T·H·E
RIFLE
B·O·O·K

In series with
The Rifle Book:

The Airgun Book
Fourth edition

The Pistol Book
Second edition

The Shotgun Book
In preparation

T·H·E
RIFLE
B·O·O·K

The comprehensive one-volume guide to the world's shoulder guns

JOHN WALTER

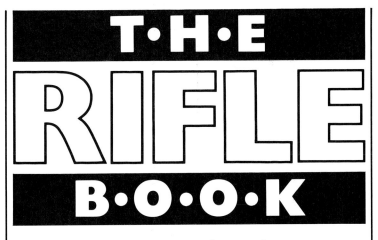

The Sauer Drilling. By courtesy of J.P. Sauer & Sohn GmbH.

ARMS AND ARMOUR PRESS

First published in Great Britain in 1990 by
Arms & Armour Press,
Villiers House, 41/47 Strand,
London WC2N 5JE

Distributed in Australia by
Capricorn Link (Australia) Pty Ltd.,
P. O. Box 665, Lane Cove,
New South Wales 2066,
Australia

• •

The information in this book is believed to be correct at the time of going to press, but neither the author nor the publisher may be held responsible for inaccuracies, changes occurring during and after publication, errors, omissions, and opinions expressed or implied.

Trademarks are reproduced throughout the book by courtesy of the relevant manufacturers and importers. They may not be reproduced from these pages without the permission of the agencies concerned.

Manufacturers, importers and promoters who consider that their wares merit inclusion in future editions of *The Pistol Book* are welcome to submit sales catalogues and associated information to the compiler by way of Arms & Armour Press.

British Library Cataloguing in Publication Data

Walter, John D., 1951-
The rifle book
1. Rifles   I. Title
683.422

ISBN 0-85368-966-0

Designed by John Walter
Origination by Service Twenty Four Ltd, Brighton, East Sussex
Printed and bound in Great Britain by Courier International Ltd., Tiptree, Essex

Contents

• •

DIRECTORY
Owing to the necessity to mix entries of differing size and design, the A – Z directory section does not always follow strict alphabetical order. The deviations are, however, comparatively insignificant.

• •

Introduction

The first book in this series, devoted to airguns and published in 1981, satisfied a market in which little attention had been given to theory; as far as pistols and rifles are concerned, however, interior and exterior ballistics have been dissected in great detail in Dr Franklin W. Mann's classic *The Bullet's Flight*, *Hatcher's Notebook*, reloading manuals, and countless other sources. I do not intend to attempt a summary here. Neither is the performance assessment system discussed in the original pistol book (1983) included, though it is as relevant to rifles as handguns and is still to be found in the current (fourth) edition of *The Airgun Book*.

The Rifle Book is simply an accessible one-volume directory. It follows in a tradition of such books, mostly produced in the USA, but aims to be more international than most of them. It probably has its origins in the first book of this type I ever bought: *The Gunner's Bible* by Bill Riviere, published by Doubleday & Company, Inc., of New York in 1965. This I purchased – for the princely sum of 15 shillings – in the summer of 1966; and if the present book fascinates its readers as much as *The Gunner's Bible* enthralled an impressionable schoolboy, I shall be well satisfied.

Some degree of selectivity is essential, as attempts to include every rifle made throughout the world are doomed to failure from the outset; not only is it impossible to obtain all the information necessary, but it is not worth devoting space to rarely encountered Eastern bloc guns at the expense – for example – of the many variants of the Winchester Model 70.

A decision was taken at an early stage to include only guns being touted commercially in 1989–90, excluding military weapons unless they are available 'over the counter'. Russian Kalashnikovs, for example, are omitted: they cannot be purchased directly from Raznoexport in the same way that Soviet target rifles are sold in the West. Chinese and Yugoslav Kalashnikov derivations, made by Norinco and ZCZ respectively, *are* included as both countries actively promote their goods outside the Eastern bloc.

Military-style weapons such as the Heckler & Koch rifles (G3, HK33, G41), Colt's AR15 series, the FN FAL/FNC, the Steyr AUG and the British Enfield System are all included on the basis of commercial availability. But arcane developments such as the Heckler & Koch G11 caseless-ammunition rifle or the US Army's Advanced Combat Rifle are omitted on the grounds that they have yet to reach production status. Details of these can be sought from recent editions of *Jane's Infantry Weapons*.

Restrictions introduced in the 1980s on the distribution of semi-automatic rifles in Britain and the USA have been ignored; guns of this class are still included in the directory, where appropriate, as *The Rifle Book* enjoys truly international distribution.

It is sometimes difficult to distinguish rifled shotguns from shotgun-style rifles; for our purposes, all double rifles (and the multi-barrel Drilling) have been included provided they chamber conventional rifle cartridges, while 12-bore 'slug guns' have been omitted.

Unless they chamber conventional metal-case cartridges such as ·45–70, black powder guns have also been omitted. With a few important exceptions, the makers of such guns proffer replica Brown Bess muskets and Hawken rifles, or tend towards one-off customization. As neither group is as easily classifiable as conventional cartridge guns, they will ultimately be covered in a separate book.

The rifle is, perhaps, the most versatile of all firearms. Its greatest weakness is simply that, even in comparatively ineffectual ·22 LR rimfire, it can still be dangerous a mile away and there are some circumstances in which the rifle cannot be substituted for a shotgun or a small pistol. Where accuracy is concerned, however, it has no peer.

The versatility of the rifle is reflected in its diversity. A glance through the directory will reveal products ranging from re-creations of nineteenth-century breech-loaders to the most modern military weapon. The range of guns is matched by the range of applications, rifles being as useful for hunting as they are for target shooting.

Of course, there is no single gun – nor single cartridge – that is suited to all applications. The optimal 'all-purpose' cartridge has been sought for much of the twentieth century, but still the basic rules are disputed. Many people would argue that the whole exercise is pointless; just as a compromise seems imminent, someone changes the guidelines and the process must begin again. New cycles bring new guns and 'new' cartridges (often re-creations of old ideas!), and each burst of enthusiasm brings fresh impetus to the gunmaking business. Some ideas are better than others, but there has never been a guarantee. Indeed, some of the best ideas have failed merely because they appeared in the wrong place at an inappropriate time; were the work of impecunious inventors who could not afford to promote them; or were snapped up by larger manufacturers simply to kill them off. This is all part-and-parcel of the gun business and, if nothing else, provides commentators with an unlimited supply of material.

Using magnum cartridges against small vermin is clearly a waste of time and money, while the extreme codification of some forms of target shooting permits nothing other than ·22LR rimfire. Some measure of selectivity is, therefore, essential. Legislation may prohibit the use of small calibres (generally ·243 or less) against deer, yet a skilled marksman is more effectual with a rifle chambering the fast-moving ·220 Swift than a novice with a ·375 H&H Magnum. The key is to hit the point of aim, an area where a rifle has no peer if correctly selected and accurately sighted.

Inspection of a 50m UIT Free Rifle target, or even a 300m service rifle pattern, will show what is required of man and equipment. Consequently, though comparatively few basic advances in rifle design have been made in the last fifty years – most of the operating principles were established in the nineteenth century – great strides have been made in production techniques and ammunition technology. This, in turn, has led to styles of shooting that seek perfection. While the Free Rifles are probably the oddest, with their proliferation of adjustable butt plates and counter-weight systems, the bench-rest shooters achieve the greatest accuracy.

Admittedly, performance of man is utterly eclipsed in unlimited bench-rest classes by the machine; when the rifle weighs 30lb or more and sits on a special rest, it could be argued that all the shooter has to do is sit back and pull the trigger. Reality is by no means as simple. Success comes from dedicated hand-loading, the most detailed attention to weather conditions, or an appreciation of the effects of heat or bedding on barrel harmonics. The results may be all but unbelievable, yet some have important repercussions for the sportsman or hunter. Advances in ammunition technology necessary to win these competitions often filter back to mass-production within a few years. The 6mm PPC round is one example of a specialist wildcat that seems set for a great commercial future.

The rifle-shooting scene, therefore, embraces many disciplines. The black powder shooter can re-create Waterloo or Gettysburg to his heart's content, or hunt for the pot in the manner of his woodsman ancestors; the dedicated shooting technologist can pursue Free Rifle, long-range or bench-rest shooting; and the more vigorous can hunt.

It is always difficult to acknowledge assistance without offending many of the individuals, companies and government bodies consulted during preparatory work. Once again, therefore, I must fall back on the overworked alphabetic list and add only that I hope to avoid offending those whose help I value most greatly.

Tamara Angerman, Oy Sako Ab; Sandy Barrett, Mitchell Arms, Inc.; Ing. Francesco Bernardelli and Pino Benetti, Vincenzo Bernardelli SpA; Amadeo Rossi SA; Embaixada do Brasil, London; Geoffrey H. Brown, Viking Arms Ltd; Malcolm and Sarah Cooper, Accuracy International Ltd; Wolfgang A. Droege, Shiloh Rifle Mfg Co.; Dynamit Nobel AG; Erma Werke GmbH; Edward C. Ezell; Federal Engineering Corporation; Val J. Forgett, Navy Arms Company; Dr Rolf Gminder; Hopkins & Allen Arms; Joachim Görtz; Colin Greenwood, Editor, *Guns Review*; Roger C. Hale, Parker-Hale Ltd; Heckler & Koch GmbH; Friedrich Wilh. Heym GmbH & Co. KG; Peter Hoffmann, Carl Walther Sportwaffenfabrik GmbH: Ian V. Hogg; Kaye Huff, American Military Arms Corporation; Israeli Metal Industries; Roy C. Jinks; JLS Arms Ltd; Viktor Kulikov, Razno Ltd; Evelyn Lau, Chartered Industries of Singapore; Lyman Products Corporation; Manufacture d'Armes des Pyrenées Françaises 'Unique'; Mauser-Jagdwaffen GmbH; Beth Mehmel, Colt's Inc.; Michael Miller, Calico; Tim Pancurak, Thompson/Center Arms; Carlo Peroni, Pietro Beretta SpA; Michael Rayment, Leslie Hewett Ltd; Remington Arms Company; Alain Renard and Chantal Bourgeois, Fabrique Nationale Herstal; Sako-Valmet; J.P. Sauer & Sohn GmbH; Karl Schäfer; Joseph J. Schroeder, Jun.; Società Armi Bresciane SRL; Springfield Armory; Jan Stevenson, Editor, *Handgunner*; Franco Testoni, Luigi Franchi SpA; Ultra-Light Arms, Inc.; Umarex Sportwaffen GmbH & Co. KG; US Repeating Arms Co.; Stephen K. Vogel, Sturm Ruger Export Company, Inc.; Paul Wahl, Paul Wahl Corporation; Hans-Hermann Weihrauch, Hermann Weihrauch KG; Paolo Zoli, Antonio Zoli SpA; and the many authors and reviewers whose works I consulted.

As progress of a book is rarely smooth, I must thank my publisher, Roderick Dymott of Arms & Armour Press, for his continued patronage; to Lionel Leventhal, now of Greenhill Books, under whose guidance this series was originally conceived; and to Paul Ford, Tony Scott and the staff of Service Twenty-Four Ltd, Brighton, for their cheerful assistance with the production work.

Lastly, but by no means least, I must acknowledge a special debt to my family for its support through a crises that spoiled the beginning of the new decade – and for humouring me while I disappeared beneath another pile of papers!

John Walter
Brighton, 1990

Operating systems

The mechanical details of the many classes of rifle are impossible to paraphrase in a few pages; their convolutions can, and do fill entire books. Particularly recommended are the late Julian Hatcher's *Hatcher's Notebook*, Frank de Haas's *Bolt-Action Rifles* and *Single Shot Rifles*, and Stuart Otteson's highly technical (if somewhat impenetrable) *The Bolt Action*. However, there are many other accessible sources and a short bibliography will be found in the appendices.

Basic classes

1. Rifles relying almost entirely on manual actions to load, extract and/or eject the spent case

This category contains most of the well-known single-shot rifles, the shotgun-type double rifles and combination weapons.

The single-shot rifle has an exceptionally long pedigree: back, in fact, to the fifteenth century when rifled barrels were used for the first time in central Europe. Rifles then developed by way of such landmarks as the American Longrifle and the Ferguson breech-loader to the Minié rifle-muskets of the mid-nineteenth century. Excepting the muzzle-loading replicas, which form a separate sub-class, the modern single-shot rifle is generally a falling-block or bolt action – or, alternatively, embodies a shotgun type break-action.

i) FALLING BLOCK SYSTEMS trace their ancestry back to the Sharps and other guns patented in the USA in the middle of the nineteenth century. Though the percussion guns were rarely gas tight, they were simple, sturdy and very durable.

The American Civil War (1861–5) not only established the merits of the metal-case cartridge, but also finally buried the classical muzzle-loading rifle-musket. In the years immediately after 1865, therefore, many block-action guns were converted to fire the new self-contained ammunition; contemporaneously, most armies – in Europe as well as in the United States of America – began to convert their rifle-muskets to breech-loading systems such as Snider's or Allin's.

Out on the broad plains of North America, the Remington Rolling Block and the 1874-model Sharps made a huge contribution to the Winning of the West. Judged against the Winchester magazine rifles of 1866 and 1873, popular but structurally weak, the single-shot rifles offered exceptionally powerful cartridges and good long-range performance. As tests proved, it was almost impossible to overload a black powder Remington.

Single-shot falling block rifles have undergone a renaissance in the last twenty years, largely owing to a handful of dedicated enthusiasts. In addition to replicas of the 1874-pattern Sharps, plus Remington

Rolling Blocks and other pre-1880 designs, many 'new' guns have been introduced. Admittedly some of them are minor redesigns of historically important guns such as the Sharps-Borchardt and the Winchester High Wall (designed by John Browning and patented in 1878), but others are more radical: the Ruger, externally somewhat Farquharson-like and by far the most influential of the mass-produced patterns, is internally pure Ruger. Other notable designs have included the de Haas, the current status of which is uncertain; the Würthrich, which owes something to a Heeren action patented in 1885; and the Blaser, which is, perhaps, the most compact of them all.

ii) BOLT ACTIONS appeared at much the same time as the first metal-cartridge falling block rifles. The father of the bolt action is generally accepted as the Prussian Johann Niklaus von Dreyse (1787–1867), though his guns used combustible ammunition and a needle igniter. However, they then paved the way first for the French Chassepot (adopted in 1866) and then the earliest Mauser, adopted by the united German army in March 1872. But though bolt-actions were adopted in France, Russia, Italy, Switzerland, the Netherlands and elsewhere, many people doubted their superiority over falling-block designs. This was especially true in Britain, where the Martini-Henry falling-block rifle remained the official service weapon until the late 1880s; consequently, sporting rifles based on actions by Martini, Henry, Farquharson, Westley Richards, Deeley & Edge and others were in vogue until the end of the century.

Neither the bolt-action nor the shotgun-type double rifle was as popular with British shooters as the falling-block action prior to 1914, except among big-game hunters. In North America, however, the lever-action magazine rifle made steady progress against guns such as the Remington Rolling Block; by 1914, falling block designs were largely confined to target shooting.

The great merit of the bolt action only became apparent with the advent and widespread distribution of magazine rifles in the last decade of the nineteenth century. The spectacular success of Waffenfabrik Mauser, Deutsche Waffen- und Munitionsfabriken, Fabrique Nationale d'Armes de Guerre and

Above

Multi-barrel guns have always been popular in central Europe. This unconventional asymmetrical design offers a shotgun above two different rifled barrels; the most popular version is the Drilling, which has two barrels above a central lower one.

By courtesy of Friedrich Wilh. Heym GmbH & Co. KG.

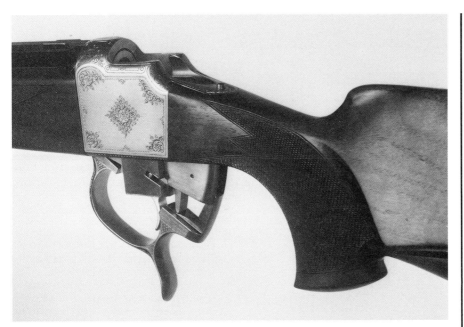

Left

The compact Blaser BL820 is among the best of the modern single-shot dropping-block rifles. Note how almost the entire action is contained within the length of the trigger guard.

By courtesy of Blaser Jagdwaffen GmbH.

Österreichische Waffenfabriks-Gesellschaft – who made bolt-action weapons in tremendous numbers – hastened the demise of the European falling block rifle in the years immediately before the First World War.

iii) SHOTGUN-STYLE RIFLES, never popular in the USA and Britain, have prospered in Europe. The most popular patterns (at least prior to 1960) were the side-by-side double and what the Germans call a *Drilling*, with two shotgun barrels above a single rifled one.

There is a widespread – but totally groundless – suspicion among devotees of falling blocks or bolts that these break-open breech systems are not robust enough for modern high-power cartridges. The reality is that the best European double rifles have always handled cartridges as powerful as the ·450 or even ·577 Nitro Expresses in perfect safety. Their great advantage lies partly in the speed with which a second shot can be fired, at least the equal of an automatic, and in the ease with which they can chamber long-case or wildcat cartridges. This is shared with most falling-block rifles, but not necessarily by bolt patterns whose feed-way dimensions may limit the maximum cartridge length. Many European authorities, if not those in North America, consider that an 8lb Drilling with two medium-calibre rifle barrels above a 16-bore shotgun provides the optimal 'all-purpose' gun.

Whether the single-shot rifle is an ideal hunting weapon is arguable. The comparative slowness of a second shot (and the absence of a magazine) suits these guns only to an expert fieldsman; in the hands of a tyro, the single-shot rifle is potentially too inhumane a tool. The double rifle is infinitely preferable, owing to the speed with which a second shot can be fired. Single-shot rifles are of inestimable value in the development of wildcat ammunition, and

on the target range. Here they can be made much more rigid than a magazine-feed version, owing to the absence of cuts in the receiver, and are often capable of the most spectacular accuracy – notably in unlimited class bench-rest shooting, most exacting of all such disciplines.

2. Rifles in which most loading, indexing and extraction and/or ejection operations are achieved by means other than direct manual control

These include most of the bolt- and pump-action magazine rifles in which feeding the cartridges into the chamber, cocking the trigger mechanism and then extracting and/or ejecting are all accomplished by mechanical means once the magazines have been filled. The curious mechanical repeating pistols of the late nineteenth century represent an extreme form, but most of the modern representatives fall into three groups.

i) BOLT ACTIONS often began life as single-shot patterns (see above), but were soon adapted to magazine systems. The earliest successful gun was the Vetterli, adopted by the Swiss Army in 1869 and subsequently by Italy. However, the Vetterli magazine was copied from the under-barrel tube found on the lever-action Henry Rifle, examples of which had been tested in Switzerland in 1866. Though the tube magazine was in vogue for twenty years – and still has its devotees – it has always had several severe drawbacks. Though ideally suited to low-power rimfire cartridges, allying large magazine capacity with simplicity, its problems arose once high-power centre-fire cartridges were used. Attempts to use spitzer (pointed-nose) bullets courted disaster; even a conventional round-nose projectile could ignite the primer of the cartridge ahead of it, should the butt be slammed on the ground during drill.

A

B

Above

Two typical side-by-side doubles: a Heym Model 88B (A) with two rifled barrels, and a Heym Model 88BF (B) with one smooth-bored.

By courtesy of Friedrich Wilh. Heym GmbH & Co. KG.

The Germans developed a flat-nose bullet for the M 71/84 infantry rifle, but the problems were never entirely overcome in French service until the end of the First World War. Modern tube-magazine bolt action rifles are almost exclusively ·22 rimfires, where the nose of pointed bullets rests on the base of the preceding cartridge. This is inherently safe, as the priming is contained in the periphery of the case-rim.

As far as the bolt-action was concerned, the ideal magazine proved to be a box – detachable like the Lee pattern, or internal like the perfected Mauser. Like bolt actions, magazines come in incredible diversity. The modern sporting preference is for an internal Mauser-type magazine, which permits an uncluttered line and cannot snag on foliage or clothing. Detachable floor plates allow the magazine to be emptied easily. Military preference remains a large-capacity detachable box, which allows instant reloading with ready-filled magazines.

A major drawback of detachable magazines is the comparative fragility of the feed-lips, and there is little doubt that the internal magazines, judged in absolute terms, are superior. It can also be argued that of the various types of internal magazine, the spool-type Schönauer magazine and its derivatives position the cartridges more accurately – and are thus more effectual – than those in which the cartridges are elevated by springs.

ii) LEVER-ACTION magazine rifles have almost as lengthy a pedigree as the bolt patterns, beginning with the Hunt Volitional Repeater in the 1840s. The first such gun to encounter widespread success was the Henry Rifle of 1859–60, which in its turn paved the way for the Winchesters of 1866 and 1873. With an occasional exception, early lever-action guns were lineal successors to the single-shot falling block rifles.

The reputation of the 1873 Winchester, which inspired a legion of copies and near-copies, was sealed

Right
The US M1903 'Springfield' rifle, perfected in the early years of the twentieth century, was a typical bolt-action military weapon. Taken from one of the many official handbooks, these drawings identify the major parts.

Right
The Grünig & Elmiger bolt action, embodied in many of the company's excellent target rifles, typifies current thinking. Note the massive receiver – broken only by the ejection port – and the sturdy locking lugs on the bolt-head. This particular gun also has an electronic trigger system.
By courtesy of Grünig & Elmiger AG.

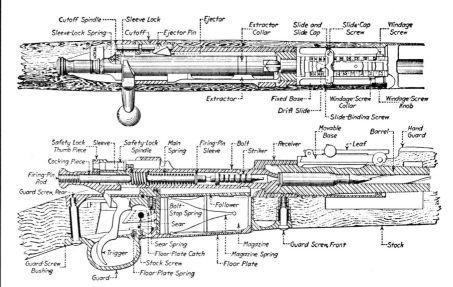

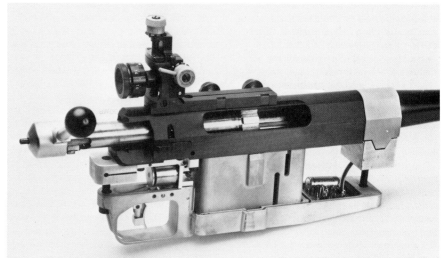

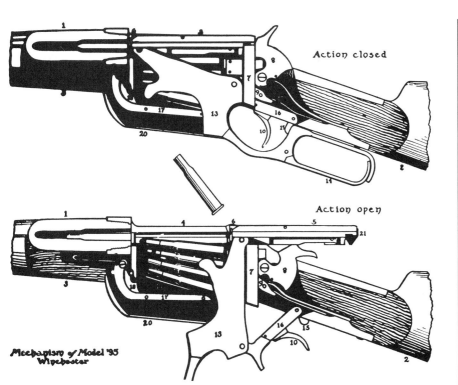

Action closed

Action open

Mechanism of Model '95 Winchester

Left

Designed by John Browning, the Winchester Model 95 lever-action rifle was among the strongest of its type. These drawings identify the major components: 1, barrel; 2, stock; 3, fore-end; 4, receiver; 5, bolt; 6, extractor; 7, locking bolt; 8, hammer; 9, sear; 10, trigger; 11, sear spring; 12, main spring; 13, finger lever; 14, finger-lever lock; 15, finger-lever catch; 16, link; 17, carrier; 18, carrier cam lever; 19, carrier cradle; 20, magazine; and 21, firing pin.

by its performance in the Wild West. Though the locking mechanism is comparatively weak, restricting the power of the cartridges to that of a large handgun, the Winchester offered a capacious magazine and could be fired rapidly with minimal practice. Though no self-respecting buffalo hunter would use one – preferring a Remington Rolling Block or a big Sharps – the cowboy and the Indian fighter had different priorities. To their minds, rapid fire and large magazine capacity far outweighed lack of stopping power at long range.

Lever-action repeaters are still extremely popular in the Americas, though less so in Europe. This is largely due to fundamental changes in the action of the Winchester, which was redesigned by John Browning until it was suited to much more powerful cartridges. The Browning-inspired Winchesters of 1886–95 persuaded other US manufacturers to develop lever-action rifles of their own. The most effectual have been the Marlin and the Savage.

The Marlin resembles the Winchester externally, but has always ejected laterally while the latter ejected upward (a drawback when it came to attach optical sights); the Savage, however, was originally made with a rotary spool magazine and a striker in place of a hammer-lock.

Winchesters, Marlins and Savages are still in production, even though the bolt action – thanks to the effects of two world wars and the military surplus market – has made considerable inroads on their popularity. Though Winchester once attempted to move from the well-established M1894 (with the short-lived Model 88) the traditionalists have never permitted it. Similarly, the Finnish Sako Finnwolf,

expensive but effectual, failed to find a niche in the US market. The only modern lever-action rifle to achieve much success, other than Winchester copies and the Marlins, has been the Browning BL22/BLR series, with a multiple-lug rotary bolt and a short-throw lever acting through a gearing system. The Browning has a most distinctive trigger unit that drops with the lever, but it lacks the elegance of the Winchester M1894 and cannot yet be regarded as a marketing triumph.

The greatest failing in lever-action guns is that, lacking the absolute strength of most bolt patterns, they cannot chamber the most powerful magnum cartridges. In addition, even market leaders such as the Winchester M94 Side Eject and Marlin 336ER use tube magazines that must be loaded with blunt or flat-nose bullets. Two new cartridges have recently been introduced for the 94XTR Big Bore, the ·307 and ·356 Winchester, but they are still loaded with aerodynamically ineffectual bullets and cannot match similar patterns chambered in bolt-action or falling-block rifles.

The comparatively low power and looping trajectory of the cartridges chambered in even the strongest lever-action rifle restrict the shooter to medium ranges; long-range varmint shooting, therefore, is undertaken exclusively with bolt- or block-action rifles in which chamber pressures may reach 50,000psi or more. According to Dynamit Nobel, the maximum chamber pressure of the current RWS ·243 Winchester loading is 51,200psi, while the ·30–06 reaches 49,800psi and even the 6·5×54 Mannlicher-Schönauer (weak by military rifle standards) generates 45,500. Excepting guns such as

11

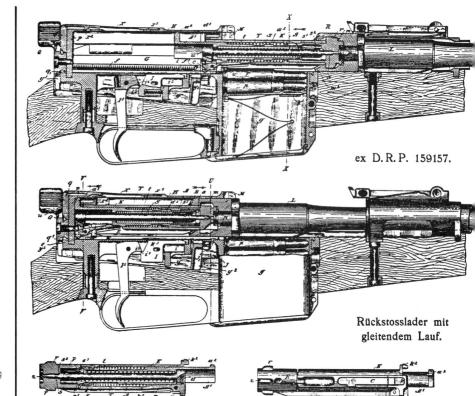

ex D.R.P. 159157.

Rückstosslader mit
gleitendem Lauf.

the Winchester Model 88, the current Savage M99 and the Sako Finnwolf, lever-actions rarely operate with pressures exceeding 35,000psi.

iii) PUMP-ACTION rifles are comparatively rare, excepting in rimfire chamberings. The mechanism was originally developed in the Spencer Repeating Shotgun, patented in 1878–82, and featured in Winchester shotguns and the Colt Lightning rifle before the end of the nineteenth century. Remaining more popular on shotguns than rifles, the pump system shares some of the advantages of the lever systems but is more compact and faster to cycle; conversely, it has a greater tendency to binding and structural failure. Pump-action rifles chambered for rimfire ammunition usually have tube magazines, while the few centre-fire versions embody boxes.

3. Guns in which loading, extraction and ejection are accomplished by the mechanism itself

The firer only needs to prepare guns of this type for the first shot – e.g., by pulling the slide back – or tripping the sear before each shot by pressing the trigger.

This category, embracing 'self-loaders' and 'automatics', is readily subdivisible. The major criterion is the strength of the breech-lock – unlocked, hesitation (partially) locked, or fully locked.

i) BLOWBACK or unlocked-breech systems comprise a heavy breech block and a stiff spring. All that opposes the backward movement of the cartridge case is the radial pressure clamping the cartridge-case walls to the chamber sides, the inertia of the breech block, a modicum of friction to be overcome as the parts move and the resistance of the recoil spring. Unless the breech block is heavy and the recoil spring sufficiently powerful, the breech opens too quickly; case-head separations and similar ammunition problems ensue. An unlocked breech, however, is essentially simple.

Unlocked-breech rifles are popular, but generally only for pistol-cartridge chamberings. Though few pistols handle powerful loadings effectually – exceptions including the Spanish Campo Giro and Astra, which handle 9mm Parabellum and 9mm Largo in perfect safety – the moving parts can be made larger and heavier in a rifle, where space is not at such a premium. Thus a Ruger blowback carbine can handle ·44 Magnum cartridges at pressures which would tax (if not actually damage) a blowback pistol. But it would be unpractical, though theoretically possible, to make a blowback rifle handling ·458 Winchester Magnum; the reciprocating masses would approach the weight of a heavy machine-gun.

Aberrant blow-forward actions have practically no application to rifle design, though one or two experimental guns have been made. These rely on the barrel being projected away from the standing breech, but are rarely as accurate or as durable as blowbacks: too much of the action moves and the effects of wear cannot be disregarded.

ii) DELAYED BLOWBACKS, also known as 'hesitation locks', are often claimed to combine the simplicity of blowbacks with the safety of a conventional breech lock. Results have varied; the best of the guns work perfectly, while the worst have been catastrophic. The most successful system has been the roller-lock, developed for the German MG.42 (locked breech) during the Second World War and subsequently extended to assault rifles (locked breech and delayed blowback). Some of the Mauser designers recommended work in Spain in the late 1940s and, by the mid 1950s, had perfected the CETME rifle. This was then licensed to Heckler & Koch in West Germany, laying the foundations of a tremendous success story. H&K has since extended the roller-lock to a series of submachine-guns, rifles and machine-guns, together with a pistol or two.

There is no doubt that the underlying principle, based on the time-delay gained while precisely placed rollers are forced out of the receiver walls and back into the bolt-head, is highly efficient. Though theoretically lacking the ultimate safety margins of a mechanically-locked breech, virtually no operating problems have been encountered with the roller system in practice. Extensively used for military purposes, its application to sporting guns is compromised only by the fluted chamber – the bane of a handloader's life.

Among the less successful hesitation locks has been the Thompson Automatic Rifle, developed immediately after the end of the First World War. This rifle was promoted to compete in the US Army trials against the earliest Garands and the toggle-locked Pedersen, which came close to becoming the

hesitation-lock success of its day. Unfortunately, the ferocity of the Thompson rifle action (which illustrated the perils of too short a delay) was such that spent cases could be embedded mouth-first into oak boards.

iii) LOCKED BREECH 'automatic' rifles have attracted the attention of inventors, engineers and manufacturers for more than a century. Initially, experiments were doomed by the absence of reliable ammunition and the reluctance of contemporary military authorities either to see simplicity as a virtue or reduce the acceptable engagement range. Though comparatively low-powered sporting rifles achieved success prior to 1914 – most notably the Winchester and Remington auto-loaders – the only military-power rifle to achieve success was the Mexican Mondragon.

Unfortunately, after the rifle had been adopted by the Mexican army in 1908, revolution plunged the country into turmoil in 1911 and prevented the guns being delivered from Switzerland. Surviving examples were purchased by the Germans in the First World War, seeing limited service in the air and in the trenches, but ultimately proved too fragile. However, the Mondragon was much more battle-worthy than the cumbersome and fantastically complicated recoil-operated Mausers of the same era.

Though the French introduced two comparatively crude gas-operated rifles during the First World War, the RSC Mle 1917 and Mle 1918, neither the British nor the Americans made much progress. Fanatical attention to the most meagre provision in unworkable specifications contributed greatly to lack of progress, as did shortages of suitable propellants. Time passed

Three typical auto-loading rifles: (A) the Russian Federov Avtomat of 1916; (B) the Belgian ABL or SAFN, sold commercially from 1949; and a Beretta-made BM59, an Italian adaptation of the Garand.

Painting by John Walter; photographs by courtesy of Fabrique Nationale Herstal SA and Pietro Beretta SpA.

A

B

C

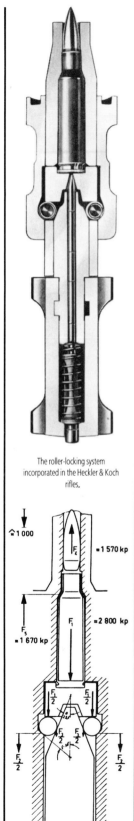

The roller-locking system incorporated in the Heckler & Koch rifles.

before designers appreciated that some cartridges were better suited to auto-loading actions than others, subtleties of case-shape and operating pressures becoming obvious only after extensive testing. Sharply tapered rimmed cases such as the British ·303 and the Russian 7·62×54R were fundamentally unsuitable; this the Russians accepted in 1916, chambering the Federov Avtomat for the 6·5mm Japanese semi-rim cartridge, but progress remained infinitesimal by 1918 if the Browning Automatic Rifle (which was closer to a light machine-gun) is excepted.

As the size of tubes and piston assemblies was less critical in a rifle than a handgun, recoil operation (preferred for pistols) gradually gave way to gas-power. Gas operation had the merits of simplicity, even though propellant fouling – gradually minimized as the years passed – forced more frequent cleaning. By the late 1930s the US Army had perfected the Garand, the Russians had the Simonov AVS and the Tokarev SVT, and the Belgians were working on what would ultimately become the ABL.

Though the Simonov failed, the Garand and the Tokarev (and the ABL after 1945) were very successful. That the perfected 1940-pattern SVT was soon taken out of production was due largely to manufacturing problems rather than inherent design faults. In view of limitations imposed by the Russian 7·62×54R cartridge compared with the 7·9mm round or even the US ·30–06, the Tokarev, with its detachable box magazine, was better in some respects than the clip-loaded M1 Garand.

Categorisation of locked-breech guns derives not from the mechanism of the lock itself – there are too many variations – but from the power source. *Gas operation* remains more popular in rifle design than recoil operation (q.v.). The power necessary to unlock the slide and force it backward is derived from the propellant, either directly (where the gas impinges on the piston or breech block) or indirectly through intermediate levers or springs. Gas operation has several advantages – the mechanism is generally simple – but propellant fouling may jam the guns unless they are cleaned regularly. Though this stricture has decreased as propellant technology advances, it has yet to be eliminated entirely. The comparatively recent problems encountered with the US M16 rifle in Vietnam provide an illuminating commentary on 'self-cleaning rifles'.

Gas-operated designs may also be less tolerant of ammunition fluctuations than recoil-operated rivals, but provision of pressure adjusters is generally sufficient answer.

Recoil operation draws power from the reaction to the moving bullet, which is opposed by an equal force moving backwards. In a 'fixed' system, such as a single-shot falling-block rifle, the rearward velocity is muted by the weight of the entire gun and the energy subsequently dissipates into the firer's arm, shoulder and back muscles. In a recoil-operated auto-loader – though some energy ultimately disappears in the same manner – part of the rearward force is harnessed to open the breech and push the breech-block or bolt back past the cocking position. Returning the parts and re-locking the breech are accomplished by springs compressed during the opening stroke.

Recoil operation is usually divided into 'short' and 'long' recoil. As definitions involving arbitrary dimensions (e.g., 'more than an inch') make no allowance for differences in cartridge-case lengths, *long recoil* is accepted as involving locked travel greater than the length of the cartridge case; *short recoil* simply requires the locked parts to travel less than case-length. This has little or nothing to do with the power of the cartridge: the cut-off dimension would be 19mm for 9mm Parabellum, about 26mm for ·22 Winchester Magnum rimfire and 76mm for ·577 Nitro Express 3″!

Virtually all modern rifles in this category embody short recoil principles, particularly if they chamber centre-fire cartridges. Many of the earliest recoil-operated weapons (such as the pre-1914 Mauser rifles) were masterpieces of the toolmakers' art, but horrendously costly to manufacture, unreliable and ineffectual; modern examples are simpler and more durable.

Breech locks

Locking systems take many guises. Among the most popular are *rotating bolts*, featured in the AR-15/M16, together with the Kalashnikov and rifles derived directly from it (e.g., the Galil and the Finnish Valmet); *tipping breech-blocks*, used in the FN FAL and the Tokarevs; and *roller- or flap-locks*, found in the Swiss StGw.57 and most of the Heckler & Koch weapons. There is little to choose between the best representatives of each group, though a multi-lug bolt rotating directly into the barrel extension is undoubtedly stronger in ultimate terms than a tipping block cammed down into the receiver: in the latter, the entire length of the breech-block between the base of the cartridge and the locking shoulder is under stress during firing. Toggle-locks and similar mechanisms, though in vogue in prior to 1930, are too difficult to machine to be cost-effective in the 1990s.

Directory

Accuracy International

BRITAIN

Trading from PO Box 81, Portsmouth, Hampshire PO3 5SJ, Accuracy International Ltd markets only the **Model PM**, a purpose-built sniper rifle standardized by the British armed forces (as the L96A1) after a series of trials lasting several years. The PM narrowly beat the Parker Hale Model 85 (q.v.), but a feature of the trials was the failure of many vaunted European and American rifles to meet the stringent performance guidelines.

Developed by a team led by Malcolm Cooper, Britain's foremost marksman, the PM was developed to satisfy a range of vital criteria. These included the 'ability to place the first shot on target anywhere in the world, in any conditions, from a clean or fouled barrel' and to provide 'such reliable accuracy so as to increase the effective sniping range considerably'. These are particularly important to the British Army, which is likely to operate anywhere from the Arctic to the South Atlantic, and from the temperate European theatre to the Hong Kong monsoons.

The PM features a triple-lug bolt with a fully enclosed head and a 60° throw, locking into the receiver immediately behind the barrel. The design of the bolt handle and the reciprocating action was carefully considered so that a trained firer can operate the gun with minimal disturbance of aim. Attention was paid to the two-stage adjustable trigger, the ease of maintenance – the striker can be removed without tools, and the extractor with a

bullet-tip – and, particularly, the design of the stock. Unlike most rifles, the PM uses two 'stock sides', made of tough plastic with an olive drab finish, which bolt onto the aluminium chassis supporting the action. This completely overcomes the effect of warping in woodwork, which (no matter how well the bedding has been undertaken) will often affect performance adversely.

PM rifles will be seen with bipods and a small monopod – called the 'Quick Action Spike' – to allow a sniper to observe his target through the optical sight without fatigue. Four basic rifles are available: **Long Range**, fitted with Schmidt & Bender PM12×42 or Leupold 10× or 16× M1 sights, and chambering 7mm Remington Magnum or ·300 Winchester Magnum; **Counter-Terrorist**, in 7·62mm NATO, with Schmidt & Bender PM6×42 or PM2·5–10×56 sights; **Moderated**, with a PM6×42 sight and a full-length sound moderator suited to 7·62mm NATO subsonic ammunition; and the 7·62mm NATO **Infantry**, with a PM6×42 sight. Excepting the single-shot Long Range pattern, Accuracy International rifles all have detachable magazines.

They are heavy, weighing in the region of 6·5kg, and initially suffered from teething troubles due largely to problems that occur when any promising design is translated into mass-production. However, use by the armed forces, SAS, police and other units has led to an enviable reputation for performance and reliability. There is no doubting that the PM is one of the best, if not *the* best bolt-action sniper rifle.

Below
Two versions of the PM sniper rifle: the standard Infantry (A), known to the British Army as the Rifle L96A1; and Moderated (B), with a full-length sound suppressor.
By courtesy of Accuracy International Ltd.

A

B

AMAC USA

The American Military Arms Corporation (AMAC), 2202 Redmond Road, Jacksonville, Arkansas 72076, succeeded to the business of Iver Johnson in the early 1980s, but continues to use the earlier tradename. Best known for its revolvers, Iver Johnson has had a long and more than usually troubled history of gunmaking. Currently, AMAC makes the ·30 **M1 Carbine** in two versions (hardwood or walnut stocked) together with a single-shot bolt-action ·22 rimfire rifle known as the Model 2000 or **Li'l Champ Bolt 22**. Intended for juniors, the latter measures 33in overall, has a 16·3in barrel and weighs about 2lb 11oz. Erma-made rimfire rifles (q.v.) are marketed in the USA as the 'U.S. Carbine ·22', 'Wagonmaster Lever Action' and 'Targetmaster Pump Action'.

AMAC also offers a large-calibre heavy-duty/sniper rifle chambered for the ·50 Browning Machine Gun cartridge. This rifle, known as the **Model 5100 LRRS** ('Long Range Rifle System'), may also be obtained for the exclusive Barrett ·338/416 round. The gun – a single-shot bolt action pattern – has a free-floating fluted barrel with a distinctive muzzle brake. A bipod is attached to the tubular receiver extension beneath the barrel, while the adjustable-length butt-piece slides on two parallel rods that protrude behind the pistol grip. The M5100 has an adjustable comb and is invariably encountered with optical sights. It is intended to strike accurately at ultra-long range, an area in which the powerful ·50 BMG is suited in all characteristics except extreme accuracy. Here, the hybrid ·338/416 is preferable as it will often better 1MOA. The ·50-calibre rifle is ideal for use against targets such as vehicles, helicopters and aircraft.

American Industries USA

Trading from 8700 Brookpark Road, Cleveland, Ohio 44129, American Industries manufactures the fascinating Calico rimfire rifles. The futuristic **M-100** comes in three basic configurations: the M-100 rifle, with a folding stock and a ribbed synthetic hand-guard; the M-100S (Sporter) with a wooden hand-guard and combination pistol-grip/butt unit; and the M-100P pistol, which is basically a rifle action with an ultra-short barrel and a pistol grip. The M-100 and M-100S share identical barrelled actions, their stocks and fore-ends being interchangeable.

The M-100 is a simple blowback semi-automatic rifle with a light alloy frame and a unique 100-round helical feed magazine. Made from high-strength thermoplastic, the magazine features a silent winder with a spring-release clutch, allowing it to be loaded without encountering spring resistance. In addition, the magazine can be left loaded with practically no spring fatigue. Two clear ports allow the state of loading to be assessed at a glance. Most unusually, the magazine lies on top of the action; tests undertaken by the leading US gun magazines have shown that the system is most efficient, in addition to being lighter-per-round than conventional box patterns. Spool magazines have been popular on bolt-action rifles for many years (e.g., the Mannlicher-Schönauer), where their merits have been proven, but are rarely encountered on modern semi-automatics. Consequently, the Calico rifle is an interesting departure from accepted norms.

AMT USA

Arcadia Machine & Tool, Inc., 6226 Santos Diaz Street, Irwindale, California 91706, is best known for a range of high-quality pistols such as the Hardballer, Back-up and Automag II. The company also offers the **Small Game Hunting Rifle** and the **Lightning**, both of which are built on a version of the Automag II gas-assisted blowback action. Game Rifles may chamber either the ·22LR or ·22 Rimfire Magnum cartridges – not interchangeably – while the Lightning comes in ·22 LR rimfire only. The Game Rifle has a heavyweight Target barrel; the Lightning may be obtained with bull or tapered patterns. The actions of both guns are satin finish stainless steel, stocked in warp-resistant fibreglass-filled nylon; the optically-sighted Game Rifle is stocked conventionally, while the skeletal butt of the open-sighted Lightning pivots forward to lie along the right side of the action.

Barrett USA

Barrett Firearms Manufacturing, Inc., PO Box 1077, Murfreesboro, Tennessee 37133, offers one of the most extraordinary rifles currently available – the ·50-calibre Model 82A1 **Light Fifty**. Advertised as 'the most cost effective means of destroying the threats that challenge your forces', this is an immense gun with an overall length of 61in, a 33in barrel and an unladen weight of 32·5lb. The Barrett cannot be confused with any other weapon; though it bears a vague external affinity with the M16, at least in the receiver area, it has a notably bulky eleven-round box magazine, a fluted barrel with a muzzle brake, straight-line construction, a skeletal butt and a bipod. It also comes with a 10× optical sight, with a special graticle graduated from 500 to 1800m.

When the Barrett first appeared, it was the subject of much ill-informed comment from writers who assumed it was a long-range sniper rifle; many authorities drew attention to the comparative inaccuracy of the ·50 Browning Machine Gun round and scoffed at the rifle's utility. However, as Barrett's literature underscores, the major purpose of the Light Fifty is to cripple much more important targets – 'compressor sections of jet engines or the transmissions of helicopters . . . make it capable of destroying multi-million dollar aircraft with a single hit delivered to a vital area'. One strike of an accurately placed ·50 BMG round, costing about $10 apiece, could theoretically achieve the same result as a far more costly missile. The accuracy of the Barrett is claimed to routinely better 2MOA with regular ·50 M33 Ball and M8 API ammunition.

ANSCHÜTZ

J.G. Anschütz GmbH, Jagd- und Sportwaffenfabrik, D-7900 Ulm/Donau, Postfach 11 28, West Germany

Founded in Zella St Blasii in 1856, Anschütz rose rapidly from humble beginnings to employ 250 people by 1914. Sporting guns were made in large numbers. Business was re-established after the end of the First World War, when air-pistols, Flobert rifles and Schützen-style falling block guns were made; Anschütz was also acting as an agency for the products of Walther, FN-Browning and Mauser at this time. Business was rebuilt again after the Second World War, once the Anschütz family had been unceremoniously bundled into western Germany in a US Army truck. J.G. Anschütz & Company was officially registered with the Ulm chamber of commerce in 1950, but some years passed before the first cartridge rifles were made. The major turning point was the introduction of the bolt-action Match-Verschluss 54 (announced in 1954), which was an immediate success. A gold medal from the prone rifle-shooting competition in the Rome Olympics (1960) laid the foundations for today's international reputation: marksmen firing Anschütz rifles took gold, silver *and* bronze medals in the Olympic smallbore rifle competitions in 1964, 1968 and 1972. By this time Anschütz had also begun to make high-quality airguns.

Below
Two of the many obsolescent Anschütz target rifles, the Model 1407 (A) and the Model 1413SM (B). The latter was intended for Free Rifle competitions, evident from the sophisticated adjustable butt plate and the palm-rest assembly beneath the fore-end.
By courtesy of J.G. Anschütz GmbH.

A

B

Product range: the company makes a wide range of bolt-action rifles, mostly for target-shooting, plus a selection of airguns. Though some 'budget price' rimfire rifles are offered, most of the products are among the finest in their classes. Many Olympic and world championships medals have been taken with Anschütz rifles, which continue to be market leaders. Many have been available in the USA through Savage (cartridge guns) and Crosman (airguns), use of whose brandnames and designations sometimes camouflages the rifles' Anschütz origins. The US firearms agency currently rests with Precision Sales International of Westfield, Massachussetts.

Discontinued models: since production of the Model 54 action began, many minor variants of the Anschütz rifles have come and gone. This is particularly true of the target rifles, where stocks have been revised periodically without changing the basic gun designations.

1400-series target rifles were replaced by the 1800-series guns in the early 1980s, differing principally in the substitution of the 5018 trigger for variants of the earlier 5071 pattern. The 1403, 1403 D and 1403 Biathlon shared the Model 64 action, while the 1407, 1407 D, 1407 Z, 1408 ED, 1408 ED Super, 1409 Z, 1411, 1411 D, 1413, 1413 D, 1413 St, 1427 Biathlon, 1432 E (·22 Hornet), 1432 ED, 1432 ESt, 1432 EKSt and 1532 (·222 Remington) all embodied the Match-Verschluss 54.

The Models 1363 E and 1365 E were simple 'Flobert I' bolt-action rifles chambering ·22 Flobert and 9mm primer-propellant ammunition respectively, while the Model 520 (or '520/61') was a ·22LR rimfire semi-automatic feeding from a detachable box magazine ahead of the trigger.

Three short-lived variations on the Flobert II bolt mechanism were known as the Models 1441, 1442 and 1443. Differing primarily in the quality of their stocks, these shared tangent-leaf back sights with the contemporary 300-series air rifles. They were replaced in the early 1970s by sporting guns built on the Model 64 action.

There were also Models 1424 (·22LR), 1524 (·22 Hornet) and 1534 (·222 Remington), built on the Match-Verschluss 64, with half stocks and Bavarian-style cheek pieces; and large – if rarely encountered – centre-fire sporters known as the Models 1568 D/St (Savage 110 action, in ·270 Winchester, 7×57 and 7×64 only) or 1574 D/ST (Krico action, in ·222 Remington, ·222 Remington Magnum, ·223 Remington, ·243 Winchester and ·308 Winchester).

Below

Three obsolete Anschütz rifles: the Model 520 (A), a ·22 rimfire auto-loader; the Model 1365 (B), a single-shot 9mm Flobert bolt-action smooth-bore; and the Model 1411 (C), a ·22 rimfire target rifle especially intended for prone shooting.

By courtesy of J.G. Anschütz GmbH.

A

B

C

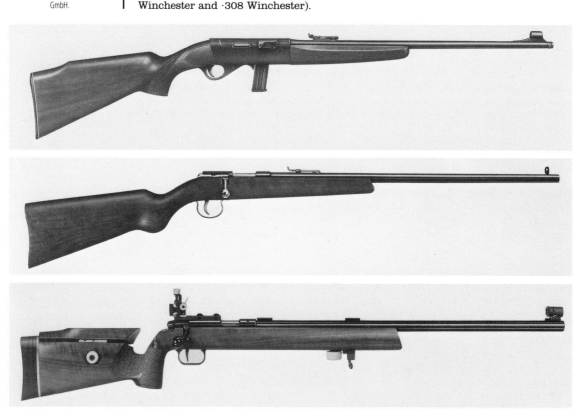

Flobert II

The simplest and cheapest of the Anschütz bolt systems is confined to the lowest grade of the company's rifles. It is amply strong enough for its task, relying on the bolt handle seat for locking, and is usually accompanied by a more-than-adequate trigger. The single-shot **Model 1388**, or 'Flobert II', which chambers ·22 primer-propelled ammunition (BB and CB Caps), is intended largely as a basic trainer. It features a hardwood half-stock, with a low Monte Carlo comb and chequering pressed into the pistol grip, and has a simple spring-leaf back sight.

All the rifles featuring the Flobert II action, apart from the Achiever (q.v.), display a radial safety on the left side of the receiver. The **Model 1449** and **Model 1450** are identical with the Model 1388, excepting that they chamber ·22LR rimfire ammunition and feed from a detachable box magazine holding five (standard) or ten (optional) rounds. The 1449 is the junior model, with a short barrel, abbreviated stock, no chequering and no butt plate; the 1450 shares the more impressive stock of the Model 1388, with panels of chequering impressed on the sides of the pistol grip.

The **Mark 2000** (·22LR rimfire) was Anschütz's basic target rifle prior to the introduction of the Achiever. It incorporates the basic simple action, but accepts the Model 6732 aperture sights and has a suitably massive barrel. Its plain hardwood stock has a low straight comb and a durable plastic butt plate. The Mark 2000 is intended specifically for novice and

junior shooters, being the lightest of all conventional Anschütz target patterns.

The **Achiever**, which weighs only a little over 2·2kg, was designed primarily to meet the regulations of the National Rifle Association of America (NRA). Though incorporating the standard Flobert II action, it has a radically differing stock with three lateral slots in the fore-end and a stippled pistol grip. The butt plate can be adjusted vertically, and spacer-plates allow the butt to be lengthened as a junior shooter grows. Unlike the rest of the Flobert II series, the Achiever has a safety catch on the right side of the action immediately behind the bolt handle. Its Model 5066 two-stage trigger can be adjusted by a gunsmith, but is usually regulated to 1,250gm. A simplified set of sights, known as the 'No.1', was developed for the Achiever in an attempt to keep price to a minimum, yet the gun still possesses the accuracy inherent in all this manufacturer's products.

Model 54 action

This elegant and highly effectual bolt action has been the cornerstone of Anschütz's success, embodied, in varying forms, in all the target rifles made prior to the introduction of the simplified Model 64 system (q.v.). Though it locks similarly to the Flobert II, the bolt-handle is reinforced by a locking lug on the opposite side of the body; every detail has been refined in a search for perfection. Anschütz trigger systems have always been among the very best, giving very

A

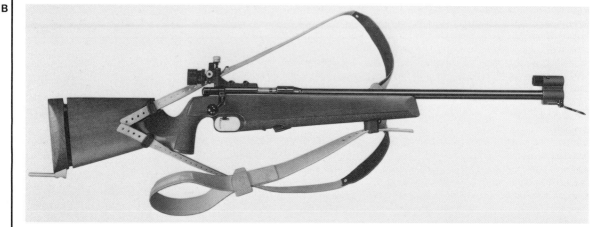

B

C

rapid lock times, and the manufacturing quality is impeccable. In addition, the company's aperture sights are widely used on other guns – a fitting tribute to the skill with which they are made.

The **Model 1422 D** (·22LR) is a typical European rimfire sporting rifle, with a well finished walnut half-stock with a schnabel tip and a contrasting pistol-grip cap. There is a rollover Monte Carlo comb, and skip-line chequering appears on the pistol grip and fore-end. Sling swivels lie on the underside of the fore-end and butt. The action, with a safety on the left side of the receiver, feeds from a detachable five-round box magazine and there is a folding open back sight. A single-stage Model 5063 trigger is standard, though double set-triggers are available as an option; the double-trigger gun is known as the Model 1422 St (Stecher, 'set trigger'). The **Model 1422 Classic** – available with either trigger system – is similar, but has a staight-comb butt and a plain rounded fore-end tip.

The **Model 1430 D** is a minor variation of the Model 1422, but has a plain stock – plainer than even the 1422 Classic – and chambers the centre-fire ·22 Hornet cartridge. The most obvious features are the absence of chequering on the fore-end and the severely curved pistol grip.

The **Model 1432 D** and **Model 1432 Classic** both chamber the ·22 Hornet round, but are otherwise mechanically identical with the 1422. Their stock designs also parallel the rimfire equivalents. The unique **Model 1432 EK St** was developed for competitions run under DJV moving-target rules. Chambering ·22 Hornet, the rifles feature a stock with a grasping groove and a deepened fore-end stippled along the length of the underside. The ventilated rubber butt plate is rarely encountered on rifles intended for moving-target work.* The 1432 EK St features the unique Model 5039 set-trigger, with a reversed setting lever at the front of the trigger-guard aperture.

Model 1433 St rifles have a full-length 'Mannlicher' stock, with a low European-style comb with minimal rollover. Stocked in walnut, these guns have skip-line chequering on the fore-end and pistol grip, and a rosewood schnabel tip. The double set-trigger is standard. The **Model 1434 D** (direct-acting single stage trigger) and **Model 1434 St** (double set-trigger) are practically identical to the 1433 pattern, apart from their half-length stocks.

Model 1522 ('Classic', 'D', 'St') rifles are all but identical with the 1422 series, though they chamber ·22 WRM instead of ·22LR rimfire, and the **Model**

1700 duplicates the 1430–1434 series in ·222 Remington instead of ·22 Hornet.

Anschütz's **Model 1803** is numerically the first of the target rifles to embody the single-shot Model 54 action. Intended for UIT standard rifle (25m) competitions, the 1803 has been made in several versions since being introduced in the early 1980s. The current pattern feaures a pale beech stock with three lateral slots in the fore-end, with extensive stippling running the length of the underside of the fore-end back as far as the trigger plate. The pistol-grip is also extensively roughened, the synthetic cheek piece is adjustable, and the butt plate can be slid vertically in its channel-piece. The standard Model 1803 has an adjustable two-stage trigger, while the 1803 D has a single-stage pattern.

The **Model 1807**, now replaced by the 1907 (q.v.), was originally made in three versions – 1807, 1807 D and 1807 Z. Only the 'Z' (Zimmerstützen, 'parlour rifle') is still available. Firing 4mm M20 primer-propellant ammunition, it is intended for ultra-short range indoor practice and is generally accompanied by a stock duplicating that of the Model 1803. However, some 1807 Zimmerstützen actions will be encountered in the newer 1907 stock.

Model 1808 rifles are intended for moving-target and metal silhouette shooting. The **Model 1808 ED Super** amalgamates a Model 54 action with a thumb-hole stock permissible for UIT Laufende Scheibe competitions. The stock has a broad stippled fore-end, an elevating comb/cheek-piece unit, and a wooden butt plate sliding in a vertical channel. Optical sights

are standard; in addition, the 1808 ED Super has a long shroud extending forward of the barrel to carry three adjustable weight collars. This is intended to facilitate a smooth swing on the target while releasing the bullet from the rifling as quickly as practicable. A 500gm single-stage trigger is standard. The **Model 1808 MS**, intended for silhouette shooting, is mechanically identical with the 1808 ED Super; however, its stock is much more conventional. There is extensive stippling under the fore-end, as well as on the pistol grip, but the butt has a fixed cheek piece and a simple solid rubber butt plate.

The **Model 1809**, still available from the factory, is a variant of the Model 1810 – described below – chambering 4mm primer-propellant ammunition to allow Free Rifle training indoors.

The **Models 1810** and **1811**, like the Model 1807, have now been renumbered '1910' and '1911' (q.v.). Mechanically, however, there are few discernible differences between the old and new models, nor do the stocks seem to vary. It is concluded that the renumbering is a marketing ploy resulting from the introduction of the new 1900-series guns. The rifles will presumably be updated when existing supplies are exhausted.

The **Model 1827 B** is intended for Biathlon matches, an arduous combination of cross-country skiing and target-shooting that is becoming increasingly popular. Biathlon guns are most distinctive, as they share unusual features such as snow caps on their sights; the muzzle is protected by a hinged cover,

Below

Typical ·22 Hornet sporting rifles built on the Model 54 action: the Model 1434 St (A), with a deluxe schnabel-tip stock and a double set-trigger; the Model 1432 EK St (B), built for DJV moving-target competitions with a special stock and a reversed trigger-setting lever in the front of the guard; and the Model 1433 St (C), a double-trigger gun with a full-length Mannlicher stock.

By courtesy of J.G. Anschütz GmbH.

A

B

C

which blocks the sight line to force the firer to swing it down before shooting begins. Four auxiliary magazines are inset in the under-edge of the 1827 B butt to facilitate reloading, the butt plate is wood (rubber would soon perish in the cold) with a short straight hook, and a special double-shoulder harness is required to carry the gun centrally on the skier's back. The 1827 uses the standard Model 54 action, with a large grasping knob suited to gloves, and has a walnut stock. It set the standards for Biathlon guns in the 1984 Olympic Games, taking all three medals.

The Anschütz **Model 1907** (·22LR) is the current designation for what was known prior to 1987 as the '1807'. The current 1907 and 1907 D, fitted with superb two-stage (5018) and single-stage triggers respectively, embody the Match 54 action and the latest 1900-series stock. This, in beech or walnut, displays an extraordinary adjustable comb/cheek piece and an extensible butt-plate mount retained by prominent synthetic snap-locks let into the woodwork. The stock also has distinctive decorative longitudinal fluting running the length of the fore-end sides.

Anschütz's Model 1910 and Model 1911 (·22LR) rifles are simply the older 1810 and 1811 renamed. This was originally simply an expedient, owing to the appearance of the Models 1907 and 1913; however, it is likely that the modernized stocks will eventually appear. The **Models 1910** and **1910 D** are intended for 50m rifle shooting, sharing the heavy barrel and match triggers of the Model 1913 Free Rifle. Their plainer stocks lack the adjustable palm-rest shelf of the 1913, and the fore-ends have been deepened to allow a standing marksman to shoot without needing an auxiliary hand rest. The multi-adjustable hooked butt plate and elevating comb/cheek-piece system of the 1913 are both retained. The **Models 1911** and **1911 D** embody the 1913-type action and heavy barrel in a stock designed specifically for prone shooting. This has a comparatively shallow fore-end and butt, and a low comb/cheek-piece unit.

Top of the company's range of target rifles, the **Models 1913** and **1913 D** are intended for 50m Free Rifle competitions. Their distinctive features include a hooked butt plate; elevating comb/cheek-piece units; an adjustable palm-rest on the pistol grip; the standard Match 54 action (right or left-handed), and a heavy barrel. A rail beneath the comparatively shallow fore-end may accept a movable hand rest, a riser block or a hand-stop. For those who wish to use the same basic gun in a number of competitions, the basic 1913 action can be fitted into an 1807-pattern stock (for 25m shooting) with a minimum of trouble.

Model 5418 MS rifles – developed largely for the North American market – are intended for metal silhouette shooting. Differing from the 1808 MS (q.v.) largely in their short large-diameter barrels, they lack the extension shroud and adjustable collar weights.

The newest Anschütz ·22 sporting rifle, introduced in 1988, the **Bavarian** (·22LR, ·22 Magnum, ·22 Hornet or ·222 Remington) is basically an amalgamation of the standard Match 54 action with a Bayernschaft or Bavarian-style stock. This has a tighter pistol grip than guns such as the 1422 or 1522, but its most obvious feature is the squared cheek piece typical of guns from this particular geographical area.

Below

Three versions of the Model 1807/1907 series, Anschütz's standard bolt-action ·22 LR rimfire 25m UIT target rifle.

Introduced in the early 1980s, this gun features a stock (shared with the LG380 air-rifle), with an adjustable synthetic comb and lateral slots through the fore-end.

The previous version, dating from about 1973, had a solid high-comb butt and lacked the fore-end slots. A left-hand action is pictured here.

The Model 1807 was replaced by the Model 1907 in 1987. Note the distinctive fluting on the fore-end, and the snap-locks in the butt.

All photographs by courtesy of J.G. Anschütz GmbH.

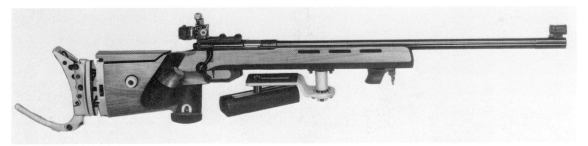

Match 64 action

This bolt action was developed to replace the Flobert II, popular in the lowest-grade sporting and target rifles but lacking the strength for magnum rimfire loads. Though some of the smaller sporting rifles made good use of the sophisticated Match-Verschluss 54, they were so expensive that a cheaper action was developed in the mid 1960s.

The Anschütz **Model 1403** is an intermediate target rifle, embodying the mechanical refinement of the Model 64 action in a simple stock. This has an adjustable butt plate, however, and stippling will be found on the pistol grip. There is a deep fore-end, with a handstop rail, and the trigger is adjustable. Several other variants of this gun, including a short-lived junior Biathlon rifle, have been discontinued.

The **Model 1415** (·22LR), the first of the sporters built on the '64' action, has a walnut-finish beechwood half-stock with a rounded fore-end and a straight comb. The current **Model 1416** (·22LR, made in D and St variants) is similar to the 1415, but has a walnut stock with schnabel fore-end tip, a low Monte Carlo comb, a cheek piece, and chequering on the fore-end and pistol grip. The 1416 DL Classic is the only rifle in this entire series to be offered with a left-hand action.

The **Model 1418** (·22LR) offers a full-length Mannlicher stock with a German-style comb and cheek piece, while the **Models 1515, 1516** and **1518** are identical with their 1400-series equivalents – excepting that they all chamber ·22 WRM instead of ·22LR ammunition. Like their near-relations, 1516 and 1518 patterns may be obtained with the single-stage No.5094 trigger instead of the two-stage 5091.

The **Model 64 MS** is a comparatively recent variant on the standard action for metal silhouette shooting and, primarily, the North American market. It shares the stock of the 1808 MS and 5418 MS (q.v.).

Above

Target rifles embodying the Model 54 action: (A) Model 1808 ED, with a thumb-hole stock and a wooden butt plate required for UIT moving-target competitions; Model 1810 (B), with an adjustable butt plate, generally used for 50m shooting; Model 1811 (C), for prone competitions, with a low comb and a shallow fore-end; and Model 1813 Olympia (D), with an adjustable butt plate and a palm-rest for Free Rifle matches.

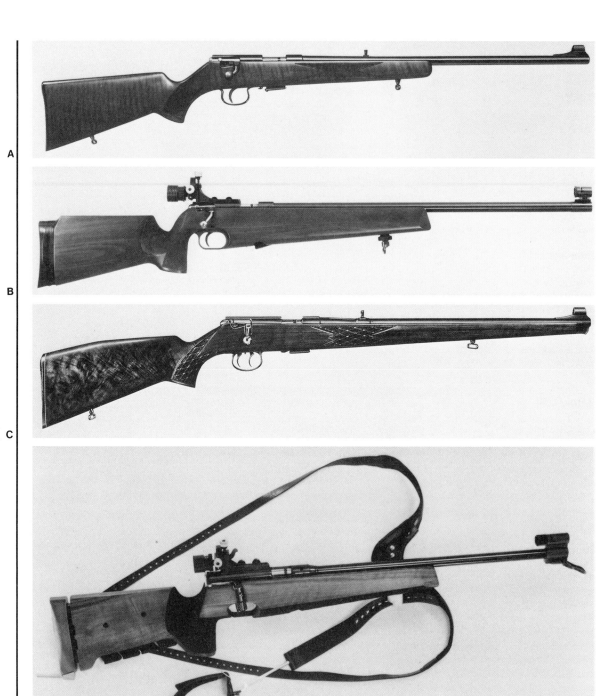

A

B

C

D

Fortner action

24

Unique among Anschütz's products, at the time of writing at least, the **Model 1827 BT** (Biathlon) rifle embodies a straight-pull bolt. Though otherwise identical with the standard Model 1827 B, the BT pattern has a distinctive cylindrical receiver with a knurled steel lever affixed vertically to the tip of the bolt-operating handle. When the lever is pulled with the index finger, the locking lugs are retracted and the bolt will come straight back; pressing the bolt closed with the thumb – an action that can be done virtually without disturbing aim – reloads the chamber and locks the bolt. Biathlon is a form of

shooting, like rapid fire, in which speed is essential; though a straight-pull bolt system is not always advantageous in centre-fire chamberings, where extraction problems may be encountered, it is a notable asset in a rimfire rifle of this type.

Semi-automatic

The **Model 525/61**, which replaced an earlier gun known as the Model 520 (or 520/61), is a conventional blowback design with a box magazine protruding ahead of the trigger, and the butt and fore-end separated by the receiver. Its features include a chequered pistol grip, a folding back sight and rails for an optical sight. A radial safety lever will be found on the right side of the trigger-guard web.

• •

Bernardelli

ITALY

Founded in 1865 but with a lineage traceable to 1721, Vincenzo Bernardelli SpA (I-25063 Gardone Val Trompia [Brescia], Casella Postale 74), is not only one of Italy's best known gunmaking establishments but also among the best. Although renowned for shotguns, pistols and revolvers, Bernardelli also makes a range of double rifles and two semi-automatic carbines.

There are two over/under doubles, known as **Sovrapposto Combinato** Serie 120 and 190; both feature sturdy box locks, double set-triggers and patented selectable extractor/ejector systems (190: ejecting mode only). The 120 has a fixed back sight on a quarter rib, its barrels have a connecting rib, and the pistol-grip butt has a squared cheek piece plus a ventilated rubber butt plate. The Serie 190 features a near-identical action, but is generally found without the barrel-connecting rib. It also has a muzzle-brake,

a plain butt with a solid butt plate; and sling swivels immediately ahead of the fore-end and on the under-edge of the butt. The Serie 190 is intended for hunting and big-game shooting. Although the gap between the barrels looks a little strange – and is deprecated by purists – it has the advantage of isolating each barrel from the effects of heating in its companion. Owing to the burning characteristics of differing propellant, and the greater friction between the bullet and bore compared with shot, this is more than a purely theoretical advantage.

Bernardelli guns are available in a combination of 12-bore and a selection of centrefire cartridges, among them 5·6× 50R Magnum, 5·6× 57R, ·222 Remington, ·243 Winchester, 6·5× 55 Mauser, 6·5× 57R, 7× 57R, 7× 65R, 8× 57, ·30–06, ·308 Winchester (7·62 NATO) and 9·3× 74R. Quality is extremely high, but investment is commensurate.

The Bernardelli **Carabine Semi-Automatiche** (CSA) presents a great contrast to the double rifles, being made with an eye to production expediency and incorporating a die-cast receiver. A simple blowback feeding from a detachable box magazine ahead of the trigger, the CSA may be obtained in 9mm Flobert and ·22 LR rimfire. The Flobert version measures about 1,110mm and has a 620mm barrel; the rimfire is merely 1,020mm long with a 530mm barrel. Weight varies between 2·35 and 2·5kg, depending on the density of the stock-wood and the magazine capacity. Flobert guns usually have plain fore-ends and a pistol-gripped hardwood stock with a Monte Carlo comb, while the rimfires' woodwork is usually chequered and better finished. Sights on the three-shot Flobert version are rudimentary, befitting the primer-propellant cartridge's inherent lack of power and accuracy, but the ten-shot ·22 LR versions are somewhat better.

Vincenzo Bernardelli

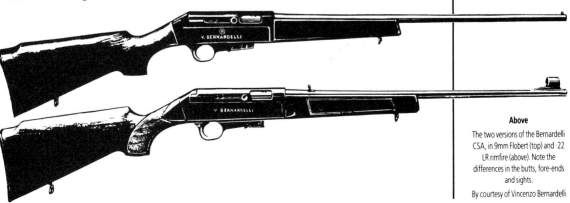

BERETTA

Pietro Beretta SpA, I-25063 Gardone Val Trompia (Brescia), Italy

Beretta is one of the few modern gunmakers with a lineage traceable back to the seventeenth century. As far as modern firearms are concerned, however, the company history begins with the approval of the Mo.1915 pistol during the First World War. Within a few years, Beretta had become one of the leading manufacturers of military-style firearms in Italy, making large numbers of pistols; rifles were made for the Italian army, as well as Greece and Japan, but a series of promising auto-loading rifles had to be abandoned with the advent of the Second World War. Production of Garand-type rifles (BM59 series – see Springfield Armory) commenced late in the 1950s, originally to re-equip the Italian army, and has led to the present generation of ·223 assault rifles. Now owned partly by Fabrique Nationale (q.v.), Beretta is still renowned as one of the world's leading gunmakers – greatly helped by the adoption of the Mo.92-F pistol by the US armed forces, and its subsequent worldwide success.

Product range: Beretta currently makes bolt-action, double- and auto-loading rifles, beautiful shotguns, and an extensive selection of pistols.

Recently discontinued models: excepting the BM59 Garand variants and earlier guns in the AR-70 series, no rifles have been completely abandoned in recent years.

A

B

Carabine Automatiche

Beretta currently offers two selectable single-shot/semi-automatic ·22LR rifles, though substantial numbers of Weatherby autoloaders (q.v.) have also been made. Locking the cocking handle down into its recess converts the rifle into manually operated bolt-action; leaving it up allows the mechanism to reciprocate automatically.

The **Tipo Olimpia** and **Tipo Super Sport** are both blowbacks, fed from detachable five- or ten-round box magazines in the stock ahead of the trigger guard. Both have walnut half-stocks, with low Monte Carlo combs, chequering on the pistol grip and fore-end, and sling swivels placed conventionally beneath the butt and fore-end. The Olimpia also has a cheek piece, which the Super Sport generally lacks. In addition, the Olimpia generally has a plastic pistol-grip cap and conventional (rather than skip-line) chequering.

Though the guns are identical mechanically, the Olimpia has a heavyweight 'target' barrel – with a phosphated anti-glare finish – and its back sight can be adjusted for azimuth as well as elevation. Both rifles will accept an optical sight above the chamber, but only the Olimpia will take an aperture back sight; this fits into the upper tang behind the receiver.

Double Rifles

Though Beretta shotguns have been marketed most successfully for many years, the company only added double rifles to its range in the mid 1980s. Two types are currently available, the box-lock over/under **S689** – in ·30–06 or 9·3x74R – and the **SSO**, which chambers either ·375 H&H Magnum or ·458 Winchester Magnum. The Berettas are usually found with straight-comb pistol-grip butts, and fore-ends of the highest quality; double triggers are standard, as is an open back sight inlet in the traditional quarter-rib. Neither the S689 nor the SSO is cheap; consequently, purchasers often specify additional engraving, to which the SSO, with its additional side plates, is ideally suited.

AR-70 and AR-70/90

The Garand-based BM59 series was extremely successful, equipping the Italian army for more than twenty years and attracting several lucrative export orders. However, the small-calibre revolution begun by the Armalite AR-15 (US Rifle M16) showed the need for a lighter gun. Beretta's designers began work in the late 1960s, and by 1972 had produced two variants of the '70.serie': the Fucile d'Assalto Mo.70 (**AR-70**) and the Carabina per Truppe Speciali Mo.70 (**SC-70**). The latter incorporates a distinctive hinged

skeleton butt and a short barrel. Both guns tap gas conventionally from the mid-point of the barrel to act on the bolt carrier by way of an intermediate piston; the rotating bolt-head carries two opposed lugs that lock into the receiver sides. A combination safety catch/selector will be found on the left side of the frame above the trigger.

Though presenting a conventional appearance, with a dropped butt rather than the more fashionable straight-line layout exemplified by the M16, the AR-70 is designed to simplify mass-production. Consequently, it incorporates stampings, pressings and synthetic furniture. However, despite extensive use of spot welding, the guns soon attained a reputation for reliability; small numbers have been acquired by the Italian armed forces, but official adoption was withheld while extensive trials were undertaken.

So many changes had been made by 1987 that the designation was advanced to **AR-70/90**. The changes are largely cosmetic, as the gas-operated rotating bolt system has been retained. The plastic furniture has been greatly simplified; the release catch has been recessed in the frame ahead of the magazine instead of exposed behind it; the safety catch/selector spindle has been extended through the frame to suit right- or left-handed marksmen; a folding carrying handle

Below

An exploded-view drawing of the AR-70 automatic rifle. Note the locking lugs on the bolt (component 20), which are rotated into the receiver walls when the action closes. The gun bears some internal affinity with the SIG SG 530 (q.v.), which Beretta apparently made under a sub-contract – permitting SIG to circumvent restrictive Swiss arms-exporting regulations.

By courtesy of Pietro Beretta SpA.

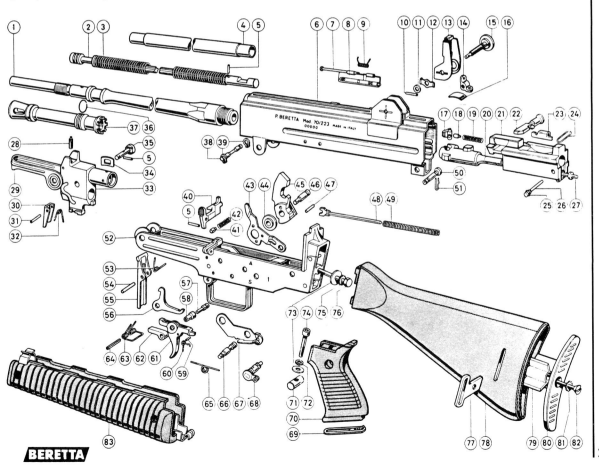

A

B

appears above the receiver; an improved folding butt is standard; and, on the standard full-length infantry rifle at least, a bipod is attached around the barrel behind the gas-port assembly. The AR-70/90 is one component in a series including a shortened carbine (SC-70/90) and a light squad automatic (ML-70/78).

At the time of writing, the Italian army's plans are uncertain; the AR-70/90 may yet have problems convincing the authorities that it is superior to the H&K/Franchi G41. Owing to the appearance of the 70/90, original AR-70 rifles remaining in the warehouse have been touted as ·223 sporting rifles. Restricted to semi-automatic fire, they are usually found with five- or ten-round magazines.

500.serie

Beretta's only bolt-action rifle, which bears an external affinity with the current Sako, is basically a Mauser; two opposed lugs lock horizontally into the receiver immediately behind the breech. However, the extractor is a small claw and the plunger-type ejector is mounted in the recessed bolt face. The standard **Modello 500** has a half-stock with a Monte Carlo comb, a North American-style cheek piece and a plain rounded fore-end tip; the **Mo.500S** is believed to have a full-length Mannlicher stock and a short barrel.

Rifles are also obtainable in Custom Grade (**Mo.500DL**), with a high-quality walnut half-stock. This has a slight hog's back comb, a European-style cheek piece, a ventilated rubber butt plate, chequering on the pistol grip and fore-end, and a schnabel tip. Williams back sights are standard on 500-pattern guns, though a similar range, **Mo.501**, accepts nothing but optical sights.

Chambered for ·222 Remington, ·243 Winchester, ·270 Winchester, ·30–06 and ·308 Winchester, the Beretta 500 is a well-made but rather unspectacular.

Blaser WEST GERMANY

Blaser-Jagdwaffen GmbH of D-7972 Isny/Allgäu, Ziegelstadel 335, makes several interesting rifles: the neat falling-block BL820 and the break-action K77A, plus the bolt-system R84 and SR850.

The **BL820**, introduced commercially in 1982, is an elegant single-shot rifle with an unusually compact falling block action contained almost entirely within the receiver (cf., Ruger No.1). Pushing the trigger-guard spur downward pivots the entire action down around a pivot at the front of the action-plate; simultaneously, the locking block drops down to expose the chamber. Once the gun has been reloaded and the breech closed, the hammer must be cocked manually. Consequently, there is no safety system. Made only in small quantities, the Blaser BL820 offers a combination of excellent design and exemplary quality that places it at the head of the field. Standard chamberings include 5·6×50R Magnum, 6·5×57R, 6·5×68R, 7×57R, 7×65R, ·222 Remington, ·243 Winchester, ·308 Winchester, ·30–06 and ·300 Winchester Magnum.

The **K77A** is a single-shot shotgun-pattern rifle, locked by a radial top-lever. However, the action also employs Blaser's patented block to lock the barrel to a separate transverse shoulder in the receiver. This relieves the receiver itself of the firing shock. A tang-mounted safety is fitted, optional exchangeable barrels are available, and the rifle readily dismantles into three major component-groups. The Circassian walnut butt and fore-end present a particularly pleasing line, while silver pistol-grip caps and engraving on the action may be provided to order. Manufacturing quality is impeccable. However, the gun is light (no more than 2·7kg) and has a considerable kick in magnum calibres: thus the sturdy rubber butt plate is advantageous. There are two minor variants, differing solely in barrel and overall lengths. The smaller of the two (580mm barrel, 1,000mm overall) chambers a selection of medium-power sporting cartridges from ·22–250 and ·243 Winchester to 7× 65R and ·30–06; the larger (610mm/1,030mm) is available only in 7mm Remington Magnum, ·300 Winchester Magnum and ·300 Weatherby Magnum.

The **R84** presents a great contrast to the K77A. The design is a quirky single-shot bolt system with three sturdy locking lugs and a short 60° bolt throw. When the bolt handle is raised, disengaging the lugs from their recesses, the entire non-rotating bolt-housing may be slid back along rails in the receiver. Consequently, there is little of the sloppiness found in many conventional bolt-action rifles. In addition, as the bolt-head locks directly into the barrel, the receiver can be made of high-grade lightweight alloy. The R84 is crammed with odd features: the safety pivots on the rear of the mobile bolt-housing, locking the bolt and the firing pin when applied, and the barrel is readily detachable. As the optical sight mounts directly on the barrel, the R84 does not required re-zeroed when a new barrel/sight combination is fitted. The butt and fore-end are made of Circassian walnut, the latter fitting over a hanger

extending from the receiver to permit the barrel to float freely. Accuracy is greatly enhanced as a result.

R84 Blasers come in two versions, one chambering standard medium-power cartridges and the other a selection of magnums; the rifles, measuring 1,040 and 1,065mm overall respectively, weigh 3·15–3·30kg. The standard pattern is available in ·22–250, ·243 and 6mm Remington, ·25–06, ·270 Winchester, ·280 Remington and ·30–06. Magnums may be obtained in ·257 Weatherby Magnum, ·264 Winchester Magnum, 7mm Remington Magnum, ·300 Weatherby and Winchester Magnums, ·338 Winchester Magnum and ·375 H&H.

The Blaser **SR850** is a modified version of the R84, sharing a similar single-shot bolt action and an exchangeable-barrel system, but has a rather more conventional appearance and an exposed hammer. Like most of these guns, the SR850 is made in very small quantities and is expensive. Quality, however, is excellent.

Browning Arms Company USA

The Browning Arms Company of Route One, Morgan, Utah 84050, handles a wide variety of handguns and shoulder arms. Though some of the pistols are made in the USA, most of the longarms are Belgian – the

Below
Three single-shot Blasers: the shotgun-style break-open K77A (A), the BL820 dropping-block rifle (B), and the quirky R84 bolt-action pattern with one of its readily detachable auxiliary barrels (C).
By courtesy of Blaser Jagdwaffen GmbH.

A

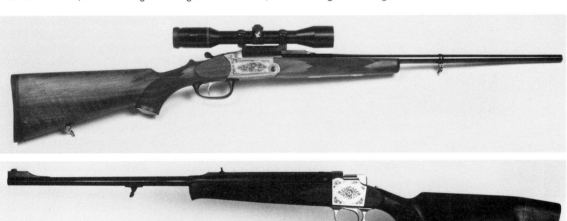

B

C

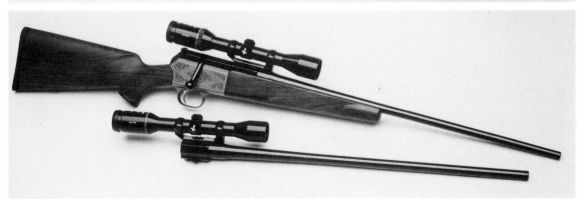

THE RIFLE BOOK
Browning
Charter Arms
Chipmunk
Classic
Commemorative Firearms

products of Fabrique Nationale Herstal (q.v.), a company with which John Browning had had the closest of links. They include the 22 Semi-Auto, A-Bolt, BAR, BL-22 and BLR, all of which are described in the relevant section.

There is also the **Model 1885** single-shot black action rifle, a recreation of Browning's 1878-patent design exploited as the Winchester Model 1885 or High Wall. Replacing an earlier re-creation, the Browning B-78 (now discontinued), the modern Model 1885 features a breech-block sliding vertically downward in the sturdy receiver when the combination trigger-guard and finger lever is pushed down. This action ejects the spent case and cocks the hammer; a new cartridge may be pushed into the chamber, whereafter closing the lever raises the breech-block again. The chamfered top leading edge of the block ensures the cartridge is pushed completely home.

The Model 1885 is the most elegant of the current genre of single-shot rifles, with an octagonal barrel and walnut woodwork. The stock has a straight English-style wrist, while the fore-end has the fashionable schnabel tip. An optical sight is a popular accessory, the barrel being suitably drilled and tapped at the breech, but the ·45–70 Government Model is supplied with open sights.

Charter Arms USA

Charter Arms Corporation of 430 Sniffens Lane, Stratford, Connecticut 06497, is best known for its revolvers, which offer a peerless combination of good quality and low price. However, the company also makes a single rifle, the ·22 LR rimfire **AR-7 Explorer** survival rifle. The Explorer is a simple blowback feeding from a detachable eight-round box magazine ahead of the trigger guard. It also dismantles near-instantaneously into four major components: butt, magazine, action and barrel. No tools are required, as the barrel is retained by a large threaded collar and the action is held in the butt by catches. The parts can then be stowed inside the hollow butt, which is made of buoyant cycolac. Combining a synthetic stock and lightweight alloy components ensures that the gun will float.

Chipmunk USA

Only a single type of bolt action is made by Chipmunk Manufacturing, Inc. of 114 East Jackson, Medford, Oregon 97501, under US patents 4,416,077 and 4,457,094. The **Chipmunk Rifles** (and the Silhouette Pistol) are single-shot rimfire patterns chambering the ·22 Short, Long or Long Rifle cartridges interchangeably, or the ·22 Magnum to special order. The rifle is about 30in overall, has a 16·1in barrel and weighs a mere 2·5lb despite having a walnut stock. Its better features include a rebounding firing pin blocked automatically to prevent accidental discharge, a pleasant trigger pull for a gun of its class, and a low-profile bolt handle that will clear the optional optical sights. The Chipmunk is specifically advertised for 'kids,

campers, backpackers, survival and trappers', though the absence of a magazine can place it at a disadvantage.

Classic USA

The product of the Classic Rifle Company, Inc. of PO Box 321, Charleroi, Pennsylvania 15022, is somewhat glibly advertised as the 'finest rifle anywhere in the world'. However, the guns are quite beautifully made, incorporating hand-finished Sako actions, Shilen barrels, and superb gloss-finished walnut stocks offering a classic profile. Whether the grandiose claim may be justified is arguable, as the Sako action, though better than all but a handful, is by no means perfection; in addition, the Classic is expensive, the Standard Grade beginning at only a little under $2,000 and the Classic Grade II costing upward of $3,500. However, the amount of skilled attention lavished on each gun assures the purchaser of smoothness and excellent accuracy to 0·5MOA or better.

Commemorative Firearms USA

Trading from 2305 South 168th Street in Omaha, Nebraska 68130, Commemorative Firearms is a distributor rather than a manufacturer. The company's place in this directory arises from a purchase of all the commemorative rifles remaining when Winchester was sold by Olin Matheson to the US Repeating Rifle Company (q.v.). Winchester had established a lucrative trade in these guns, but the new owners were concerned more with products than historical tradition, and immediately re-sold the special guns to Commemorative Firearms. At the time of writing, only a few of the many commemorative lever-action Winchesters produced since 1964 (see Table) are still available in any numbers. They include the **Canadian Pacific Railroad Gun**, with 24in barrel and a three-quarter length magazine, a pewtered receiver and a 'CPR' branded butt; the **US Border Patrol Gun**, a short Model 94 with a blued receiver displaying the Border Patrol patch and badge; the **Calgary Stampede Gun**, with a 'CS' branded butt, and a suitably engraved and pewter-plated receiver; the **Saskatchewan Diamond Jubilee Gun**, with a burnished silver receiver (suitably engraved) and a silver medallion inlet in the butt; and the **Great Western Artists Guns**, commemorating Charles M. Russell or Frederic Remington. Engraved in Italy, receivers of the Great Western Artists gun feature adaptations of Russell's paintings 'In Without Knocking' and 'Wild Meat for Wild Men', or, alternatively, Remington's 'Cowboy' and 'A Dash for the Timber'. The guns originally sold for $2,500, but an idea of the declining interest in such special editions – a greatly overworked genre in recent years – may be gauged by the current price of a mere $799.

Details of the basic rifles, now marketed by US Repeating Rifle Company, will be found in the Winchester section.

Recent commmemoratives

WINCHESTER.

Guns marked with an dagger (†) were assembled and finished in Canada.

1 of 1000 (M1894 carbine, set comprising one ·22 and a ·30−30, 1979)

'66' Centennial (M1894 carbine and rifle, ·30−30, 1966)

Alaskan Purchase (M1894 carbine, ·30−30, 1967)

Alberta Diamond Jubilee (M1894 carbine, standard and cased issues, ·38−55, 1980)

American Bald Eagle (M1894 carbine, ·375, 1983); two patterns − Silver and Gold

Annie Oakley (M1894 carbine, ·22, 1982)

Antlered Game (M1894 carbine, ·30−30, 1978)

Apache† (M1894 carbine, ·30−30, 1974)

Bicentennial Carbine (M1894 carbine, ·30−30, 1976)

Boy Scouts of America (M1894 carbine, ·22, 1985)

Buffalo Bill Centennial (M1894 carbine and rifle, ·30−30, 1968)

Calgary Stampede (M1894 Trapper, ·32, 1981)

Canadian Centennial (M1894 carbine and rifle, ·30−30, 1967)

Canadian John Wayne (M1894 carbine, ·32−40, 1981)

Canadian Pacific Railroad (M1894 rifle, Standard, Members and deluxe issues, ·32, 1981)

Cherokee† (M1894 carbine, ·30−30, 1978)

Cherokee (M1894 carbine, ·22, 1978)

Cheyenne† (M1894 carbine, ·44−40, 1977)

Cheyenne (M1894 carbine, ·22, 1977)

Chief Crazy Horse (M1894 carbine, ·38−55, 1983)

Comanche† (M1894 carbine, ·30−30, 1975)

Cowboy (M1894 carbine, ·30−30, 1970)

Eagle Scouts of America (M1894 carbine, cased, ·22, 1985)

Golden Spike (M1894 carbine, ·30−30, 1969)

Great Western Artists (M1894 carbine, two patterns, ·30−30, 1982 and 1983)

Illinois Sesquicentennial (M1894 carbine, ·30−30, 1967)

John Wayne (M1894 carbine, ·32−40, 1981)

John Wayne 'Duke' (M1894 carbine, ·32−40, 1981)

John Wayne '1 of 300' (M1894 carbine, cased, ·32−40, 1981)

Klondike Gold Rush† (M1894 carbine, ·30−30, 1975)

Legendary Frontiersman (M1894 rifle, ·38−55, 1979)

Legendary Lawman (M1894 Trapper, ·30−30, 1978)

Limited Edition I (M1894 carbine, cased, ·30−30, 1978)

Limited Edition II (M1894 carbine, cased, ·30−30, 1980)

Little Big Horn Centennial† (M1894 carbine, ·44−40, 1976)

Lone Star (M1894 carbine and rifle, ·30−30, 1970)

Louis Riel (M1894 Trapper, standard and deluxe issues, ·30−30, 1985)

Nebraska Centennial (M1894 carbine, ·30−30, 1966)

Northwest Territory (M1894 rifle, ·30−30, 1970)

NRA (M1894 carbine and musket, ·30−30, 1971)

Oklahoma Diamond Jubilee (M1894 rifle, ·32−40, 1982)

Oliver F. Winchester (M1894 rifle, ·38−55, 1980)

Royal Canadian Mounted Police (M1894 musket, ·30−30, 1973) − also made as a special "Member's Model"

Saskatchewan Diamond Jubilee (M1894 carbine, standard and cased issues, ·38−55, 1981)

Sheriff Bat Masterson (M1894 carbine, ·30−30, 1979)

Sioux† (M1894 carbine, ·30−30, 1976)

Statue of Liberty (M1894 carbine, ·30−30, 1986) − accompanied by a statuette

Texas Ranger (M1894 carbine, ·30−30, 1973)

Texas Sesquicentennial (M1894 rifle, cased with a matching bowie knife, ·38−55, 1986)

Texas Sesquicentennial (set consisting of an M1894 carbine and a rifle, cased, ·38−55, 1986)

Theodore Roosevelt (M1894 carbine and rifle, ·30−30, 1969)

US Border Patrol (M1894 Trapper, ·30−30, 1981)

Wells Fargo (M1894 carbine, ·30−30, 1977)

Winchester 120th anniversary (M1894 rifle, ·44−40, 1986)

Winchester and Colt (M1894 rifle and Colt M1873 revolver, ·44−40, 1984)

Wyoming Diamond Jubilee (M1894 carbine, ·30−30, 1964)

Yellowboy Indian (M1894 carbine, ·30−30, 1971)

COLT

••

Colt's Inc., 150 Huyshope Avenue, Hartford, Connecticut 06102, USA

A company with a long and tortuous history, Colt began life as the Patent Arms Manufacturing Company in Paterson, New Jersey. This venture was liquidated in 1842, however, and not until the early 1850s did Colt's percussion-ignition revolvers find lasting success. Vast numbers of revolvers have been made ever since, alongside Colt-Browning automatic pistols and a wide range of machine-guns.

Until recent years, Colt was not known as a mass-producer of rifles. Though small numbers of the Colt Lightning pump-action had been made at the turn of the century, the company's reputation has been that of a pistol-smith; only when the Armalite AR-15 was adopted by the US Army (as the M16 rifle) did the balance change. Though beset by problems – fallibility of the M16 in Vietnam in the early days, arguments with the US Treasury, labour disputes – production of M16 and AR-15 sporters continues today. Occasional attempts have been made to market more conventional sporting rifles, including the Sauer Model 90 and a re-creation of the Sharps-Borchardt, but none has been outstandingly successful. Currently, therefore, Colt still relies on the AR-15/M16.

Product range: Colt makes pistols, revolvers and a series of rifles based on the AR-15.
Discontinued models: excepting some of the M16/AR-15 variants, no US-designed gun has been discontinued in recent years – though the original AR-15 Sporter (without bolt assist) was upgraded to AR-15A2 in 1983. From 1975 onward, Colt distributed 'Colt-Sauer' Drilling and bolt-action sporters in North America. Though offered under unfamiliar titles, and sometimes incorporating differing furniture, these were simply bought from Sauer (q.v.). It is suspected that the agreement lapsed when Sauer was purchased by SIG – one of Colt's competitors in the military market-place – but that sufficient guns were on hand to permit sales to continue into the mid 1980s. The Colt-Sauers are described below. In addition, in 1970, Colt purchased the Sharps Rifle Company of Utah (unrelated to the nineteenth-century firm of the same name), which had planned to make a series of rifles on a modernized Sharps-Borchardt action developed by Art Swinson. Unfortunately for aficionados of falling-block actions, the project subsequently failed and surviving rifles are rarely encountered.

Below

A futuristic view of a Pilkington Kite image-intensifying sight mounted on a Colt-made M16A1 rifle.

By courtesy of Pilkington PE Ltd.

AR-15/M16 series

The Armalite AR-15 was developed by the Armalite Division of the Fairchild Engine & Airplane Company in the mid 1950s, to the designs of Eugene Stoner. After protracted US Army trials, the small-calibre lightweight rifle failed to overcome the ingrained prejudice of senior officers who, almost to a man, preferred the more powerful M14. Just when all had seemed lost, the AR-15 had been adopted by the US Air Force in January 1962 as the 5·56mm **Rifle M16**; the first contract, for 8,000 guns and 8·5 million cartridges, was agreed with Colt on 23rd May 1962. A new era had begun.

The US involvement in Vietnam had already led to the procurement of AR-15 rifles for the Vietnamese army (ARVN); the low weight and good handling qualities of the Armalite were well suited to the smaller stature of the Vietnamese soldiers. Though diehards continued to advocate retaining the M14, unexpectedly backed by experts who believed in keeping the M14 while the SPIW projects were being 'perfected' (ultimately, these all failed), 85,000 XM16 rifles were acquired for airborne and US Army Special Forces in 1963.

The XM16 was successful enough, but the army smallarms experts recommended the addition of a manual bolt-closing system even though the air force vehemently opposed it; for a time, the army's modified XM16E1 (reclassified **M16A1** in 1967) was made alongside the USAF M16 until purchasing was rationalized and the latter gun dropped from production.

The history of the M16 series in Vietnam is well known. Owing to unsatisfactory propellant and universally poor maintenance, M16 rifles rapidly fouled and became unserviceable. However, once this problem had been overcome, a modified buffer had reduced the cyclic rate, and the bore and chamber had been chromed, the M16 became a popular battle-proven tool.

The action taps gas from the mid-point of the barrel to impinge directly on the bolt carrier (the primary source of fouling) and rotate the bolt-lugs out of engagement. It is capable of single-shot or fully automatic fire: the selector, combined with the safety catch, appears on the left side of the receiver above the trigger guard. A hinged plate covers the ejection port, opening automatically as the first round is ejected if the firer forgets to do so manually. The AR-15 is comparatively easily identified, as the standard rifle has a distinctive fixed carrying handle/back sight mount above the receiver and notably 'straight-line' construction to minimize muzzle-climb while firing automatically. The butt, fore-end and pistol grip are all synthetic mouldings.

Several differing models have been made. The original **XM16** and **M16** lacked the bolt-closing plunger that protrudes from the right side of the **M16A1** (formerly XM16E1) receiver immediately in front of the joint with the butt. The **M16A2** incorporates a three-round burst fire system; a modified back sight adjustable for azimuth and elevation; stronger furniture; and optimal 1-in-7 rifling twist for the standard NATO ball ammunition. A moulded shield, behind the ejection port on the right side of the receiver, prevents extracted cases being thrown into the faces of left-handed firers.

Among the most unusual derivatives is the **Port Firing Weapon M231**, basically a stripped M16A1 adapted to lock into the firing ports on the standard M2 tracked infantry carrier. Unlike the standard guns, however, the M231 lacks sights,* fires from an open bolt and has a sliding bent-wire butt.

The **Commando** is an AR-15 with a short barrel and a sliding butt, known to the US armed forces as the **XM177**. Guns in the series have included the basic

* The periscope sight is an integral part of the vehicle, and cannot be detached; however, the upper surface of the M231 carrying handle can be used as a rudimentary sight when the gun is removed from its housing.

XM177, with a ten-inch barrel and a large flash-hider;
the XM177E1, with a bolt-assist; and the XM177E2,
no more than an E1 with its muzzle adapted to launch
grenades.

At the time of writing, commercial versions of the
AR-15 series include **AR-15A2 Sporter II**, combining
the heavy barrel (introduced to the US Army in 1985)
with a conventional back sight adjustable for
elevation only; the **AR-15A2 Carbine**, a shortened
version of the Sporter II with a collapsible butt; the
AR-15A2 H-Bar, a commercial variant of the M16A2,
with improved sights, a case-deflector and the heavy
barrel; and the **AR-15A2 Delta H-Bar**. Intended for
police marksmen and SWAT teams, but also useful for
hunting, the Delta model consists of a standard AR-
15A2 H-Bar, selected for accuracy, with a rubber-
armoured 3–9af01.003 optical sight on a special
mounting bracket and a detachable cheek piece on the
butt. When the special components are removed, the
only obvious distinguishing feature is the white-
bordered red triangle insignia let into the pistol grip.
Announced in 1986, the first batches of Delta rifles
were released in February 1987.

The Colt-Sauers

These rifles were available in two action-lengths:
short, for ·22–250 Remington, ·243 and ·308
Winchester; and *standard/magnum* for ·25–06
Remington, ·270 Winchester, 7mm Remington
Magnum, ·30–06, ·300 Weatherby Magnum and ·300
Winchester Magnum. The guns had American walnut
stocks with Monte Carlo cheek pieces, rosewood
pistol-grip caps and fore-end tips, and ventilated
black rubber butt plates. Polyurethane wood finish
was standard, metalwork being blued. The **Grand
Alaskan** rifle, available only in ·375 H&H Magnum,
was stocked in the manner of the other magnums but

had open sights. The **Grand African**, in ·458
Winchester Magnum, was similar to the Grand
Alsakan excepting that the stock wood was bubinga.
A general description of the action will be found in the
Sauer section.

CETME SPAIN

The CETME rifle was the prototype of the Heckler &
Koch G3 (q.v.), though the two designs have diverged
in recent years. Once the German-designed roller lock
had been perfected in Spain, latterly under the
auspices of Centro de Estudios Técnicos de Materiales
Especiales, production of the 7·62×51 **Modelo B**
(or Modelo 58) rifle for the Spanish army began in the
factory of Empresa Nacional Santa Bárbara de
Industrias Militares SA, Joaquin Garcia Morato 31–
6°, Madrid 10. The Mo.58 resembles the first G3, but
has a wooden butt and a folding bipod under the fore-
end; the back sight also differs markedly. The Mo.58
has been offered commercially as the **Modelo C** –
generally encountered with a wooden fore-end – and
the current **Modelo E**, with a distinctive synthetic
fore-end and a short bipod with telescoping legs. The
5·56mm **Modelo L** is a lightened refinement of the
basic roller-lock rifle with a one-piece synthetic
butt/pistol grip assembly; **LC** is identical, apart from a
short barrel and retractable butt.

Santa Bárbara also makes the conventional Mauser
C-75 bolt-action rifle for sporting and snipers' use.

Czechoslovak State Factories

Nationalized after the revolution of 1948, the Czech
firearms industry currently consists of a group of
small semi-independent factories and several large
government arsenals. Guns are exported by
Merkuria, ČSSR-Praha 7, Argentinska 38.
ZKK rifles were designed by the Koucký brothers,

apparently in 1959–62. Based on the preceding ZG47 Mauser, considerably modified, they appeared in the West in 1964. ZKKs are undoubtedly the best sporting rifles made in the Soviet bloc. Even though the woodwork and chequering may fall short of the best Western European standards, the guns are effectually designed and strongly made; they also have a pleasing appearance, the blued barrel and bright-finish bolt contrasting with the parkerized receiver.

The **ZKK600** (1,095mm overall, 3·1kg) embodies a short action suited to ·222 Remington, ·222 Remington Magnum, ·243 Winchester and ·308 Winchester; medium-action **ZKK601** rifles (1,110mm, 3·25kg) chamber ·270 Winchester, 7×57, 7×64, ·30–06, 8×57 or 8×68S; and the largest, **ZKK602** (1,150mm, 4·2kg), currently handles ·358 Norma, ·375 H&H or ·458 Winchester magnums. Straight-comb butts are standard, Monte Carlo stocks being optional.

The ·22 Hornet **ZKW465** and ·222 Remington **ZKB680** (1,075mm, 2·63kg), often known as 'Hornet' and 'Fox' respectively, incorporate a simplified bolt system and detachable box magazines; **ZKM452** (·22LR) has an even simpler action, locked by turning the bolt handle down into its seat, and its magazine lies some way ahead of the trigger.
Rimfire auto-loaders include the **ZK581** (another

Koucký design) and a refinement designated **ČZ511**, with a heavier barrel and an improved stock.

The **Brno Super Express** double rifle has a side-lock action, skip-line chequering on the fore-end, and a straight-comb pistol-gripped butt; it also has an unusually broad rib between the barrels. Chambering 7×65R, ·375 H&H Magnum or 9·3×74R, it is about 1,020mm long and weighs 3·8–4kg. Brno's combination guns include **ZH304** and **ZH324**, chambering 7×57R and 12- or 16-bore shotgun cartridges respectively. They have an extraordinary-looking box lock credited to Václav Holek; the rifle barrel is uppermost, the reverse of usual practice. About 1,030mm overall, they weigh about 3·3kg.

The **Brno Super** is a conventional double-barrel over/under gun, with side locks and the 12-bore shotgun above the 7×65R rifle.

Designed by a team led by Josef Čermák and made in the ČZ factory in Uhersky Brod, the **Samopal vz.58** has been offered commercially with a butt and fore-end made of wood fibres impregnated in plastic resin (vz.58P); with a mounting bracket for infra-red or image-intensifying sights (vz.58Pi); or with a laterally-folding butt (vz.58V). These assault rifles superficially resemble the Kalashnikov, but are locked by a P.38-type tilting block rather than a rotating bolt.

Below
Three typical ČZ rifles – ZKK601 (A), with the optional Monte Carlo-comb stock and an optical sight; the ·22LR ZKM452 Fox (B); and the Brno Super Express double rifle (C), showing the distinctive ultra-broad rib between its barrels.
By courtesy of Karl Schäfer.

A

B

C

Daisy USA

Best known as a maker of airguns, Daisy Manufacturing Company (PO Box 220, Rogers, Arkansas 72757) has occasionally flirted with cartridge weapons – including the abortive Daisy-Heddon VL system of the 1960s, which was supposed to combine the advantages of both with the drawbacks of neither... but failed on all counts. Currently, Daisy's only cartridge rifles are the **Legacy** series. Designed by Jerry Haskins, these are interesting departures from the traditional gunsmithing approach typified – for example – by the Ruger M7022 and rely greatly on Daisy's unrivalled experience with high-strength synthetic materials. One of the most interesting features is the detachable trigger unit, which can be removed for safe keeping; another reminder that though Daisy is widely regarded as a toymaker, owing to its air- and gas-guns, rimfire rifles are far from being toys.

The brief to Haskins appears to have been to develop guns that incorporated visual references to American shooting heritage. Consequently, the Legacy rifles display an odd combination of an octagonal barrel (interchangeable with the smooth-bore shotgun patterns) and synthetic wood-grain stocks. With the exception of a solitary semi-automatic embodying a seven-round detachable box magazine, the Model 2203, all the Legacy guns have a turning-bolt action. The single-shot Model 2201 and the Model 2202, which has a detachable ten-shot rotary magazine, are offered alongside single-shot (Model 2221) and magazine-feed shotguns (2222). There are also combination kits with exchangeable rifled and smooth-bore barrels (Models 2231 and 2232). The Daisy rifles are not as sturdy as some of their traditionally-made rivals, though more than adequate for the power of the rimfire cartridges they chamber. Yet they are very competitively priced and, owing to an effectual distribution system, will surely make an appreciable impact.

Dakota Arms USA

Trading from HC55 Box 326, Whitewood Road, Sturgis, South Dakota 57785, Dakota Arms, Inc. was formed by the amalgamation of Don Allen Inc. and H.L. Grisel – two companies with extensive gunmaking experience. The objective was to produce small quantities of the Dakota 76 rifle, basically a Winchester Model 70 built to the original standards rather than what many people see as the coarsened mass-production pattern of the 1980s. Thus the Dakota 76 has a Mauser-type claw extractor, and the ejector functions only when the bolt has reached the end of its travel; the trigger is a simple-but-rugged adjustable pattern; the three-position safety characteristic of the Model 70 is retained; and the trigger-guard/floor-plate assembly is machined out of a single piece of bar stock. The Dakota also has a special combination bolt-stop, gas shield and bolt guide patented by Peter Grisel.

There are two basic versions of the Dakota 76, which, owing to the amount of special handwork, has acquired a reputation for silky-smooth operation. The Safari Grade (·375 H&H Magnum and ·458 Winchester Magnum only) incorporates a one-piece magazine box unit and a specially selected gloss-finished walnut stock with a Monte Carlo comb and cheek piece. The simpler Classic grade features a more restrained stock design, with a straight comb and – generally – a somewhat duller sheen. Dakota actions, right- or left-hand, can be acquired separately; neither guns nor actions are cheap (the guns started at $1,750 in 1989), but quality always demands a price.

DuBiel USA

Formed in 1975 by Dr John Tyson and Joseph DuBiel, son of the gunmaker John DuBiel, this company (1724 Baker Road, Sherman, Texas 75090) crafts – 'manufactures' is hardly appropriate – small numbers of a bolt-action rifle with a patented five-lug system. The bolt design allows the extractor to pass between two lugs rather than requiring one to be partially cut away, and gives an unusually short 36° locking motion. Other features include a neatly shrouded cocking piece, a longitudinally sliding tang safety (omitted from thumbhole-stock guns), and a pivoting magazine floor-plate locking lever reminiscent of pre-1939 Mauser sporting rifle practice. DuBiel rifles are really custom made, so the stocks may take virtually any form requested by the customer; generally only the best French walnut is used, chequered at 22 lines to the inch. Purchasers may choose maple or wood laminate at no extra cost. DuBiel rifles are expensive, prices beginning at $2,500 at the end of 1989. They may be chambered for virtually any cartridge currently obtainable and are guaranteed to be able to group less than 1·5MOA with factory ammunition. Demand often exceeds production capacity, even though most guns are made to order; delivery time may be as much as six months.

Dumoulin BELGIUM

The products of Dumoulin Frères et Cie SA of Liège are encountered only rarely outside Europe. They include bolt-action sporting rifles, originally built on the FN Mauser action but now apparently incorporating Sako patterns. The standard Mauser-action model, modified by the addition of a Winchester M70-type safety catch, is called **Bavaria** or **Diane** (octagonal or round barrels respectively). It may be obtained in a profusion of chamberings: ·22–250, ·222, ·222 Remington Magnum, ·223, ·240 Weatherby, ·243 Winchester, ·25–06, 6mm Remington, 6·5×57, 6·5×68, ·264 Winchester, 7×57, 7×64, ·270, 7mm Remington Magnum and Remington Express (·280 Remington), ·300 Weatherby, ·300 Winchester, ·30–06, ·308 Norma Magnum, 8×68S, ·338 Winchester, ·375 H&H Magnum, 9·3×64 and ·458 Winchester Magnum.

The rifles will usually be encountered with European-style walnut stocks and quick-detachable swivels. Barrels are invariably of Böhler steel, but Dumoulin rifles are not cheap: the Bavaria started at about £1,500 in 1988.

The Dumoulin **African Safari** rifle, built on Mauser or Finnish Sako actions, is designed for big-game hunting. Distinguished by a classic English-style stock, with a straight comb and an elegant cheek piece, the African Safari features a pistol-grip cap of buffalo horn and a solid rubber butt plate. Rifles are available in most popular high-power chamberings – 6.5×68, ·264 Winchester, 7mm Remington Magnum, 7mm Weatherby Magnum, ·300 H&H Magnum, ·300 Weatherby Magnum, ·300 Winchester, 8×68S, ·338 Winchester, ·340 Weatherby Magnum, 9·3×64, ·375 H&H Magnum, ·404 Jeffrey, ·416 Rigby, ·416 Hoffmann and ·458 Winchester Magnum. Others will be made to special order. The African Safari rifles weigh 8·5–9lb, depending on calibre, and are thus more easily controlled than the lighter Bavaria and Diane in the most powerful calibres. However, even a 9lb gun is difficult to control in ·458 Winchester Magnum. Largely custom-made, their prices began at £2,250 in 1988.

The company also offers two double rifles, the box-lock **Pionier**, with Greener cross-bolt and Holland & Holland-type ejectors, and the side-lock **Prestige**. The latter offers a choice of chopper-lump or Classic Ernest Dumoulin barrel systems, has a quarter-rib and gold-plated internal parts to withstand the ravages of time and corrosion. Built to special order in any calibre imaginable, these guns will stretch a purchaser's resources appreciably: the Pionier began at $5,500 in 1988, while even the most basic of the ten grades of Prestige cost nearly £15,000. And there is also a lengthy waiting list!

Erma WEST GERMANY

Best known for its handguns, Erma-Werke GmbH (D-8060 München-Dachau, Postfach 1269) also makes cartridge rifles, blank-firers and a re-creation of the US Gallager percussion-ignition carbine.

Auto-loaders modelled on the US M1 Carbine include the blowback **EM122*** (·22LR, 900mm overall, 2·55kg), with a standard military-pattern half-stock and a ten- or fifteen-round magazine; Modell 70 or **EGM1** (·22LR), similar to EM122 but with a plain butt, a sporting-pattern front sight and a five-round magazine; and **ESG22** (·22 WMR, 965mm, 3·05kg), featuring a gas-operated locked breech and a refined stock with a Monte Carlo comb.†

Lever-action Erma 'Winchesters' include **EG712** (·22 Short, Long and LR) – 910mm overall and weighing about 2·4kg – with a straight-wrist butt and a tube magazine holding fifteen (·22LR), seventeen (·22 Long) or 21 rounds (·22 Short). **EG73** rifles, similar externally to EG712 but 4cm longer and 150gm heavier, chamber ·22 WMR and have twelve-round magazines; **EG76** chambers 4mm M20 primer-propellant cartridges and has a ten-round magazine.

Erma also makes a EG76-type lever-action blank-firer (EG294), an electronic version for target practice (EG80 Ermatronic) and even a similar-looking airgun (ELG10).

EG722 is a pump-action EG712 derivative, made in all three ·22 rimfire chamberings with identical magazine capacities to its lever-action prototype. Two ·22LR rimfire bolt-action rifles – **E61** and **E62** – have also been produced; single-shot and magazine-fed respectively, they are about 970mm long and weigh 2·2–2·3kg.

* Also known as as 'EM1', which may have been its original designation.

† The standard military-stype stock and hand guard can be fitted on request.

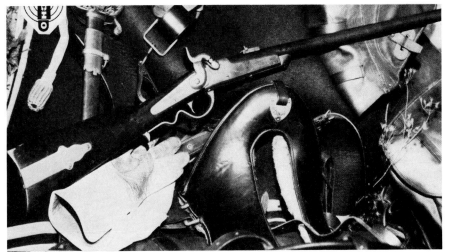

Left

Two typical Erma products: the EM122, one of the many ·22LR auto-loading derivatives of the US M1 Carbine; and the replica Gallager percussion-ignition carbine.

By courtesy of Erma-Werke GmbH.

FN

Fabrique Nationale Herstal SA, Branche Défense et Securité, B-4400 Herstal (Liège), Belgium

Fabrique Nationale was founded in 1889 to make Mauser service rifles. It has since grown to become one of the world's largest gunmaking establishments – in addition to manufacturing products ranging from aero-engines to tennis racquets. After the dislocation of two world wars, and the decline of the Mauser rifle in favour of auto-loaders, the 7·62mm FAL became the NATO standard. The rifle has since sold in more than ninety countries and remains front-line issue in many of them. However, despite investing extensively in Beretta, FN's smallarms business has declined perceptibly in recent years; the large-calibre FAL is now regarded as obsolescent, and the perfected 5·56mm FNC enjoys nothing like the dominance of its parent.

Product range: handguns, shotguns, sporting rifles, and military weapons ranging from pistols to heavy machine-guns.

Recently discontinued models: the *CAL,* or Carabine Automatique Légère, was the first 5·56mm version of the FAL. Successful enough to sell to several armies – though never in huge numbers – it has now been replaced by the FNC. Only recently discontinued, the ·22LR *T-Bolt* had a straight-pull bolt and a detachable five-round box magazine.

Military rifles

Below

The FN sniper rifle is built on the last of the FN-Mauser actions. Note the bipod and the extraordinary design of the adjustable-comb butt.
By courtesy of Fabrique Nationale Herstal SA.

The basis of FN's success has been the **FAL**, or Fusil Automatique Léger (LAR, 'Light Automatic Rifle'). This gas-operated rifle was based on the SAFN, developed shortly before the Second World War and introduced commercially in 1949. However, its construction was greatly simplified until, after protracted trials, it became the NATO standard. The

FAL is a thoroughly conventional weapon, locked by a tilting bolt copied from the Russian Tokarev; a lack of originality is often advantageous in weapons, however, and the Belgian gun is sturdy and reliable.

FAL-type rifles have been manufactured throughout South America, in Germany and Austria, in Britain (Rifle L1 series), in Canada, in South Africa and elsewhere. FN currently offers the standard **Type**

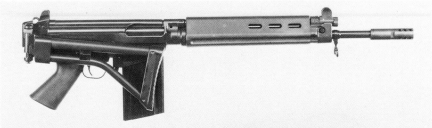

Three of FN's military rifles: the standard 7·62×51 FAL, Type 50-00 (A); the short-barrelled Type 50-63 Para (B); and the 5·56mm FNC (C).
By courtesy of Fabrique Nationale Herstal SA.

50−00 selective-fire rifle with nylon furniture, a fixed butt, a tubular flash-suppressor, and parkerized finish. It is 1,090mm long and weighs about 4·25kg without its magazine. **Type 50−64 Para** has a tubular-frame butt, folding laterally to the right, but is otherwise similar to the infantry model; **Type 50−63** is identical to the standard Para model except for its short barrel (458mm instead of 553mm) and fixed 300m battle sight. It lacks a hold-open or carrying handle, and the cocking handle folds against the receiver. An **FAL HB** or Type 50−41, intended as a light support weapon, has a special heavy barrel, a sturdier hand guard, nylon or wood furniture, a combination flash suppressor/muzzle brake, and a folding bipod attached to the muzzle. Owing to the design of the barrel, which cannot be changed quickly, the 7·62mm HB (1,150mm, 6·73kg with a loaded twenty-round magazine) has never been as popular as the standard infantry rifle.

The 5·56×45 **FNC** ('Fabrique Nationale Carabine') has probably been perfected too late to dominate a small-calibre market in which the US M16A1 remains the market leader. However, the FNC is well made, sturdy and effectual enough to persuade Belgian, Swedish and other armies to adopt it.

A gas-operated selective-fire rifle locked by a rotating bolt, the FNC has been designed specifically for mass production: heavy-duty pressings and welded seams provide ample evidence. The standard rifles − **Types 2000** and **0000** (1-in-7 and 1-in-12

rifling respectively) − have 45cm barrels giving them an overall length of 997mm with the folding butt extended; a fixed polyamide butt is optional. Barrels and chambers are chromed to extend useful life, and there is a three-round burst fire system. Standard long-barrel rifles accept a tubular-handle bayonet and can fire grenades.* The Type 2000 weighs 4·36kg with a loaded thirty-round magazine.

Short rifles, **Types 7000** and **6000**, have 36cm barrels, measure 911mm overall and weigh 3·7kg unladen. Semi-automatic 'Law Enforcement' variants are made for police and security services, but are otherwise identical with the short-barrel FNC. **Type 7030** has 1-in-7 rifling for the Belgian SS109 bullet, while **Type 6040** has the 1-in-12 pattern suited to the US M193.

Sporting auto-loaders

The **BAR**, or Browning Automatic Rifle, is an elegant gas-operated centre-fire design locked by seven lugs on the bolt engaging the receiver. A patented combination hinged floor-plate/detachable box magazine is fitted, allowing the box to be replenished without necessarily removing it, and the safety features are exemplary. Two variants are made: **Affût** − with a conventional adjustable back sight − and **Battue**, with a small folding leaf let into a quarter rib. Standard rifles have plain walnut pistol-grip butts and fore-ends, extensively chequered, but deluxe Grade IV examples will be richly decorated.

* Guns can be supplied with the standard US M8 knife bayonet, which requires a different muzzle fixture.

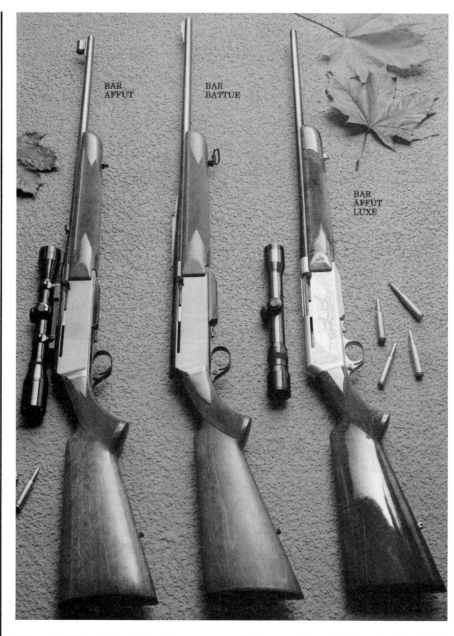

BARs are 1,097 (standard) or 1,146mm long
(magnums), and weigh 3·4 – 3·7kg; they currently
chamber ·270 Winchester, 7mm Remington Magnum,
·30 – 06, ·308 Winchester (Affut only), and ·300
Winchester Magnum. Magnum rifles have six-groove
twist instead of four, and their magazine capacities
are restricted to four rounds instead of five.

The **BAR 22**, a blowback ·22LR rimfire auto-loader,
resembles the centre-fire BAR externally. However, it
has a fifteen-round tube magazine beneath the barrel,
measures 972mm overall and weighs a mere 2·85kg.
The Browning **Automatic 22** dates back to the early
years of the twentieth century. Its most distinctive
feature is the loading port in the butt, the tube
magazine running backward from the receiver.

Unlike many rimfire auto-loaders, the Automatic 22
will feed Short and Long Rifle cartridges
interchangeably; maximum capacity is eleven Short
or sixteen Long Rifle rounds. The gun is 940mm
overall and weighs 2·15kg unladen.

Bolt-action sporters

Since the demise of the FN-Mauser, Fabrique
Nationale has exhibited a schizophrenic attitude
towards centre-fire bolt action rifles. The current
BBR rifle offers a nine-lug bolt with a 60° throw and a
combination hinged floor-plate/box magazine with a
patented scissors elevator, but is otherwise
conventional enough. Quality is very high, though
the oddly angular cocking-piece shroud spoils the

guns' looks. The standard rifle currently has a Monte Carlo stock with a high-gloss finish.† A Williams ramp back sight may be replaced with a Battue rib and folding leaf on request. BBR rifles chamber ·270 Winchester, 7mm Remington Magnum, ·30–06 or ·300 Winchester Magnum, magazine capacities being four regular or three magnum rounds.

FN has also made small numbers of the **FN-Sauer**, though production may now have ceased. Based on the Sauer Model 90 (q.v.), the FN version has a massive forged-steel receiver separating the fore-end from the hog's back combed butt. Chequering graces the pistol grip and the fore-end, and a ventilated rubber butt plate is standard. The lock time of 2·77 milliseconds is very fast for such a long action. Chamberings have included ·270 Winchester, 7×64, 7mm Remington Magnum, ·30–06, ·300 Winchester Magnum and 8×68S.

Lever- and pump-action sporters

The **BLR** is the current FN-made centre-fire lever-action rifle, locked by a seven-lug rotating bolt and fed from a detachable four-round box magazine. This is amply strong enough to handle ·243 and ·308 Winchester cartridges, giving the BLR an advantage over most other lever-action repeaters. Its trigger system is mounted on the actuating lever assembly, moving with the finger lever to prevent pinching. However, despite the traditional appearance of the straight-wrist butt, the rifle does not yet enjoy the reputation it deserves: too many marksmen seem to prefer the larger capacity of a tube magazine to the considerable advantages of a box!

FN's **BL 22** is a rimfire diminution of the BLR, featuring a 33° lever-throw and a locking block instead of a rotating bolt, A tube magazine, beneath the barrel, holds fifteen ·22LR, seventeen ·22 Long or twenty-two ·22 Short cartridges. The **BPR 22** is simply a pump-action BAR 22, with a tube magazine handling up to eleven ·22 WMR or fifteen ·22LR cartridges; 933mm overall, the gun weighs 2·85kg unladen.

Combination guns

As part of an extensive range of high-quality shotguns, Fabrique Nationale offers the **Browning Express** rifle in 7×65R and 9·3×74R. The standard box-lock action – side locks are available on super-deluxe guns – is reinforced to withstand the greater pressures generated by rifle ammunition, there are several patented features, the back sight is let into a quarter rib, and the quality of wood and metal is exemplary. Indeed, the highest grades of engraving are works of art rather than mere firearms.

GIAT FRANCE

Groupement Industriel des Armements Terrestres (F-92211 Saint-Cloud, 10 place Georges Clemenceau), offers several rifles commercially.

The 5·56×45 **FAMAS** is an extraordinary-looking bullpup assault rifle, with a carrying handle/sight-channel running virtually half the length of the gun to justify its nickname 'Le Clairon' ('the bugle'). However, the delayed blowback action works too near its limits and the French may well replace the FAMAS in the near future. Ejection can be changed from right to left merely by re-positioning the extractor and reversing the cheek piece.

FR-F1 (7·5×54 or 7·62×51) and **FR-F2** sniper rifles (7·62×51) are adaptations of the pre-war bolt action MAS36. However, though popular with the French army and police, neither rifle has sold extensively abroad.

† A selection of differing finishes, including traditional oil-rubbed, is available to order.

Below
This Browning Express 124 is typical of FN's excellent over/under double rifles; like most of them, it can accept an exchangeable shotgun barrel cluster.
By courtesy of Fabrique Nationale Herstal SA.

Bottom
The 7·5×54 French FR-F1 sniper rifle is an odd-looking design, based on the pre-war rifle MAS36. This particular gun has folding open sights, though the rifles are usually encountered with an optical sight.
By courtesy of Ian Hogg.

Federal Engineering USA

The products of Federal Engineering Corporation
(3161 North Elston Avenue, Chicago, Illinois 60618)
barely classify as rifles, being more justifiably
labelled 'machine carbines'. Chambering ·22 LR
rimfire (XC-220), ·45 ACP (XC-450 or 9mm
Parabellum (XC-900), they all make use of genuine
Colt AR-15 action components – mostly in the trigger
group – and offer parkerized steel parts (an optional
Teflon coating is recommended if the guns are to be
used in extreme climates). The back sight bridge is
grooved to accept an optical sight mount, but is
usually encountered with a Williams aperture sight.
Virtually all the parts are machined and then welded
together; quality is good for weapons in this class and
reliability is usually exemplary.

Feinwerkbau WEST GERMANY

Feinwerkbau–Westinger & Altenburger GmbH & Co.
KG of D-7238 Oberndorf/Neckar, Neckarstrasse 43,
founded in 1948, began to make high quality airguns
in the early 1960s. So successful did this business
become, and so many European and world
championships gained with them, that the company
diversified into small-bore rifles in the late 1970s. The
goal was to provide airguns and cartridge rifles with
the same stock design to satisfy multi-discipline
marksmen. This aim has largely succeeded, as
Feinwerkbau rimfire rifles now jostle with the best of
Anschütz, Walther and other designs worldwide. Top
of the range is the **Modell 2000 Super Match**,
intended for Free Rifle shooting. The gun is
immediately recognisable by its beige-colour
laminated stock, intended to maximize warp
resistance, and by the proliferation of angular
accessories: a fully-adjustable hooked butt plate, an
elevating comb, the optional palm rest, a muzzle-
weight bar and adjustable over-barrel
handguard/weight assemblies. The action is a
conventional bolt pattern, made for right- or left-
handed firers, but the rifle's glory lies in its patented
electronic trigger. By careful attention to the current-
paths, Feinwerkbau managed to develop a system
needing neither a switch (leak-losses are so low that
the battery is left permanently on) nor a warning
light, as the warm-up time is a mere three seconds.

The standard small-bore rifle is currently the
Modell 2600, which mates the laminated stock
design of the 600-series air rifles with the bolt-action
of the Modell 2000 Super Match. The cheek piece may
be elevated, and the butt plate slides in a channel that
automatically adjusts rake with changes in height.
The gun features a floating barrel, standard
Feinwerkbau aperture sights, and a mechanical
trigger in which careful design reduces lock time to a
minimum.

Older Feinwerkbau small-bore rifles of the **2000
series** are still available. These amalgamate the
general lines of the Feinwerkbau 300 air rifle with a
predecessor of the '2600' bolt action and mechanical
trigger. They are much more conventionally finished,
with stipple-roughened walnut – or occasionally
beech – stocks. Four variants are made: the Modell
2000 UIT Standard, with a stippled fore-end and a
plain butt; the 2000 UIT Universal, identical
mechanically but with an adjustable comb; the 2000
UIT Junior, with a shortened barrel, fore-end and
butt; and the 2000 UIT Laufende Scheibe for moving-
target shooting, which has a wooden butt plate, an
elevating comb/cheek piece, a handgrip-and-weights
system on a rail beneath the heavy barrel, and optical
sights.

Feinwerkbau rifles are undoubtedly among the
leaders in their fields, but the garish appearance and
angular design of the newest examples has yet to meet
universal favour.

Francotte BELGIUM

Currently trading from Rue de Trois Juin 109 in
Herstal, "Auguste Francotte et Cie, Fabricants
d'Armes" – a trading name of Auguste Francotte–
Précision Liègeoise – claims a lineage back to 1805,
though there have been several changes of ownership
in the interim. Current products include **double rifles**
with back-action side- or Anson & Deeley box-locks,
plus a solitary bolt-action rifle. The double rifles are
typical of this almost exclusively European genre,
offering excellent quality at a price – starting at
725,000 Belgian francs in 1989 – which can soar once
the otherwise plain actions have been engraved. They
have chopper-lump barrels of chrome nickel steel,
quarter ribs with multi-leaf back sights, and are

Photographs by courtesy of Feinwerkbau – Westinger & Altenburger GmbH & Co.

Feinwerkbau®

Above

The Feinwerkbau Model 2000 Junior ·22LR rimfire target rifle, with a special short barrel and an abbreviated stock.

Above

The Feinwerkbau Model 2600 small-bore rifle. Note the free-floating barrel and the most distinctive laminated stock.

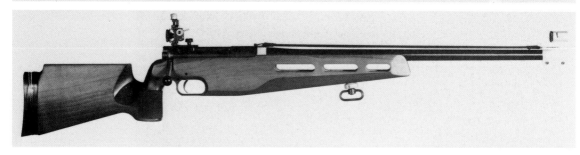

A

B

C

Above

Three Grünel target rifles: a 300m full-bore pattern (A) built on a Swiss military Kar.31 Schmidt-Rubin action, with a heavy barrel and a special stock; a Matchkugelbüchse (B), built on a proprietary bolt action with a set-trigger system; and a ·22LR rimfire UIT Standard rifle (C), with an Anschütz-pattern stock and a 'mirage band' above the barrel.

invariably ejectors. Some guns will be found with twin triggers, the forward one often folding, while others will have single selective set-trigger systems. Butts and fore-ends are made of the finest European or Circassian walnut, the purchaser being offered a wide choice of style. A simple butt with a straight comb and a pistol grip is deemed standard; however, a Monte Carlo comb is commonly specified in cases where optical sights are to be fitted. The Francotte **bolt-action**, which is substantially cheaper than company's double-barrelled rifles, is a refined but otherwise quite standard Mauser. It is generally encountered with its back sight on a quarter-rib; a classic straight-comb pistol grip stock of the finest walnut; and the restrained decoration typical of European-market guns.

Grünel SWITZERLAND

Grünig & Elmiger AG, Jagd- und Sportwaffenfabrik, of Malters, is best known for sub-calibre inserts for the Swiss Parabellum and other handguns, bolt-action target rifles and some excellent sights.

The earliest Grünig & Elmiger rifles were based on the Swiss Kar.31 service rifle, with a Schmidt-Rubin straight-pull bolt, but modern weapons are built around the company's own action. However, stocks and other components are usually bought in from Anschütz. Among the guns currently available are bolt-action **Matchkugelbüchsen** – Standard and

Luxus – with a distinctive trigger system in which the rear lever is set by pushing forward on the 'reverse trigger' in the front of the guard. These guns generally have solid beavertail fore-ends and freely floating barrels, and can be obtained in chamberings ranging from ·222 Remington to 8× 68S. Light patterns weigh about 3·8kg, but the heavy guns may reach 5kg.

The **Matchgewehr UIT Standard** – available in ·222 Remington, ·243 Winchester, 6·5× 55 Mauser, 7·5 Swiss or ·308 Winchester (7·62 NATO) – offers an Anschütz-pattern stock with lateral slots in the fore-end, allied to a Grünel bolt action. Trigger pull is regulated to 1,500gm and quality is extremely high. The **Matchgewehr 300m LM** (Liegendemodell), shares the action of the UIT Standard but is specifically designed for shooting in the prone position. Consequently, the stock has a shallower fore-end and the comb and butt plate are noticeably higher. Most guns made after 1985–6 will be found with an elevating comb.

Grünig & Elmiger's **Target 200** features a purpose-built stock as well as the company's bolt action and an electronic trigger, while the **Super Target 200/40 Free Rifle**, available in the standard calibres listed previously, features a special thumb-hole stock, a hand-rest beneath the fore-end and an adjustable hooked butt plate. The Super Target 200/40 has replaced the similar **Matchgewehr 300m**, which embodied a conventional mechanical trigger and an Anschütz stock.

Virtually all these rifles feature a 'mirage band', a long matted strap running forward from above the chamber to the front sight base. This prevents unwanted reflection from the barrel surface disturbing the sight picture, yet is isolated from the worst effects of barrel heating.

Harrington & Richardson USA

Once trading from Gardner, Massachussetts, the long-established Harrington & Richardson, Inc., collapsed in 1988. The rump of the company continues as the New England Firearms Company (q.v.), but all but a solitary example of the H&R rifles have gone. Prior to its demise, however, H&R made a series of bolt- and break-action patterns. New guns may still be purchased from dealers' stocks.

The brand-leader was the **Model 340**, a centrefire sporter built on a Swedish Husqvarna-made Mauser bolt action (H&R rifles made during the 1970s used Sako patterns). Offered in a selection of chamberings, including ·243 Winchester and 7mm Mauser, the M340 was an elegant well-finished rifle with a classic stock profile. But it could not hope to compete with the newest US-made guns, in particular the Ruger M77, at a time when H&R was struggling financially.

At least part of H&R's demise seems to have been due to the introduction of the **Model 5200**, a ·22 LR rimfire bolt-action. Though the rifles were well made and quite attractive, certain features – the cheap looking bolt handle and the flimsily stamped trigger blade – weighed against them. The H&R products could not compete against rival guns being brought in from Germany, particularly Anschütz and Krico patterns, nor ultimately against the Ruger 7722. The 5200 Match Rifle was particularly unlucky, as it offered very good performance at an acceptable price and had the publicly-exploitable merits of being American-made.

Below

Grünel target rifles: the Target 200 (A), with a proprietary bolt action and an electronic trigger; and the conventional Matchgewehr 300m (B), with a mechanical trigger and an Anschütz-type stock.

By courtesy of Grünig & Elmiger AG.

A

B

Left

The Harrington & Richardson Model 340 rifle, with the magazine floor-plate open. This particular gun embodies a Swedish Husqvarna-Mauser action.

45

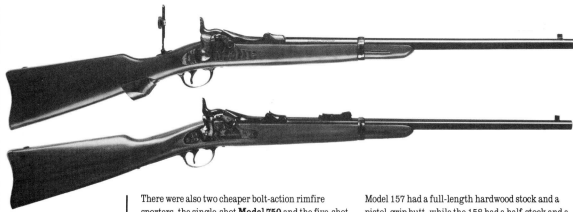

Above

Harrington & Richardson's re-creations of the 'Trapdoor Springfield' carbines, Models 174 (top) and 171 (above).

There were also two cheaper bolt-action rimfire sporters, the single-shot **Model 750** and the five-shot **Model 865**. Both were well made, but had little else to offer a highly competitive market. The same strictures applied to the two small ·22 rimfire semi-automatics, the **Models 700** and **700 deluxe**. The only US-made auto-loaders chambering the ·22 WMR cartridge, the guns received considerable critical acclaim when they were introduced. However, as so often happens, the praise could not offset the comparative scarcity and high cost of magnum rimfire ammunition. Ironically, the Model 700 may have encountered greater success had it chambered the ubiquitous ·22 LR!

Harrington & Richardson also made single-shot break-action rifles patterned on the company's most basic exposed-hammer shotguns, with a thumb-catch lock on the right side of the receiver behind the breech. At the time of the company's demise, these included the **Models 157** and **158**, plus a convertible **Model 058 Combination Gun** and the **Model 258 Handy Gun II** (which was simply a short-barrelled 058 with Hard-Guard electroless nickel finish). The Model 157 had a full-length hardwood stock and a pistol-grip butt, while the 158 had a half-stock and a straight wrist. Barrels measured 22in, giving an overall length of about 37in and a weight of 6–6·5lb. The 157 chambered ·22 Hornet and ·30–30 only, while the 158 was additionally available in ·38 Special/·357 Magnum and ·44 Magnum. The Combination and Handy Guns could exchange 22in rifled barrels chambering ·22 Hornet, ·30–30, ·38 Special/·357 Magnum and ·44 Magnum with a 26in 20-gauge smooth-bore.

H&R was responsible for two versions of the ·45–70 1873-model or 'Trapdoor Springfield' carbine, with 22in barrels, an overall length of about 41in and a weight of 7–8lb. The **Model 171** had an engraved lock plate, a ladder-pattern back sight and a colour case-hardened receiver; the **Model 174**, loosely based on the so-called "Officer's Rifle" of 1875, substituted a vernier tang-sight for the military ladder and had a detachable metal pistol grip. The replicas were popular with 'Trapdoor aficionados', as they were sturdily made of far superior material to most imports.

HECKLER & KOCH

●●

Heckler & Koch GmbH, D-7238 Oberndorf/Neckar, Postfach 1329, West Germany

Founded in Oberndorf in 1949, to refurbish and manufacture machine tools in the aftermath of the Second World War, H&K has now taken over much of the mantle of the once-great Mauser smallarms operations. This is none too surprising, since the company's success has been based on a roller-lock breech developed by Mauser engineers in 1942–3 and embodied successfully in the experimental StG.45 (M) [Gerät 06] series) before hostilities had ended. Huge quantities of G3 rifles have been made world-wide – it is service issue in more than twenty countries – and production has been licensed to several other manufacturers. However, though the G3 and its small-calibre derivatives – HK33 and G41 – have been most successful, H&K has staked a considerable amount on the perfection of its caseless-cartridge G11 project.

Product range: in addition to the military rifles, H&K makes pistols, submachine-guns, sporting guns and machine-guns embodying the basic roller-lock action. Blow-back pistols and sporting rifles, signal pistols, grenade launchers and a vast range of accessories are also manufactured in Oberndorf.

Recently discontinued models: very few. The HK33A2 (fixed butt), HK32A3 (retractable butt) and HK32KA1 (short barrel, retractable butt) were variants of the HK33 series, chambering the Russian 7·62×39 round instead of 5·56×45; they were comparatively unsuccessful, owing to the availability of millions of cheap Kalashnikovs chambering the same cartridge, and are now rarely encountered.

G3 series

These rifles, which have been made in varying guises since the late 1950s, share an identical delayed blowback action. Designed in Germany in the early 1940s but subsequently perfected by German emigré engineers in Spain, the principle is extremely simple: when the gun fires, part of the pressure generated in the cartridge case pushes the cartridge-case head back against the bolt-head. However, before the bolt can move back, vertical rollers must be disengaged from the receiver walls; though this takes no more than a few milliseconds, chamber pressure has dropped to a point where the action can open safely.

Though theoretical objections have often been made against this system, owing to the lack of a positive mechanical lock at the instant of firing, there is little doubt that it works well. It is true that the Heckler & Koch rifles have quite violent operation cycles – fluted chambers are used to facilitate extraction – and are not always as tolerant of fluctuating ammunition pressures as conventional designs, but there have been few complaints from the military users. Excepting the Belgian FAL, the Kalashnikov and possibly the US M16, the G3 is the most successful post-war military rifle; in addition, uniquely, it has spawned a whole family of derivatives.

The original G3 variants included the G3A3 and G3A4, with fixed and retractable butts respectively. Among the current versions, however, there is far greater variety.

The **G3 INCAS** – made with fixed or retractable butts – are standard rifles with an integral infra-red laser sighting system for use in poor light. The gun is conventional enough, excepting that it has a laser projector built into the front of the cocking-handle tube. The laser is activated by a catch above the tip of the fore-end behind the front sight. To operate the system, the firer must lock the detachable Philips Elektro-Spezial BM 8028 image-intensifying goggles into his face mask. The target is found with the aid of these goggles, the sights are roughly aligned, and the laser projector is switched on; a small dot of bright light then appears on the target out to 300m in starlight conditions. The gun can be fired once the dot has been laid accurately, significantly increasing chances of a hit. There is little doubt that the system works well enough in ideal conditions; however, the cumbersome goggles and the lack of peripheral vision reduce general utility appreciably.

The **G3-TGS** – 'Tactical Group System' – is a G3 variant with an integral single-shot HK79 grenade launcher replacing the fore-end/hand-guard assembly, and an additional radial sight on the right side of the fore-end. The HK79 breech drops down to load, controlled by a latch under the breech and the striker must be cocked manually before each shot. An auxiliary thumb trigger lies on the left side of the frame above the barrel. 40mm grenades can be projected to a maximum distance of 350m, including high-explosive fragmentation patterns, hollow-charge and anti-barricade grenades, smoke and flare loadings, CS and CN gas canisters, plus baton and 'dazzle' rounds.

An interesting combination weapon, the G3-TGS has proved popular and effectual. The grenade launcher brings with it the penalty of extra weight – 1·5kg, raising the gun weight to 5·4kg (fixed-butt pattern) – but this is not sufficient to be unbearable.

The HK33 series was originally essentially similar to the G3 rifles, but chambered the 5·56×45 round adopted by NATO to replace the 7·62×51 pattern. The HK33E was appreciably lighter than the standard G3 – weighing 3·65kg with a fixed butt (originally known as the HK33A2) or 4·00kg with the retractable pattern (HK33A3) – while the short-barreled HK33EK (formerly HK33KA1), only available with a retractable butt, weighed 3·9kg. The standard guns were 920–935mm overall, depending on the butt design, while the short pattern measured 865mm. Magazines held 25

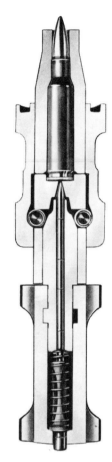

rounds apiece, and a standard 4×24 optical sight was often encountered.

Current versions of the HK33E have a modernized ambidexterous safety catch/selector system incorporating a three-short burst-fire mechanism; a simpler pistol-grip sub-frame than their predecessors; and baked-on forest green ('C' suffix) or desert sand ('S' suffix) camouflage finish to reduce absorption of heat at high temperatures. The forest-green finish **HK33EC A2** has a fixed butt; the **HK33EC A3** has a retractable butt; and the **HK33KC** amalgamates the retractable stock with a short barrel. The HK33ES A2, HKE33S A3 and HK33KS are identical, but offer sand finish.

Guns in the GR3 series, launched in 1988, resemble the current HK33. However, they all have simple 1·5× optical sights on a permanent receiver-top mount. No open sights are fitted, though the optical system is adjustable for elevation and azimuth. The dimensions of the GR3 rifles duplicate those of the HK33, though they are all about 300gm heavier than their direct equivalents. There are currently six variants: GR3C A2, GR3C A3 and GR3KC with forest green finish; GR3S A2, GR3S A3 and GR3KS with sand camouflage.

The **Gewehr 41** is an improved form of the HK33, from which it differs in minor details. These include a folding carrying handle and a 'bolt-assist' on the right side of the action behind the ejection port, inspired by the US M16A1. The guns will accept STANAG magazines, fittings and grenade launchers. They have been made in several differing forms, differing principally in their fittings. Current guns display synthetic butt/pistol grip sub-frames and ambidexterous safety catches. The safety mark is a white diagonal cross superimposed on a white bullet in a rectangular border, other settings including single shot (one red bullet in a closed border), three-shot bursts (three red bullets in a closed border) and fully automatic (seven red bullets in an open-end border). The basic fixed-butt G41, in 5·56×45, is 997mm long and weighs 4·1kg; with a retractable butt, it is 985mm overall and weighs 4·3kg. Short-barrel guns (**G41K**) measure 13cm less overall.

The **G41 INKAS** is essentially similar to the G3-INKAS described above, with an integral infra-red laser projector, and is used in conjunction with Philips Elektro-Spezial BM 8028 image-intensifying goggles. It is made with fixed or retractable butts, and in short-barrelled form. Similarly, the **G41-TGS** and **G41K-TGS** are standard standard G41 rifles with an integral 40mm HK79 grenade launcher. They were originally made with ladder-pattern sights on top of the receiver

A

B

ahead of the back sight, but more recent patterns have a conventional radial sight on the right side of the fore-end.

Heckler & Koch rifles are well made and, as they have proved surprisingly accurate for guns of their class, a series of sniper rifles has been offered.†

The most conventional of these are the **G3 SG/1** (7·62×51) and **HK33 SG/1** (5·56×45), which retain most of the features of the standard rifles. However, in addition to optical sight mounts, they each have a raised auxiliary comb on the butt, bipods, and a special set-trigger system that reduces the trigger-release pressure appreciably (from 26N to 12–15N). The set-trigger is automatically disconnected if burst or automatic fire is selected. Both rifles can be obtained with five-round magazines, saving weight compared with the standard twenty- (7·62mm) and 25-round (5·56mm) versions. A special 1·5–6× sight with a range-finding reticle is standard on these two rifles.

The **MSG3** and **MSG90** are both built on standard G3 actions, limited to semi-automatic fire only, with specially regulated (but otherwise conventional) triggers. They also embody bolt assists to reduce cocking noise. Developed specifically for the West German armed forces, the MSG3 features an adjustable comb and butt plate, a fixed-leg bipod, and conventional open sights in addition to the optical sight bracket. It has a standard-weight barrel and will be found with five- or twenty-round magazines. The MSG90 is a variant of the MSG3 with a special heavy 60cm barrel and a bipod with adjustable legs. It lacks open sights and measures about 1,165mm overall; weight is some 6·4kg (cf., MSG3: 1,100mm and 5·3kg).

The **PSG-1** ('Polizei-Scharfschützengewehr 1') is the ultimate refinement of the H&K roller lock system, though it was introduced some years before the MSG3 and MSG90. PSG-1 offer a butt with a 'saddle' cheek piece similar to those found on some H&K light machine-guns, an adjustable butt-plate, and a heavy 65cm barrel. The standard 6×42 optical sight features powered illumination and a range-finding reticle; there are no open sights. Among the most obvious features of the PSG-1 are the anatomical walnut pistol grip with a synthetic palm-shelf. Bipods can be obtained on request, but a small tripod rest is more popular. Owing to the sturdy barrel, the PSG-1 weighs 8·1kg without magazine and tripod, and measures 1,208mm overall.

Sporting autoloaders

Heckler & Koch makes a number of sporters in addition to military weapons. The smallest in the series –

† In a trial undertaken specially for *Guns of the Elite* (Arms & Armour Press, 1987), standard optically-sighted G3 Zf and G41 Zf, fired with a wrist support, placed thirty consecutive shots inside a 6cm circle at 100 metres. A PSG-1 placed all its shots in a 31mm circle at the same distance.

Left and below

Variations on a theme: the Heckler & Koch HK33ES A2 (A) with sand finish, the standard bayonet and a 4×24 optical sight; the GR3C A2 (B), with a fixed butt and an integral optical sight; an original ladder-sight G3 TGS (C); and a G41 (D) dismantled into its major components.
By courtesy of Heckler & Koch GmbH.

C

D

HK270 and **HK300** – are blowbacks chambering ·22LR and ·22WRM respectively, but both share typically H&K lines. Standard HK270 guns offer a plain walnut stock with a schnabel-tip fore-end and a distinctive German hog's back comb. They also have standard H&K military-style rotary drum back sights. The HK300, larger and somewhat heavier, features a refined stock with a squared cheek piece, chequering on the pistol grip and fore-end, and swivels on the underside of the butt and fore-end. It retains the distinctive trigger-guard/magazine housing design of its smaller relation. Thin white spacers accompany the butt plate and pistol-grip cap. Open sights comprise a laterally adjustable blade and a vertically adjustable notch; however, many guns will be encountered with H&K's clamp-locked optical sight mounts. Magazine capacity of the HK270 and HK300 is limited to a mere two rounds for the indigenous market, though five- and twenty-round magazines can be supplied for export.

The larger sporters all embody the standard roller-lock mechanism. The **HK630**, **HK770** and **HK940** are similar-looking guns, with folding cocking handles on the right side of the breech, and squared trigger guard/magazine floor-plate units. Magazine catches lie in the front of the trigger guard and radial safety levers

are let into the left side of the stock. Stocks are generally walnut of impeccable quality, with hog's back combs, squared cheek pieces, and chequering on the pistol grip and fore-end. Schnabel fore-end tips and white-line spacers accompanying the butt plate and pistol-grip cap complete the decorative effect. All guns are fitted with swivels under the butt and fore-end, and have folding-leaf back sights; multi-slot muzzle brakes are also standard.

The **HK630** chambers ·223 Remington, measures 1,070mm overall and weighs 3·2kg; the **HK770**, in ·308 Winchester (7·62×51 NATO), is 1,130mm long and weighs 3·6kg; while the **HK940**, the largest and most powerful of the series, chambers ·30-06. It weighs 3·9kg and measures 1,200mm overall. Magazines contain two rounds to satisfy West German law, though three- and nine-round patterns (four and ten in ·223 Remington only) are available for export. HK770 and HK940 rifles may also be obtained with shortened barrels (HK770K and HK940K), or in highly decorated de luxe versions.

The **SL-6** (·223 Remington) and **SL-7** (·308 Winchester) carbines, incorporating the roller-lock system, are very plain by sporting standards; indeed, they offer a three-quarter length stock with a hand

Below
Two of the many sniper rifles derived from the basic G3: MSG90 (A) and PSG-1 (B). Note the variations in fore-end, butt, bipod/tripod and sights.
By courtesy of Heckler & Koch GmbH.

A

B

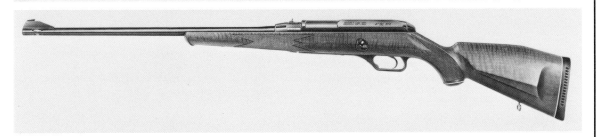

guard over the barrel and a sling-anchor plate let into the left side of the butt. Standard military-type sights are fitted, and radial safety levers appear in the left side of the fore-end above the front of the trigger guard. The magazines hold a mere two rounds for the West German market, though three- (four in ·223) and ten-round patterns are available for export. The SL-6 measures 1,015mm overall and has a 450mm barrel; the SL-7, which has a 430mm barrel, is 1,010mm long. Both rifles weigh about 3·8kg without their magazines.

Above

Heckler & Koch's sporting rifles include the HK270 (A), the SL-7 (B) and the HK770 (C) – all of which embody the roller-locking system proven in the military weapons.

By courtesy of Heckler & Koch GmbH.

Left

A longitudinal section of the G3.

By courtesy of Heckler & Koch GmbH.

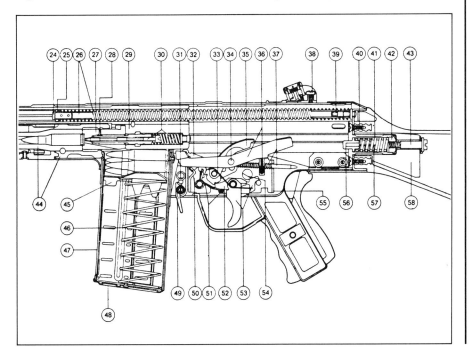

HEYM

●●

Friedrich Wilh. Heym GmbH & Co. KG, D-8732 Münnerstadt, Coburger Strasse 9

Established in Suhl in 1865, Heym made sporting guns until the end of the Second World War, the company's reputation being firmly established when the first hammerless Drilling was patented in Germany in 1891. Production of sporting guns resumed after the First World War had ended, continuing with scarcely an interruption until 1945. Operations were subsequently re-established in the small Bavarian town of Münnerstadt, where the first post-war firearms were made in 1952.

Product range: Heym makes a series of excellent shotguns, combination guns, double rifles, bolt-action rifles and single-shot falling-block patterns based on Ruger No.1 actions.

Recently discontinued models: apparently none, apart from older versions of the current guns. Some variants of the SR 20 were made for Mauser-Werke Oberndorf (q.v.) in the 1970s and sold under the Mauser-Jagdwaffen banner.

Model 20

This is a conventional bolt-pattern rifle, with a Mauser action and a full-length guide rail to prevent binding. Two sturdy lugs on the bolt head engage recesses in the receiver immediately behind the chamber, and the internal box magazine hold three (magnum) or five (standard) cartridges. The safety catch lies on the rear right side of the action behind the bolt handle: thumbed back, it allows the bolt to be opened even though the gun cannot fire. The medial position locks the bolt into the receiver.

SR 20 rifles can be obtained with single-stage, adjustable or double set-triggers. Elegant stocks of French walnut feature a Monte Carlo comb, a cheek piece, a ventilated rubber butt plate, and a pistol-grip with a Wundhammer Swell. Chequering graces the pistol grip and fore-end.

Variants of the basic rifle include **Model SR 20N** (right- or left-hand actions), a standard Monte Carlo half-stock gun — with a rosewood pistol-grip cap and schnabel fore-end tip — available in 5·6×57, ·243 Winchester, 6·5×55 Mauser, 6·5×57, ·270 Winchester, 7×57, 7×64, ·30−06, ·308 Winchester and 9·3×62. The guns are 1,130mm long, have barrels measuring 595mm and weigh about 3·18kg. **SR 20G** rifles are similar to SR 20N, excepting that they chamber magnum ammunition — 6·5×68, 7mm Remington Magnum, 8×68S, ·300 Winchester Magnum and ·375 H&H Magnum. Their barrels measure 650mm, making them

Below

Variants of the standard Heym bolt-action rifle: the SR 20 Classic (A), with a straight-comb butt; an SR 20L (B), with a Mannlicher-style stock and an exaggerated pistol-grip cap; and the SR 20 Match (C) with its hefty competition stock.

Courtesy of Friedrich Wilh. Heym GmbH & Co. KG.

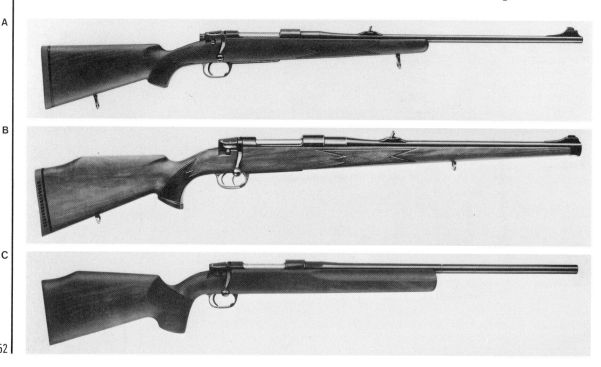

commensurately longer and slightly heavier than the otherwise comparable 'N' patterns. The **SR 20L** carbine features a 510mm barrel and a full-length Mannlicher-style stock. It is available in all regular calibres excepting 9·3×62. The **SR 20 Classic** is identical with the SR 20N, but has a straight-comb butt, a rounded fore-end tip and a shallower pistol grip. In common with all the guns in this series, the SR 20 Classic is supplied to order with engraved actions or carved stocks.

The **SR 20 Fiberglas** features a synthetic stock – classically styled, in brown or black – while the **SR 20D** (Drückjagdbüchse) has a short barrel and ventilated sighting rib suited to snap-shooting, though otherwise comparable with the standard SR 20N. Lastly, the Heym **SR 20M** (Match) rifle is intended for competition shooting. Available in 6·5×55 Mauser and ·308 Winchester only, as a single-shot or with a conventional magazine, it has a deep pistol grip and a broadened fore-end with a grasping groove. It weighs 4·3kg without sights and measures 1,130mm overall.

The Heym **Model SR 40** is a short-action version of the SR 20N, chambering ·222 Remington, ·223 Remington or 5·6×50 Magnum. It measures 1,115mm overall and generally weighs 2·95kg.

Model 22

Designed for hunters who seek excellent quality at a competitive price, the Heym Model 22S is a two-barrel over/under combination gun with an engraved duraluminium receiver. Though a conventional break-open action locked by a top lever, the 22S embodies a separate cocking system controlled by a sliding catch on the upper tang. The strikers can be uncocked merely by thumbing the catch back, or by releasing the top lever and opening the action. A barrel selector appears on the left side of the action above the front of the trigger guard, the trigger is generally a single 'set' design, and an 'all-ways' inertia safety prevents discharge should the gun be dropped or struck accidentally. The **Model 22S** and **Model 22SM** (the

latter for magnum ammunition) feature a walnut fore-end and butt, the latter with a straight comb and an ovoid cheek piece. Chequering appears on the pistol grip and fore-end; the butt plate is solid rubber; swivels will be encountered beneath the butt and on the lower barrel; and a rail above the breech accepts optical sight mounts. Standard chamberings are ·22WRM, ·22 Hornet, ·222 Remington, ·222 Remington Magnum, 5·6×50R Magnum, ·243 Winchester, 6·5×57R and 7×57R. The shotgun barrel is usually 16- or 20-bore, though 12-bore (2¾in cases) is optional on the 22SM. The **Model 22SZ** duplicates the standard pattern, but its barrels are detachable. Heym Model 22 rifles measures about 1,015mm overall, with 610mm barrels, and weigh about 2·5kg.

Models 33, 35 and 37

These are all Drillinge, with box- (Model 33) or side-locks (Models 35 and 37) controlled by a conventional top lever. All guns have a special cocking device for the lower barrel in the form of a slider mounted on the upper tang. They have double set-triggers, the foremost of which (with the 'set') fires the lower barrel, and the lock plates are extensively engraved. A safety catch will be found on the left side of the butt above the rear trigger. The **Model 33** Drilling, with double under-lugs and a Greener cross-bolt extension, has an oil-finish walnut stock and an imitation horn trigger guard. Arabesques decorate the standard version, while the deluxe patterns feature oakleaf-and-game engraving on the action body.

The side lock of the **Model 35** and **Model 37**, with double under-lugs and Greener cross-bolts, is shared with the Models 55 and 88 (q.v.). The Model 35 has a distinctive butt with a hog's back comb, a Bavarian 'Imperial' cheek piece and skip-line chequering; it also has massive integral bases for optical sight mounts. The Model 37 is more conventional, with a plainer butt, ovoid cheek piece and traditional chequering.

Side locks generally offer greater opportunity for engraving than box locks, and so the Model 37 deluxe

Above

Heym's 22S (A), shown here in a 1974-vintage photograph, is a competitively priced over/under combination gun with a duraluminium receiver. The Model 35 (B) is a sturdy and effectual triple-barrel Drilling, a richly decorated deluxe 1988-vintage example being pictured.

By courtesy of Friedrich Wilh. Heym GmbH & Co. KG.

model is more popular than the corresponding Model 33 amongst the élite. Standard chamberings include 12-, 16- and 20-bore; 5·6×50R Magnum, ·222 Remington, 5·6×57R, ·243 Winchester, 6·5×57R, 7×57R, 7×65R, ·270 Winchester, ·30–06, ·308 Winchester, 8×57 and 9·3×74. However, the **Model 37B**, which has two rifle barrels above one 20-bore shot pattern, is available only in 7×65R, ··30–06, 8×57 and 9·3×74. The guns are all about 1,065mm long, though weight varies from 3·2kg for the Model 33 to 3·85kg for the Model 37B.

Models 30 and 38

These are 'Heym-Rugers', built on the US-made Ruger No.1 action but stocked and engraved in European style. The two patterns differ only in their round (HR 30) or octagonal barrels (HR 38). The guns are usually fitted with single set-triggers, plus traditional open sights or claw mounts for optical equipment. They are stocked in French walnut, both half-length (HR 30 and HR 38) and Mannlicher styles (HR 30L Carbine only) displaying Bavarian cheek pieces with scalloped lower edges. Standard actions are engraved with game-and-oakleaf motifs, but the Model HR 38 Exclusive has additional side plates extending back from the receiver. These extensions are so well fitted and finished that they appear to be integral with the receiver forging itself.

Excepting the carbine, which is available only in standard chamberings, the Heym-Rugers can be obtained in ·243 Winchester, 6·5×57 and 6·5×57R, 6·5×68R, ·270 Winchester, 7×64, 7×65R, ·300 Winchester Magnum, ·30–06, ·308 Winchester, 8×68S and 9·3×74R. They are 1,015–1,065mm overall and weigh 2·95–3·20kg.

Model 55

Displaying an Anson & Deeley-type box lock, with double under-lugs and the Kerstenschloss (double Greener cross-bolts), the **Model 55B** double rifle is a

variant of the 55F shotgun and 55BF combination guns. The rifles usually feature select walnut furniture – the butt having a German cheek piece and slight hog's back comb – and a back sight is let into the traditional quarter-rib. The action is engraved with scroll-and-game motifs.

Model 55 BSS deluxe combination guns are similar to the standard 55B, but are built on side-lock actions to display the engravers' skills to greatest advantage; the best of them are true works of art, though not always suited to hard use. 'B' and 'BSS' guns are available in a selection of chamberings, including 7×65R, ·30–06, ·308 Winchester, 8×57, 9·3×74R and ·375 H&H Magnum. They are 1,065mm long and – depending on the woodwork – weigh about 3·4kg.

The **Model 55BS**, the Bergstutzen or 'mountain rifle', is supplied with rifled barrels chambering different cartridges, and with twin set-triggers. The upper barrel fires 5·6×50R Magnum or ·222 Remington, while the lower one can be chambered for any of the standard Heym cartridges.

Model 88

This is a classical side-by-side double rifle, embodying Anson & Deeley box- (88 B) or Purdey/Greener side locks (88 BSS) and all the many refinements to be expected of Heym. Sliding safety catches are mounted on the upper tang, and loaded-chamber indicators are inlet in the top of the action body alongside the top lever. All Heym side-by-side double rifles incorporate double under-lugs and Greener cross-bolt locks, and can be supplied with extractors, ejectors or the company's special Selective Ejector. The standard guns usually display American-style butts with Monte Carlo combs, while the deluxe patterns invariably have straight combs. The latter feature English scroll engraving on the action and gold-line inlay on the breech. Excepting the heavy **88 B Safari** (·458 Winchester Magnum and ·470 Nitro Express only), which weighs 4·5kg, the Heym Model 88 weighs 3·4–

Below

Heym-Ruger falling-block rifles include the HR 30L Carbine (A), with a full-length Mannlicher stock; the standard HR 30 (B), with a short fore-end and a round barrel; and the HR 38, similar to the HR 30 but with an octagonal barrel. Note the decoration on the two deluxe guns, and the distinctive Bavarian cheek piece on the butts.

A

B

C

By courtesy of Friedrich Wilh. Heym GmbH & Co. KG.

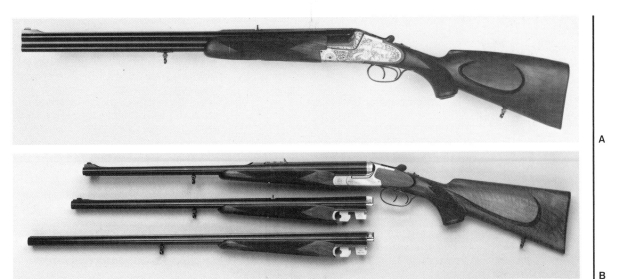

3·8kg; barrels measure 635mm, giving an overall
length of about 1,065mm. Standard and deluxe rifles
may chamber ·30–06, 8×57, 9·3×74R or ·375
H&H Magnum, though alternatives are available to
order. Heym also makes a Model 88 shotgun (88F) and
a combination rifle (88 BF), the barrel-clusters being
readily interchangeable.

Howa JAPAN

Howa Industries (Sukaguchi, Shinkawa-cho,
Nishikasugai-gun, Aichi) has made actions for
Weatherby (q.v.) for some years; once the exclusive
licensing agreement had expired, Howa began to offer
rifles under its own name. These are conventional
Mauser-type bolt actions, with dual opposed lugs on
the bolt head. Three gas ports are cut into the
underside of the bolt body. The monobloc receiver is
machined from a forged steel billet, and the magazine
is a conventional detachable floor-plate pattern. The
rifle presents a conventional appearance, excepting
the distinctive angular web ahead of the trigger
guard that houses the magazine release catch. The
tapered barrels are generally fitted with Williams
back sights, though the receiver is drilled and tapped
for optical sight mounts. Known as the **Model 1500**,
the guns are available as standard/deluxe sporters,
with tapering barrels; as heavy-barrel varmint rifles
(·223 and ·22–250 Remington only); or as **Big Game
Magnums**, chambered only for 7mm Remington
Magnum and ·300 Winchester Magnum cartridges.
Hunter rifles have elegant classic-style walnut stocks
with a straight comb and uncapped pistol grip, the
effect being spoiled only by the white-line butt plate
spacer. **Trophy** guns have Monte Carlo combs, plus
pistol-grip caps accompanied by white spacers. A
lightweight rifle known as the **Lightning**, with a
synthetic CarboLite stock, may be obtained in 7mm
Remington Magnum, ·270 and ·30–06. The weight
thus saved amounts to about 225gm. Howa rifles are
still uncommon outside the Far East and North
America.

Interarms USA

With its headquarters at 10 Prince Street, Alexandria,
Virginia 22313, Interarms manufactures and
distributes a wide range of guns – including Howa,
some Rossi and Walther rifles, details of which will be
found in the relevant sections. There is also a series of
Mauser-action sporting rifles known as the
Whitworth, **Viscount** and **Mark X**. Made in
Yugoslavia, these are covered in the Zastava
section.

Imbel BRAZIL

Industria de Material Belico do Brasil (Avenida das
Nações Unidas 13.797, CEP 04794 Saõ Paulo) makes
the FN FAL under licence. Used by the Brazilian army
as the Mo.964, as well as being offered commercially
(see Springfield Armory), the rifle has provided the
basis for the 5·56mm **MD1**. This small-calibre
derivative, which measures about 990mm overall and
weighs 3·8kg, has a folding butt and a short hand
guard. A blowback ·22LR rimfire training adaptation
of the FAL is being made under the designation
MD2.

IMI ISRAEL

Israeli Metal Industries (IMI), POB 1044, Ramat
Hasharon 47100, makes Galil assault rifles, Desert
Eagle pistols and munitions.

Adapted from the Russian Kalashnikov by way of
the Finnish m/62, the standard selective-fire
5·56×45 **ARM** Galil measures 980mm overall and
weighs 4·2kg with its bipod and carrying handle; a
shortened version (**SARM**) has a barrel measuring
330mm rather than 460mm; and a 7·62×51 version
is designated **AR**. Galils are now encountered with
synthetic rather than wooden fore-ends; apart from
the folding butt, their elongated pistol grips are
distinctive.

A semi-automatic **Galil Sniper** rifle (7·62×51,
1,115mm overall, 6·4kg), made for police and
security-service use, has a heavy barrel with a

Below

The standard 5·56mm Israeli Galil ARM. Note the design of the fore-end, the length of the pistol grip, and the position of the selector/safety lever (marked 'S A R').

By courtesy of Ian Hogg.

muzzle-brake/compensator, a folding wood butt and a bracket for a Nimrod 6×40 optical sight or an image intensifier.

The 7·62×51 **Hadar II** is a semi-automatic Galil action in a distinctive threequarter-length stock with a safety lever set into the left side of the pistol grip. Hadars are 980mm overall and weigh 4·35kg.

Jager ITALY

Armi-Jager is best known for a series of ·22LR rimfire pseudo-assault rifles. These include full- and carbine-length variants of the AR-15 (known as the Armi-Jager M16A1/22 and CAR15/22 respectively), as well as the Kalashnikov, Galil and FAMAS. Jager's AR15 rifles are particularly convincing, as the small magazine is contained within a dummy housing; the rimfire Kalashnikov suffers by comparison.

Kassnar
USA

Kassnar Imports, Inc., of PO Box 6097, Harrisburg, Pennsylvania 17112, distributes bolt-action rifles under the brandname **Churchill**. These comprise the Highlander and Regent, disguising that they are made in Italy by FIAS (q.v.) as 'Carabina Modelo Rover'. The 'Highlander Combo' is simply a standard gun supplied with a 3−9× 32 Kassnar Vista-scope in place of the Williams-pattern open back sight. Conventional-looking centre-fire designs, with a Mauser-type action and a spatulate bolt handle, they are distinguished almost entirely by their stocks: the Highlander has an English style straight comb, while the Regent features a Monte Carlo pattern. The safety locks the trigger, allowing the bolt to be opened to unload or inspect the chamber.

These photographs of the Armi-Jager ·22LR blowback replicas of the CAR-15 (above) and AR-15 (below) show just how convincing such guns can be. The small magazines protruding below the dummy magazine block are the most obvious giveaway.

By courtesy of Mitchell Arms, Santa Ana.

A

B

C

KRICO

•••

Krico GmbH, Jagd- und Sportwaffenfabrik, D-7000 Stuttgart 61, Postfach 61 02 55

The last twenty years has brought a considerable change in the fortunes of this gunmaking company, founded as Kriegeskorte & Co. shortly after the end of the Second World War. Little more than just another European gunmaker in 1970, Krico has now joined the leaders in the field; partly due to astute marketing, and a link in the USA with Beeman, this has also been due to the efficiency of the company's elegant and individualistic sporting guns.

Product range: Krico makes a series of bolt-action rifles, ranging from rimfire trainers to powerful centre-fire sporters, as well as a single ·22LR semi-automatic. Krico rifles will also be encountered under Beeman and RWS brands.

Recently discontinued models: excepting minor variants of the current products, generally differing in stock profile or fittings, very few guns have been abandoned.

However, there has been a single-shot ·22LR junior rifle known as the 120E; in addition, prior to the current 300 and 400 series, there were earlier ·22LR rimfire (302E, 304ST) and ·22WMR (352E, 354ST) patterns. The guns with numbers ending in '2' appear to have been analogous to the present 300D and 400D, while those ending in '4' were similar to the 320L and 420L. The Krico 120SA was a basic magazine-feed rifle with a Krico-Kitzmann breech.

The oddest of the Krico rifles was the 360S2 Biathlon, made in small numbers alongside the comparatively conventional 360S Biathlon. The photograph reproduced here shows how strange the S2 pattern looked! Neither gun proved capable of challenging the market leader, the Fortner-system Anschütz 1827BT; both were soon abandoned.

Above

Obsolescent Krico rifles have included the single-shot ·22LR rimfire Model 120E (A); the 354ST (B), a ·22 Hornet rifle, with a full-length Mannlicher stock and a detachable box magazine; and the extraordinary 360S2 Biathlon (C), which is rarely confused with other guns!

By courtesy of Krico GmbH.

57

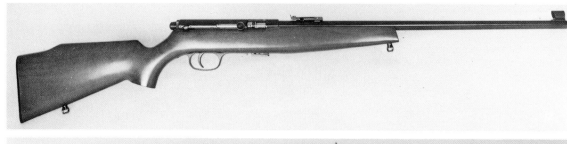

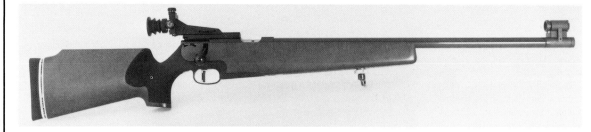

Above

The ·22LR rimfire 260EA (A) is the only auto-loader currently offered by Krico; the ·22LR or ·22WRM Model 320L (B), with a Mannlicher stock and a hog's back comb, is typical of the company's smaller rifles; and the Model 330S (C), recently discontinued, provided an effectual low-cost target rifle.

By courtesy of Krico GmbH.

Model 260

The Model 260EA is an inexpensive ·22LR rimfire blowback auto-loader, distinguished by excellent quality and reliable performance. Accompanied by detachable box magazines containing two, five or ten rounds, the 260EA can be used as a single-loader when required. It has a walnut-finish hardwood half-stock with a low Monte Carlo comb; a rubber butt plate; chequering on the pistol-grip and fore-end; and sling swivels placed conventionally beneath the butt and fore-end. A radial safety catch lies on the right rear side of the receiver, while a tangent-leaf back sight will be found on the barrel ahead of the receiver ring. Like all these guns, the 260EA has dovetail grooves for an optical-sight mount.

Series 300

Rifles in this group all feature a sturdy bolt action locked by the bolt-handle base turning down into its seat in the receiver. This is more than adequate for the pressures of the ·22LR or ·22WRM cartridges the 300-series chambers.

The basic model is the **Krico 300E**, which shares the stock design and single trigger of 260EA (q.v.); the **Krico 300D** amalgamates the basic action with a double set-trigger unit. It also has a deluxe walnut half-stock with a shallow schnabel tip on the fore-end. The **Krico 320L**, mechanically identical with the 300D, has a full-length Mannlicher stock with a hog's back comb, a squared Bavarian-style cheek piece and a decorative pistol-grip cap. The 300D and 320L both have fixed

back sights, adjustable for azimuth only by driving them across their mount-block dovetail.

Several target-shooting adaptations of the 300 action have been offered. The **Krico 330S**, only recently discontinued, was a single-shot UIT 25m target rifle with a conventional competition stock and aperture sights. It had an adjustable butt plate, extensive stippling on the pistol-grip, and an accessory rail inlet under the fore-end; unfortunately, it did not prove capable of challenging the domination of Anschütz and Walther in this particular discipline. The ·22LR **Krico 340**, intended for DJV moving target competitions, features a deep butt with a squared cheek piece, a fixed wooden (or rubber) butt plate, and a broad 'beaver tail' fore-end. Stippling is applied extensively to the pistol grip and under the fore-end. The 340, which can only be used with optical sights, has a heavy barrel and the standard double set-trigger.

Destined for moving-target competitions, the **Krico 340S** has a distinctive stock with seven slots in the fore-end. Unlike the standard 340, it also has sling swivels. The **Krico 340S Silhouette** was developed especially for North American competitions. It is somewhat similar to the 340, but has a single trigger and a short barrel. The half-stock lacks the deep broad fore-end of its near-relation; it also has a ventilated rubber butt plate.

Series 400

These guns are essentially similar to the 300-type equivalents. However, they chamber the centre-fire ·22

Hornet cartridge and have an auxiliary locking lug behind the bolt-handle base. Though this allows compressive stresses to be generated in the bolt body during the firing cycle, the Krico rifles are extremely well made of good material and the margins of safety are high. The **Krico 400E, 400D** and **420L** are otherwise identical with their rimfire cousins. There are also two target rifles: the **Krico 430S** and **Krico 440S** are centre-fire versions of the models 340 and 340S respectively.

Series 600

These centre-fire sporters are currently available in nine chamberings: ·17 Remington, ·222 Remington and Remington Magnum, ·22–250 Remington, 5·6×50 Magnum, 5·6×57, ·223 Remington, ·243 Winchester and ·308 Winchester. They all share a Mauser-type action in which twin opposed lugs lock horizontally in the receiver. All Krico sporter stocks are walnut, with a distinctive hog's back comb and Bavarian-type cheek piece, though there are appreciable differences in the fore-ends. Safety catches appear on the right side of the action behind the bolt handle, and there is a very distinctive synthetic cocking-piece shroud enveloped in the receiver walls. The Krico action performs as smoothly as it looks.

The basic model, **Krico 600A**, has a half-stock with a shallow schnabel tip to the fore-end, and a thin rubber butt plate. Sling swivels are supplied as standard, but not open sights. **Krico 600D** rifles are identical with the 600A type excepting that they have better woodwork, ventilated rubber butt plates, neater schnabel tips, and factory-installed open sights. The

Krico 620L has a short barrel and a full-length Mannlicher stock. Like the 600D (but not the 600A), it has a machine-jewelled bolt. All three guns have spherical bolt knobs and a double set-trigger.

The deluxe **Krico 600DL** has a specially selected stock with a more ostentatious pistol-grip, a rosewood schnabel tip and an elegant spatulate handle on the machine-jewelled bolt. Front sling swivels lie on the barrel instead of under the fore-end. **Krico 620DL** rifles are similar, excepting that they have a full-length stock with a metal schnabel tip. Deluxe Krico guns all have standing open-notch back and gold-plated barleycorn front sights. They will also be found with the standard double set-trigger, a single set-trigger, or either of two match patterns.

Among the target rifle derivatives are the single-shot **Krico 630S** (·222 and ·223 Remington, ·243 and ·308 Winchester), intended for DJV 'hunting' competitions. This gun has a half-stock with a deep fore-end, and a massive butt with a low Monte Carlo comb and a fixed ventilated rubber butt plate. The magazine-fed **Krico 640S** and **640S Sniper** are essentially similar, sharing the standard seven-slot match stock of the 340S (q.v.). However, the Sniper variant has an adjustable butt plate and an elevating comb. It also has a muzzle brake on its phosphated barrel, a single set-trigger and an enlarged bolt-handle knob. Krico 640S rifles are available in ·222 and ·223 Remington, ·22–250 Remington, ·243 and ·308 Winchester, and 6·5×55 Mauser; Snipers are only available in ·222 and ·223 Remington, and ·243 and ·308 Winchester.

The **Krico 640L** is a dual purpose target/sporting gun, incorporating the 640S action in a comparatively

Below

Krico's larger rifles include the distinctive ·22LR rimfire Model 340S (A), intended for DJV moving-target competitions; the Model 600 (B), with a compact action handling centre-fire cartridges up to ·308 Winchester; and the Model 620L (C), a carbine variant of the basic 600 series with a full-length stock.

By courtesy of Krico GmbH.

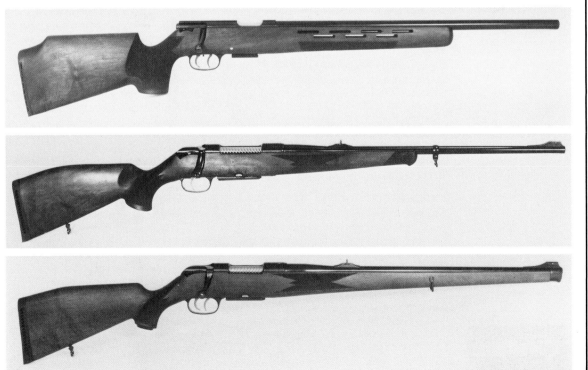

A

B

C

Above

The Krico Model 640L (A), intended for sporting use, features the standard compact action – as does the 640 Sniper (B), with its characteristic slotted fore-end and elevating comb. The Model 720L (C) has a long action and can handle cartridges with cases measuring as much as 68mm.

By courtesy of Krico GmbH.

slender half-stock with a rounded rosewood fore-end tip.

Series 700

The rifles in this series – 700A, 700D, 700DL, 720L and two deluxe versions – are identical with corresponding variants in the 600 group. Befitting the powerful cartridges it chambers, however, the 700 action is substantially longer and heavier than the medium 600. Options include 6·5×55 Mauser, 6·5×57, 6·5×68, 7×57, 7×64, 7mm Remington Magnum, 7·5×55, ·30–06, ·300 Winchester Magnum, 8×68S, 9·3×62 and 9·3×64. The solitary 700-action target rifle, the **Krico 740S**, is essentially similar to the 640S (q.v.)

• •

Kimber USA

Kimber of Oregon, Inc. (Clackamas, Oregon 97015) is a comparatively new name among prominent US gunmakers – but one which may eventually join the élite group headed by Ruger. Kimber's first gun was the **Model 82** ·22 rimfire sporter, a rugged and extremely well-made bolt action with twin rear locking lugs, a precisely adjustable trigger and flush-fitting magazines. The rifle is not cheap: prices began at about $600 in 1989. However, the Kimber offers a walnut stock, a polished steel pistol-grip cap and a chequered steel butt plate to entice purchasers. The action is much stronger than many rival rimfire rifles, Kimber rightly regarding such

'over engineering' as an asset rather than a liability. There are two models, 82A and 82B, but the differences are comparatively insignificant.

An indication of the efficacy of the basic Kimber ·22 rifle is that the US Army adopted a modified Model 82 (known as the **M82 Government Model**) for training purposes in the summer of 1987. This gun is immediately identifiable by its heavy barrel, extra-deep fore-end and a butt with adjustable spacers. It is interesting to note that no US-made rimfire ammunition initially proved capable of satisfying the army's stringent requirements: acceptance trials utilized Eley Tenex. The results included ten-shot groups as small as ·235in at 50 yards.

The Kimber **Model 84 Mini-Mauser** was designed expressly for the ·222 family of centre-fire cartridges. It combines some of the features of the pre-1964 version of the Winchester Model 70 – the spring-loaded ejector and the three-position cocking-piece safety – with others from the proven 1898-type Mauser. The result is a sturdy and effectual rifle; the Kimber is expensive, once again, but quality is a determining factor in most purchases.

The first of the **Big Game Rifles** appeared in mid-1988, chambered for cartridges up to the ·375 H&H Magnum. Somewhat similar in concept to the Model 84, it combines the best of Mauser and Winchester practice in a most appealing package. The Mauser provides the basic locking and breeching system with an inner collar to contain gas leaks; the claw-type extractor; the magazine system and the

bolt-stop. From the Winchester Model 70 comes the trigger; the ejector, which rides under rather than through the left locking lug; and the three-position safety. The action is beautifully finished of the best materials, and is stocked – in classic style – in Claro or (in better grades) European walnut. A small action, for cartridges based on the ·308 case (7·62mm NATO), and a magnum version handling cases as large as the ·505 Gibbs are expected to be in production by 1990.

Kimber rifles can be stocked in Classic (Claro walnut and 18-line chequering) or Custom Classic (figured walnut and 22-line chequering) styles; both options have chequered steel butt plates and polished pistol-grip caps, but only the latter has a contrasting ebony fore-end tip. A full-length 'Continental' stock – in regular and Super grades – can also be obtained if desired. 'Mini-Classic' styling, available only for the Model 82A, amalgamates the Government Model action with a sporting-style stock.

The jewels of the Kimber range are the 'Super America' models, which are special guns with extra finish, selected figured Claro or quarter-sawn straight-grain English walnut stocks; beaded cheek pieces; extensive borderless 22-line chequering; and Niedner chequered-steel butt plates. Additional options include ebony fore-end tips; a barrel quarter-rib with folding multiple-leaf sights; skeleton pistol-grip caps or butt plates; and chequering on the bolt-handle knob. Available on the M82, M84 and Big Game Rifle, the package is not particularly expensive when one considers that the result is virtually a custom gun: in 1989, prices started in the region of $1,200.

Krieghoff WEST GERMANY

The products of H. Krieghoff GmbH, Jagd- und Sportwaffenfabrik (D-79 Ulm/Donau, Boschstrasse 22), are exclusively fine-quality shotguns and shotgun-style hunting rifles. The latter are made in two basic styles – over/under double rifles and *Drillinge*, distinctive three-barrel guns of a pattern especially popular in central Europe. Though the Krieghoff guns are never cheap, they are among the very best. The Neptun Primus and Ulm Primus, for instance, are often celebrations of the gunsmith's art.

Krieghoff's **Plus** is a box-lock Drilling with two hammers, the action body being satin-nickelled aluminium alloy. Unlike many guns of this basic type, which cock on opening the action, the Plus incorporates the patented Krieghoff 'Kickspanner' cocking mechanism. This is used much like the push-button found on most ball-pens: pressing it forward cocks the hammers, but an additional push uncocks them. The rear trigger fires the left upper (shotgun) barrel, while the front, or set-trigger, can be selected to fire either the right (shotgun) or under (rifle) barrel by a catch on the right side of the action immediately behind the top lever – set to 'K' (Kugel) for the rifle barrel and 'S' (Schrott) for the shotgun. The Plus has oil finished German-style walnut woodwork, with a generous pistol grip and a distinctive cheek piece. Swivels lie on the rifle barrel ahead of the short chequered fore-end, and on the under-edge of the butt. A folding back sight is let into the matted top-rib, which will also accommodate Krieghoff's proprietary claw mounts for optical sights. Unlike some other Krieghoff Drillinge, the barrels

Left

The Neptun Drilling is seen here in its decorative Primus (deluxe) form, and with two shotgun barrels above a single central rifle. Quality of these pieces is very high.
By courtesy of H. Krieghoff GmbH.

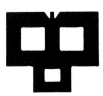

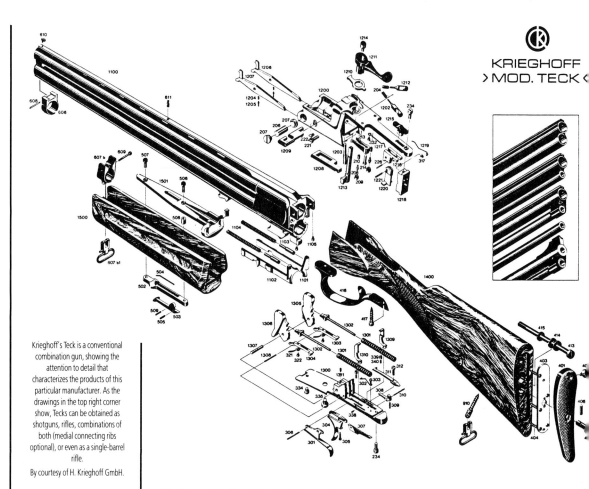

Krieghoff's Teck is a conventional combination gun, showing the attention to detail that characterizes the products of this particular manufacturer. As the drawings in the top right corner show, Tecks can be obtained as shotguns, rifles, combinations of both (medial connecting ribs optional), or even as a single-barrel rifle.

By courtesy of H. Krieghoff GmbH.

* Though traditionalists dislike the absence of barrel-connecting rib, there is little doubt that floating barrels are more effectual. Krieghoff's catalogues recommend that 7–10 seconds should be left between successive shots when firing a 'ribbed' double-rifle continually; and, if the rifle barrels are differing calibres, no rapid firing should ever be attempted.

of the Plus are all soldered together. The smooth-bore barrels are chambered for 12-bore cartridges measuring 70 or 76mm (2¾ or 3in), while the rifle barrel will accept ·22 Hornet, ·222 Remington, 5·6× 50R, ·243 Winchester, 6·5× 55 Mauser, 6·5× 57R, 7× 57R, ·270 Winchester, ·30–06 Springfield, 7× 64, 7× 65R, ·308 Winchester, 8× 57 or 9·3× 74R. Options for the double rifle are restricted to 20-bore, ·30–06, 8× 57 and 9·3× 74R. All barrels measure 635mm, the length of pull is 370mm and the guns weigh 3·18–3·30kg.

The **Trumpf** is similar to the Plus, but longer-established; indeed, it is the most popular of the Krieghoff Drillinge. The Greener box-lock action features an earlier form of the Kickspanner system in which the rifle barrel may be cocked by pressing forward on a tang-slider or uncocked by pulling it back again. What appears to be a selector, on the left side of the action beside the cocking catch, is the shotgun-barrel safety: forward to fire, back to lock. Like most shotguns, the strikers for the smooth-bore barrels cock on opening. The guns are generally encountered with two triggers, the forward lever – a set-trigger – firing the rifle barrel if its mechanism has been cocked. However, an optional non-selective trigger may be specified; this fires the right barrel first, then the left one. If the cocking slide has been

activated, the two upper barrels are isolated to allow the trigger to fire the lower barrel.

Trümpfe may be obtained as a double rifle with a solitary shotgun barrel, or as a side-by-side shotgun with a rifle barrel below. In addition, in the latter guise, the purchaser may request a free-floating rifle barrel suited to rapid fire.* The stock, construction and features otherwise parallel the Ultra (q.v.) excepting that steel or alloy action bodies are offered. Unlike its near-relation, the Trumpf can also be obtained in 16- or 20-bore. The Trumpf-L is simply a shortened version, with 55cm barrels, an overall length of 97cm and a weight of about 3·1kg. It is available in 12- or 16-bore (12/70 and 16/70 only), and any of the standard rifle calibres.

The **Neptun** is essentially similar to the Trumpf, but the locks for the shotgun barrels are mounted on side plates. Available in the same calibre options as the Trumpf, sometimes with a free-floating rifle barrel, the standard Neptun features a steel body engraved with hunting scenes and arabesques. The Neptun Dural is similar, but has an alloy body. The Neptun Primus is the deluxe version, with specially selected stocks and extensive inlaid engraving.

The **Teck** is an over/under double rifle, shotgun or combination rifle/shotgun, with optional floating barrels (rifle/shotgun only). The action is similar to the Trumpf, but lacks the separate cocking mechanism: the standard Teck action cocks on opening, and a safety catch replaces the tang-slider. However, the optional Teck Handspanner cocks on opening only when the safety is in the forward position. Twin triggers are standard, though a simple single trigger system is also available. Tecks are available in the same calibre combinations as Trümpfe, though the double rifles are only obtainable in ·30–06, 8× 57, 9·3× 74R, ·375 H&H and ·458 Winchester Magnum.

The double rifles have an open back sight on a quarter rib, while the combination guns have folding leaf on a solid full-length rib; shotguns have a plain ventilated rib. Light scroll engraving is standard on the steel or dural bodies, but deluxe patterns may be obtained on request.

The **Ulm** is a variant of the Teck with side locks rather than a box-lock body. It is also usually specified in its deluxe (Ulm Primus) form, when it becomes a work of art rather than a mere firearm. It may also be obtained with Krieghoff's special Single/Double Trigger. The rear trigger will fire the lower barrel, while the front one – which can be set to a finer pull than its companion – usually fires the upper barrel; however, if required, the front trigger can fire both barrels sequentially.

Lebeau-Courally BELGIUM
One of the legacies of the Liège gun trade, now a shadow of its former self, Lebeau-Courally was formed about 1910 to make fine sporting arms. Its current products include two types of double rifle, one with an Anson & Deeley/Purdey Bolt box lock and the other with a Holland & Holland-pattern side-lock action. Both patterns are generally fitted with ejectors. Available in 8× 57, 9·3× 74R, ·375 H&H Magnum and ·458 Winchester, the guns have quarter ribs with fixed- or folding-leaf back sights, elegant French walnut stocks with a cheek piece, chequered pistol grips and steel pistol-grip caps. Claw-pattern optical sight mounts can be supplied to order, as can various patterns of engraving. Double or single non-selective triggers may be encountered. Quality is very good; prices are generally commensurately high.

Ljutic
USA
Ljutic Industries, Inc., of PO Box 2117, Yakima, Washington 98907, makes a series of futuristic 'Space Guns' – a term that describes their unorthodox construction with consummate accuracy. The **Space Rifle** (available in ·22–250, ·30–06, ·30–30 and ·308) features straight-line layout with a walnut pistol grip, fore-end and butt-cover. The single-shot rifle has a push-button trigger, adjustable to six degrees of sensitivity, and only six major moving parts. Optical sights are carried on high mounts, the configuration precluding the use of conventional open sights. Owing to the major axis running through the barrel, the breech and the tubular receiver extension (or 'butt'), the sturdily made 8·5lb Space Gun is very easily controlled. Its extraordinary appearance, however, shocks most traditionalists. In addition, Ljutic products are far from cheap: the shotguns started at $3,695 in 1989.

Left

The Krieghoff Ultra-S is a deluxe over/under combination gun, fitted with side- rather than box locks to receive additional engraving. This particular gun has the shotgun barrel uppermost and a double trigger.
By courtesy of H. Krieghoff GmbH.

MANNLICHER

Steyr-Daimler-Puch AG, A-4400 Steyr, POB 1000, Austria

Ferdinand Ritter von Mannlicher (1848–1904), trained as a railway engineer, is among the best-known names in firearms history. His guns were originally made by Österreichische Waffenfabriks-Gesellschaft AG, founded in 1864 ('OEWG'); by 1914, they were service issue in Austria-Hungary, the Netherlands, Romania and Greece. The importance of the guns declined after the end of the First World War, when many of the Habsburg dominions were freed and many armies adopted the ubiquitous Mauser. Austria, the Netherlands and Greece remained loyal Mannlicher users. After 1938, when Austria was assimilated into Germany, the Steyr factory – merged with Daimler and Puch in 1934 – was put to making Mausers and only regained its independence in 1945. Production of sporting guns was ultimately resumed in the early 1950s The reputation of the Mannlicher rifle persists today even though its front-line military career is now over. Steyr-Daimler-Puch also makes the so-called Armee-Universal-Gewehr or AUG, which is becoming increasingly popular.

Schnitt a-b.
durch Trommel u. Gehäuse.
(1/2).

Right

Sectional drawings of an early Mannlicher-Schönauer rifle, known as the Modell 87/88, showing the action open (A) and closed (B). From *Repetier- und Automatische Handfeuer Waffen der Systeme Ferdinand Ritter von Mannlicher*, Wien, 1900.

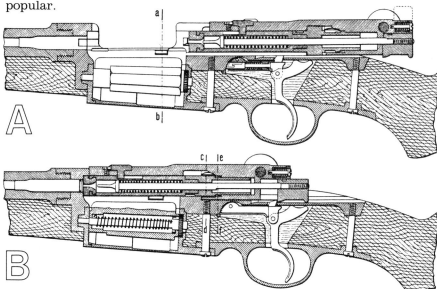

Product range: Steyr-Daimler-Puch makes pistols, submachine-guns, automatic rifles, bolt-action rifles and machine-guns, as well as vehicles ranging from motor cycles to light tanks.

Discontinued models: the Mannlicher sporters made after production resumed in 1953 were based on the pre-war patterns, which in turn duplicated the Greek Mannlicher-Schönauer adopted in 1903. This featured a split-bridge receiver, with the bolt handle locking down ahead of the bridge, and a removable bolt head. The spool magazine was effectual enough, but the action was obsolescent; though the Mannlicher still had champions, it slowly fell from grace as optical sights became increasingly common. Split-bridge receivers almost always require special optical sight mounts. The company's designers were put to work on something better. After extensive research in the 1960s, a new military bolt-action Mannlicher – the Scharfschützengewehr or SSG – appeared in 1969. By moving the bolt handle behind the bridge, a much more compact action was produced. This now provides the basis for all the current bolt action sporters. The lightweight SL and L-pattern actions were introduced first, to be followed by the 'M' and 'S' designs (in 1974–5). A Model 72 rifle, built on a differing action,[*] was used as a stop-gap for several years.

Model 69

Sometimes called 'M67' after the year in which development was completed, these guns all share a turning-bolt action in which the six lugs (in two rings of three) lock into the receiver behind the magazine when the bolt handle is turned down into its seat. Though this places a substantial part of the bolt body under compressive stress during firing, the Mannlicher action has proved to be very sturdy – it is, after all, beautifully made – and the drawbacks are largely theoretical. By moving the lugs back behind the magazine, the designers were able to place the magazine so that cartridges feed directly into the chamber. This effectively shortens the action by deleting the space for the locking lugs ahead of the magazine behind the breech. In addition, the strain of recoil is transmitted to the stock in an area where it is comparatively strong – rather than ahead of the magazine-well where the wood is thin.

In combination with a perfected detachable spool magazine, which presents the cartridges to the bolt more consistently than a conventional thin-lipped box, the current Mannlichers have a reputation for flawless feeding.

The standard Model 69 bolt has a neat spatulate handle, ideally placed above the mid-point of the trigger aperture, and a sliding safety catch lies on the right of the receiver immediately behind the bolt handle. A distinctive feature of all current Mannlichers is the

"monk's cowl" cocking-piece shroud, shared with practically no other rifle. The magazines have a skeletal spool inside a tough transparent Makrolon casing, enabling the firer to check the state of loading merely by removing the magazine; the sniper rifles, however, may be encountered with conventional box magazines. One of the few advantages of boxes is that, size for size, they hold more cartridges than the rotary pattern. No import to a sportsman, this feature is of much greater value to a soldier.

The lightest of the rifles is the **Model SL** ('Super Light'), available in ·222 Remington, ·222 Remington Magnum, ·223 Remington and 5·2×50 Magnum. The guns feature an ultra-compact action and a hammer-forged barrel; the double set-trigger is standard, though a single-trigger system can be supplied on request. An open blade front sight lies atop a muzzle ramp, and a small folding leaf-pattern back sight appears some distance in front of the receiver. There are three basic SL variants: one gun with a half-stock, one with a full-length stock,† and a Varmint model with an odd-looking half-stock and a heavy barrel. In addition, otherwise standard half- and full-stocked rifles in ·222 Remington can be obtained with heavy barrels. Excepting the varmint pattern, which is characterized by stippling on the pistol grip and a series of short grooves cut in the fore-end, the stocks have skip-line chequering on their fore-ends and pistol grips, low Monte Carlo combs with minimal roll-over,

plastic pistol-grip caps and rubber butt plates.

The **Model L** ('Light') rifles, supplied in the same diversity as the SL, chamber 5·6×57, ·243 Winchester and ·308 Winchester.

The **Model M** (Medium) action duplicates the Model L, excepting that it is larger and heavier, and can handle longer cartridges. The standard chamberings are 6·5×57, ·270 Winchester, 7×64, ·30−06 and 9·3×62, plus three others − 6·5×55 Mauser, 7·5×55 and 7×57 − available to special order. Left- and right-handed Model M rifles are stocked in the manner of their smaller cousins. However, the rubber recoil pad is ventilated and a contrasting fore-end tip, cut diagonally, is accompanied by a thin white spacer. The **Model M Professional** is identical mechanically, but has a synthetic Cycolac stock with 'chequering' moulded into the pistol grip and fore-end. However curious these stocks may look, and regardless of how much purists dislike them, they are practically warp-proof. Their great dimensional stability helps to maintain point-of-impact in extreme climates. In addition, unlike wood, they are unaffected by scratches, oil and grease.

The **Models S** and **S/T** (Standard and Standard/Tropical) are similar to the half-stocked 'M' patterns; both are supplied with the double set-trigger, though the single-trigger pattern is available to special order. S and S/T receivers are lengthened and strengthened to withstand the rigours of high-power magnum cartridges. Consequently, the tropical rifle weighs more than 4kg. The rifles all have conventional pistol-grip stocks with low Monte Carlo combs and ventilated rubber butt plates. Rosewood fore-end tips, cut diagonally, are separated from the stock-wood by a thin white spacer; so, too, are pistol-grip caps. Sling swivels are standard. The back sight on the tropical rifle is mounted on a distinctive squared block.

Standard rifles may be obtained in 6·5×68, 7mm Remington Magnum, ·300 Winchester Magnum, 8×68S and ·375 H&H Magnum; tropical rifles are made only for 9·3×64, ·375 H&H Magnum and ·458 Winchester Magnum. Magazine capacity is four.

Steyr-Daimler-Puch offers **Luxusmodelle** in addition to the standard rifles. Though these are readily distinguished by their stocks, they also incorporate mechanical changes. The synthetic spool magazines have been substituted by three-round box magazines, accompanied by conventional metal floorplates, and the safety catch has been replaced by a slider on the upper tang; in addition, the single trigger system, set by pushing the trigger-lever forward, is standard rather than an option. The stock is greatly refined, with none of the slightly hunchbacked appearance of the standard rifles. It has a longer pistol grip, a Bavarian-style cheek piece and a perceptible hog's back comb. Excepting the Model S, which requires greater thickness of wood to handle recoil, all half-stocked guns offer a delicate schnabel tip of contrasting rosewood − without the white spacer − and the front sling swivel will be found on the barrel rather than under the fore-end.

The metalwork of Luxusmodelle may be engraved and the stock-wood carved to order. The Mannlicher offers unusual possibilities for engraving, owing to the size of the receiver and the shape of the cocking-piece shroud. However, the guns often look oddly archaic when so treated; restraint in stock carving, particularly, is usually for the best!

The excellence of material, allied with superb handling qualities, endows the Mannlicher with a reputation for accuracy. Steyr-Daimler-Puch has capitalized on this by developing a sniper rifle − the **Steyr-Scharfschützengewehr** (SSG or SSG-69) − and two target-shooting versions, Sport and Match-UIT. The sniper rifle of the Austrian army as well as many military/police forces worldwide, the standard SSG is essentially similar to the **Sport-Modell**. However, the former usually offers a detachable box magazine while the latter has the standard synthetic spool. The metal parts of the SSG are usually phosphated to eliminate reflections, while the sturdy stock has extensive stippling on the pistol grip and fore-end. Alternatively, an olive-green Cycolac stock may be obtained; butt-plate spacers can adjust the guns to individual firers. The **SSG PII** is simply a modification of the standard gun

with a heavy barrel and a large bolt-handle knob instead of the slender spatulate type. SSG PII rifles do not have open sights.

Available only in ·243 and ·308 Winchester, the **Match-UIT** – single-shot, or feeding from a ten-round box – looks quite unlike any other gun in the series. Its extraordinary stock is cut away to allow the barrel to float freely, the exiguous fore-end being entirely stippled to improve grip. The straight bolt handle, angled downward, has a large synthetic grasping knob; the trigger is adjustable longitudinally within the angular stamped-strip guard; aperture sights are standard fittings; and a woven 'mirage band' runs from the receiver ring to the front sight.

AUG

The 5·56mm Armee-Universal-Gewehr (AUG), sometimes known as the Model 77, was developed specifically for the Austrian army. Though another of the voguish bullpups, the AUG embodies additional unorthodox features. There are six main construction groups: barrel, receiver, trigger, bolt, magazine and butt. Changing the barrel will transform the AUG into a light support weapon, a carbine or even (with a special magazine and bolt unit) an effectual submachine-gun.

Though there is only a single synthetic frame, in black or olive green, the AUG System offers six barrel assemblies – 350, 407 and 508mm without sights; 508mm with a front sight; 508mm with an integral

M203 grenade launcher; and a heavy 621mm pattern, with bipod. There are receivers with the standard integral optical sight, an open back sight, or adapted to take conventional optical sight mounts ('N' pattern). Then there are three triggers and three bolts: semi-automatic, and two types of selective unit allowing open- or closed-bolt operation. Magazines hold either thirty or 42 rounds.

Gas is tapped from the barrel, then strikes one of the bolt-carrier guide rods to rotate the bolt out of engagement with the barrel extension. This is conventional enough, though open to criticism on the grounds that the action is asymmetric: in common with objections to current Mannlicher sporting rifles, however, these are entirely theoretical.

The external appearance of the AUG is futuristic, even by current standards. This is largely due to the synthetic 'frame' or butt/pistol-grip unit, which accepts an alloy receiver with steel inserts, and the low power optical sight bracket cast integrally with the receiver. Magazines are transparent plastic, allowing the contents to be assessed at a glance but adding to an aura of unreality; there is a prong-type flash suppressor; and a fore-grip, which assists speedy barrel removal, appears immediately ahead of the trigger guard. There is no selector – light pressure fires single shots, further pressure gives automaticity – and a cross-bolt safety catch runs through the frame. Ejection can be changed from right to left merely by changing the bolt and

replacing the ejection-port cover. The standard selective-fire rifle is the **AUG-A1**; the **AUG-P** (Polizei or Police) is generally a short-barrelled version, selective-fire or semi-automatic only, firing from a closed bolt.

AUG rifles have performed well in most recent competitive trials, and have been adopted by Australia, Eire and Malaysia in addition to Austria. Unlike many of their direct competitors, Steyr-Daimler-Puch prefers precision casting to welding; this, plus the use of sturdy synthetics for the frame, appears to promote better reliability and longer life than some rival designs.

Manurhin FRANCE

Manufacture de Machines du Haut-Rhin (F-68200 Mulhouse, 10 Rue de Soultz) is best known among gun connoisseurs for making Walther pistols under licence. However, the company also makes a version of the Swiss SIG SG542 (q.v.) together with hunting/sporting derivatives of the basic design known as the **Fusil Semi-Automatique Manurhin** (FSA-MR, in ·222 Remington) or **Carabine Semi-Automatique Manurhin** (CSA-MR, ·243 Winchester). Perhaps surprisingly, the 'carbine' is longer and slightly heavier than the rifle.

Mayer & Grammelspacher WEST GERMANY

Founded in the Bavarian town of Rastatt in 1890, Dianawerk Mayer & Grammelspacher GmbH & Co. KG (D-7550 Rastatt, Karlstrasse 34) is best known for its 'Diana'-brand airguns. However, like Feinwerkbau

(q.v.), Mayer & Grammelspacher decided to capitalize on the success of the airgun business by introducing its first ·22 rimfire target rifle in 1979. The goal was to persuade marksmen to use the company's products in several disciplines by matching stock profiles and handling characteristics.

Though M&G's cartridge guns – derivatives of the basic **Model 820** – have yet to achieve the success of the Feinwerkbaus, they have certainly established a niche in their market. This is due in no small part to a marketing relationship with Dynamit Nobel; consequently, Diana 820 rifles will also be encountered under the RWS brand.

The basic 820 range currently comprises four guns: the single-shot **820S** or Standardgewehr, chambering ·22LR rimfire and sharing the stock of the Model 75U T01 airgun; the **820K**, a shortened version of the 820S, intended for moving-target shooting, with an optical sight, a short barrel, a muzzle weight and a distinctive wooden butt plate; the 1988-vintage **820L**, which shares the odd-looking stock of the Model 100 air-rifle; and the **820F**, a heavy Free Rifle with a thumb-hole stock and an adjustable hooked butt plate. The Model 820SF is a variant of the 820 with the sight-line raised about 10mm to suit the 'head up' shooting position. The Dianas all feature a trigger system adapted from the airgun pattern, which can be adjusted in many differing ways. Thus the trigger lever can be moved longitudinally within the guard, and the synthetic trigger-lever blade can be turned laterally to suit the firer.

Right
The Merkel Modell 210E, typical of the combination guns made in the German Democratic Republic. The shotgun is placed conventionally above the rifled barrel.
By courtesy of Karl Schäfer.

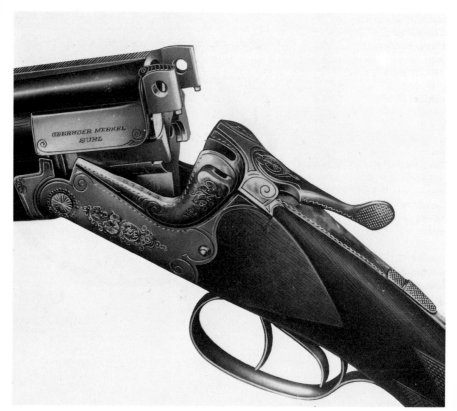

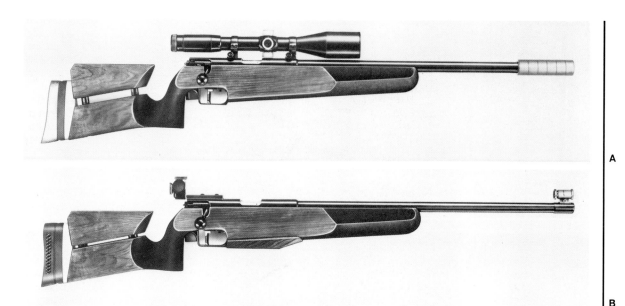

Merkel EAST GERMANY

The once-independent Gebrüder Merkel & Co., tracing its lineage back to 1781, disappeared into the nationalized GDR firearms industry immediately after the end of the Second World War. Production of fine shotguns and double rifles recommenced soon afterwards, however, and examples are still available in the West through Suhler Jagdwaffen (DDR-6000 Suhl, Wilhelm-Pieck-Strasse 16). The guns are expensive, but worth the investment. They are made of the best materials; offer excellent walnut stocks; and may be obtained with engraving which, at its finest, will satisfy the most discerning client.

Merkel double rifles, as well as the combination guns, are conventional superposed-barrel designs with Kersten (box) locks and Holland & Holland-type side-lock triggers to allow greater strength immediately behind the breech: Merkel shotguns often have 'Blitz' lockwork mounted on the trigger-plate, which is potentially less sturdy. Holland & Holland ejectors are used, with a sliding safety catch on the tang above the stock-wrist. The standard guns – Models 213 and 213E (the former non-ejecting), plus rifles 223 and 223E – feature semi-deluxe European walnut stocks, their locks and side plates being lightly engraved with arabesques, hunting scenes and animals. The deluxe guns – models 313E and 323E – are essentially similar to the standard patterns, but have better stocks plus 'English Scroll' engraving on the action and the side plates. Some guns can be obtained in matched sets, with exchangeable rifle and shotgun barrels.

Unlike some of the similar-looking Merkel shotguns, the double rifles and combination guns invariably have double triggers (the foremost being a set-trigger) and fixed or folding-leaf back sights. Shotgun barrels may be 12-, 16- or 20-bore, while the rifles may be chambered for cartridges from ·22 Hornet up to 9·3×74R and ·375 H&H Magnum.

Mitchell USA

Mitchell Arms, Inc., of 3411 Lake Center Drive, Santa Ana, California 92704, is primarily an importer. A wide range of shoulder arms is handled, including Yugoslavian-made Kalashnikov adaptations and Italian rimfire versions of the Galil, M16, AK-47 and MAS. In addition, however, Mitchell promotes a conversion kit for the Charter Arms AR-7 (q.v.) providing a telescoping butt and a vented barrel shroud.

Mossberg USA

O.F. Mossberg & Sons, Inc. (7 Grasso Avenue, North Haven, Connecticut 06473), a renowned maker of shotguns, once also proffered a range of centre- and rimfire rifles. As these were losing ground to more effectual rivals, they were discarded in 1988.

The range at the beginning of the 1987 season included bolt-action **Model 1500** rifles (Grade I, Grade II, Mountaineer and Varmint versions), with internal magazines; the **Model 1550**, with a detachable box magazine; and the deluxe **Model 1700** Classic Hunter. Introduced in 1979 to replace older and less effectual bolt-action rifles of the 800 series, the Model 1500 came in a selection of calibres, including ·223 and ·22–250 Remington, ·243 and ·270 Winchester, 7mm Remington Magnum, ·30–06 and ·308 Winchester, plus ·300 and ·338 Winchester Magnum. Though well made and effectual enough, the Mossberg rifle could not compete with the Winchester M70, Ruger M77 or Remington 700.

By 1987, none of Mossberg's bolt-action, lever-action and auto-loading rifles survived. Three years previously, there had been two versions of the Model 479 ·30–30 lever-action; the Models 353, 377 Plinkster and 380 ·22LR rimfire auto-loaders; and the bolt-action 144 Target (·22LR), 341 (·22 Short, Long and Long Rifle) and 640K Chuckster (·22 WMR).

Left
The Marlin lever-action rifle has a pedigree stretching back into the nineteenth century. This Model 444SS shows how the receiver is cut to allow lateral ejection, a feature that gave Marlins an advantage over almost all but the most recent Winchesters.

MARLIN

•••

The Marlin Firearms Company, 100 Kenna Drive, North Haven, Connecticut 06473, USA

Claiming origins dating back to 1870, this gunmaker sprang to prominence with the introduction of a lever-action rifle designed by John M. Marlin. The Model 1881 was the first of a series that has lasted to the present day; at least the equal of the contemporary Winchesters, it also offered the merits of a solid-top receiver and lateral ejection after modifications had been made in 1891. Marlin thereafter rose to become a leading member of the US gunmaking fraternity, making machine-guns and military rifles during the First World War.

Product range: the company currently makes a range of lever- and bolt-action rifles, some auto-loaders and a single-barrel shotgun.

Recently discontinued models: the ·22LR Model 990, introduced in 1979 and discontinued in 1986, was a tube-magazine variant of the Model 995 described below. In addition, most of the Marlin rimfire auto-loaders were once also encountered under the 'Glenfield' brandname; and there have been versions of the Model 336 (particularly) with differing stock fittings. The 336ER or 'Extra Range', for example, was the standard Model 336 with a longer barrel and a three-quarter length magazine similar to that of the current Model 444.

Models 9 and 45

These are identical auto-loading blowback carbines, chambering 9mm Parabellum and ·45 ACP respectively. The guns are unremarkable mechanically, though, as their receivers are machined from a solid steel block, durability is better than many diecast rivals.

They incorporate a seven- or twelve-round detachable box magazine (·45 and 9mm respectively), a Garand-style safety in the front of the trigger guard, and an automatic hold-open to retain the bolt after the last round has been fired and ejected. An additional safety mechanism prevents the guns being fired if the magazine is not in place.

The carbines have one-piece hardwood half-stocks, with rubber butt plates, and sling swivels appear beneath the butt and fore-end. Open sights are supplied, though the receiver-top is drilled and tapped to accept optical sight mounts. The guns measure 35·6in overall and weigh a little over 6lb unladen.

Models 15, 25 and 780–3

Marlin's bolt-action junior rifles are all built on the same system, locked by turning the bolt handle down into its seat. This is quite adequate for the comparatively low pressures generated by rimfire ammunition; in any case, the guns cannot fire until the action is securely shut. A rocking safety catch lies on the right rear of all receivers.

The smallest Marlin is the **Model 15Y** or 'Little Buckaroo', a single-shot junior gun with an abbreviated fore-end and a short butt. The **Model 25** shares the 15Y action, but has a longer barrel – 22in compared with 16in – and a full-size stock. The stock has a pistol grip and a low Monte Carlo comb, but lacks chequering. The guns feed from seven-round detachable box magazines and have simple open sights, though the receiver is grooved for optical-sight mounts.

The guns of the 780 series, which preceded the Model 25, offer American walnut stocks with nylon butt plates, white-line spacers, and chequering impressed into the pistol grip and fore-end. They also have a better-quality metal trigger guard, and a sturdier semi-buckhorn back sight. **Model 780** embodies a seven-shot detachable box magazine, while **Model 781** has a tube magazine similar to the lever-action Model 39 (q.v.); this holds seventeen ·22LR rimfire or twenty-five ·22 Short cartridges. The guns are 41in overall and weigh 5·5–6lb, depending on magazine configuration.

A

B

C

A

B

The **Models 25M** and **25MB Midget Magnum** (·22WMR only) are essentially similar to the Model 780, with detachable seven-round box magazines. White-line spacers are omitted from the hardwood stocks, the back sights are simple open notches, and the Midget Magnum has a truncated stock. Its barrel measures a mere 16·2in compared with 22in for the other guns in the series.

Models 782 and **783** are similar to the Model 25M, excepting that they have genuine American walnut stocks; white-line spacers and nylon butt plates; and chequering on pistol grip and fore-end. The 782 rifle has a detachable box magazine, while Model 783 embodies the standard tube. All guns accept optical sight mounts.

Models 30, 336, 444 and 1895

These are classical Marlin lever-action rifles with a lengthy pedigree dating back to the Model 1893. Though changes were made in the 1930s and then in 1948, resulting in the Models 36 and 336 respectively, the gun is substantially the original excepting that a round bolt and an ejection port have replaced a squared block and cut away receiver. All Marlins of this type now incorporate a hammer-block safety system.

The standard **Model 336CS**, available in ·30–30 or ·35 Remington only, has a 20in barrel. Its pistol-grip butt and plain fore-end display high-gloss 'Marshield' finish, while the butt plate and pistol-grip cap are accompanied by white-line spacers. The guns have prominent ejection ports on the right side of the receiver, directly above the loading gate, and bear a superficial resemblance to the Winchester M1894; however, the Marlin has an unmistakable lever-pivot block beneath the receiver ahead of the trigger. The rifle weighs 7lb and measures 38·5in overall.

Model 336LTS (·30–30 only), introduced late in 1987, amalgamates the mechanical features of the 336CS with a straight-wrist butt, a plain rubber butt plate and a 16·5in barrel. Magazine capacity is reduced from six rounds to five.

The **Model 30AS** (·30–30 only) is basically a budget-price 336CS with an ultra-plain hardwood pistol-grip butt and simpler sights, while the **Model 444SS** (·444 Marlin only, five-shot) is a strengthened 336-type action accompanied by a 22in barrel and a three-quarter length magazine tube. The **Model 1895SS**, offered only in ·45–70, is identical with the 444SS apart from chambering; however, its magazine capacity is restricted to four rounds, and the enlarged loading gate breaks into the lower line of the ejection port. The large-bore Marlins measure 40·6in overall and weigh about 7lb 9oz unladen.

Model 39

This is an adaptation of the original M1891 rifle, the first lever-action repeater to chamber ·22LR rimfire. The standard **Model 39AS**, introduced in 1988, is stocked in the fashion of the 336CS (q.v.). However, a squared breech-bolt reciprocates in the right receiver wall and a patented quick-release locking plug closes the magazine tube. The standard 39AS has a large magazine capacity: nineteen ·22LR or twenty-six ·22 Short rounds. Measuring 40in overall, the guns weigh 6lb 8oz. The **Model 39TDS** is essentially similar, but its barrel measures a mere 16·5in (instead of 24in) and magazine capacity is reduced to ten ·22LR or sixteen ·22 Short cartridges. It also has a straight-wrist stock and a squared operating lever.

Models 60, 70, 75 and 995

These are blowback auto-loaders, predecessors of the Models 9 and 45. They share the traditional Marlin rounded receiver; cross-bolt safeties in the web behind the trigger; and (excepting the Models 70 Papoose and 995) plain walnut-finish hardwood half-stocks with pistol grips and low Monte Carlo combs. The **Model 60** and **Model 75** are tube-magazine repeaters differing

only in length (40·5 and 36·5in respectively); they can hold seventeen and thirteen ·22LR rimfire rounds but, unlike the bolt actions in this calibre, will handle neither ·22 Short nor ·22 Long. Automatic hold-opens are provided on the tube-magazine guns.

The **Model 70HC** and **70P** or Papoose are box-magazine variants of the Model 60, capacities being seven (standard) or 25 rounds (optional). The 70HC rifle has an 18in barrel and a manual hold-open, while the Papoose, introduced in 1986, features a straight-comb butt, a minimal half-stock, and a detachable 16·2in barrel retained by a large knurled collar. It weighs a mere 3lb 9oz, compared with 5lb for a Model 70HC or 995.

The **Model 995** (·22LR only, 36·2in overall, 5lb) is simply a deluxe Model 70, though it is the oldest of the trio. Sole survivor of the 990-series guns introduced in 1979, it has a walnut stock with a white-line spacer and a nylon butt plate; chequering is impressed on the pistol grip and fore-end. A semi-buckhorn back sight is usually let into the top surface of the barrel.

Model 1894

This is a version of the original 1893-pattern Marlin rifle, retaining the squared breech-bolt that forms part of the upper right receiver wall. When the action is opened, the block slides back to expose the chamber; ejection is lateral rather than vertical, which facilitates the use of optical sights. Helpfully, the receiver top now

has a non-reflective matt finish. All the guns in the series have tube magazines, and all have traditional straight-wrist American walnut stocks. The **Model 1894M** chambers ·22WRM, has a ten-round magazine, and a white-line spacer accompanying the nylon butt plate; the **M1894S** is similar, but has a rubber rifle-type butt plate and can be chambered for ·41 Magnum, ·44 Remington Magnum/·44 Special or ·45 Long Colt; the **M1894CS**, stocked similarly to the M1894M, has an 18·5in barrel (instead of 20in), a nine-shot magazine and chambers ·357 Magnum/·38 Special; and the **Model 1894CL**, with a 22in barrel and a half-length magazine holding six rounds, may be obtained in ·25–20 or ·32–20 WCF.

Navy Arms Company USA

Trading from 689 Bergen Boulevard, Ridgefield, New Jersey, Navy Arms is one of the pioneers of modern black powder shooting. Indeed, the compant's president, Val Forgett, has been greatly honoured by Italy for contributing so much to the growth of the country's gunmaking industry. Though Navy Arms Company acquired the black powder division of Ithaca Gun Company and Classic Arms Company in 1977, and now makes many of its own handguns, most of the more complex re-creations – including Henry, Winchester and Remington Rolling Block replicas – are purchased from Parker-Hale, Pedersoli, Pietta or Uberti.

Below

Marlin Models 70 and 75C (A and B respectively) are conventional blowback auto-loaders chambering ·22LR rimfire cartridges, while the Model 1894 (C) is a version of the Model 39 lever-action repeater with a straight-wrist butt.

By courtesy of The Marlin Firearms Company.

A

B

C

MAUSER

Mauser-Werke Oberndorf GmbH, D-7238 Oberndorf/Neckar, Postfach 13 49, West Germany

The name of Peter Paul Mauser (1838–1914) is enshrined in the annals of rifle design as the father of the metallic-cartridge bolt action, even though his original company – Gebrüder Mauser & Co. – has been through many changes since 1874. The success of small-bore Mausers throughout the world between 1889 and 1918 laid a base from which the Third Reich diversification arose. However, just as Germany collapsed in 1945 so did Mauser-Werke AG. Not until the late 1950s did the rump of the once-powerful arms-making concern regain measurable success, though operations have been greatly expanded since then. Once again, Mauser's name appears in the top hundred German manufacturing companies; smallarms, however, provide a mere fraction of the total.

Product range: Mauser still makes aircraft cannon, while marketing a selection of rifles – some of which have been made by Heym and Voere (q.v.) – together with the last few Mauser-Parabellum pistols. In recent years Mauser has become much more generous with its trademark, licensing the mark to Umarex for use on items such as blank-firers, airguns and knives.

Recently discontinued models: from 1969 until the mid 1970s, Mauser-Jagdwaffen marketed a series of conventional Mauser-action rifles under the model-designations 2000, 3000 and 4000. Seen as a safeguard against the failure of the radical Modell 66 to gain widespread acceptance, they were made by Heym (q.v.). The Modell 2000 was available in ·270 and ·308 Winchester, or ·30–06. Introduced in 1969, it was replaced in 1971 by the Model 3000, which featured skip-line chequering but lacked open sights. A similar 3000 Magnum (7mm Remington Magnum, ·300 Winchester Magnum and ·375 H&H Magnum) had a longer barrel and magazine capacity restricted to three rounds instead of five. The Modell 4000 was a short-action variant of the 3000, chambering ·222 and ·223 Remington. Supplied with open sights, it had a solid rubber butt plate instead of a ventilated pattern. Though the Heym-made Mausers were abandoned in the mid-1970s, they provided the inspiration for the Modell 77.

Below

Mauser's Model 66 rifle embodies a novel, but nonetheless interesting short bolt action with the operating handle ahead of the trigger guard. This gaudy gun is typical of those made to special order; whether baroque decoration meets with approval or not, the standard of the workmanship is irreproachable.

By courtesy of Mauser-Werke Oberndorf GmbH.

Modell 66

Mauser did not recommence production of sporting guns until the mid 1960s. When it did, the Modell 66 (known as the '660' in North America, 1966–74) created a sensation: virtually all the traditional Model 98 features had gone! The new rifle offered an unusually short action created by interposing the magazine between the trigger and the receiver, rather than placing the units in tandem. A further reduction was made by telescoping the bolt and the bolt carrier: the bolt handle is raised, the bolt retracted until the handle strikes the bolt-carrier bridge, and then bolt and carrier run back together over the small of the stock. Consequently, although the Modell 66 appears to have a solid-bridge receiver, it also has the bolt handle *ahead* of the bridge.

The plunger-type ejector and claw extractor are both carried in the recessed-face bolt head. A 'silent safety' will be found on the right side of the cocking piece shroud, while the bolt-release catch protrudes from the right side of the stock above the trigger. The extraordinary design of the action forced important changes in the trigger system, which is carried on a broad sub-assembly made in the guise of a U-shape pressing.

Modell 66 barrels are readily exchangeable. The cap-head bolts retaining the receiver ring and the back sight block are loosened, whereupon, once the action has been opened, the barrel/receiver ring assembly can be replaced. Shutting the action, which automatically indexes the barrel, allows the bolts to be replaced.

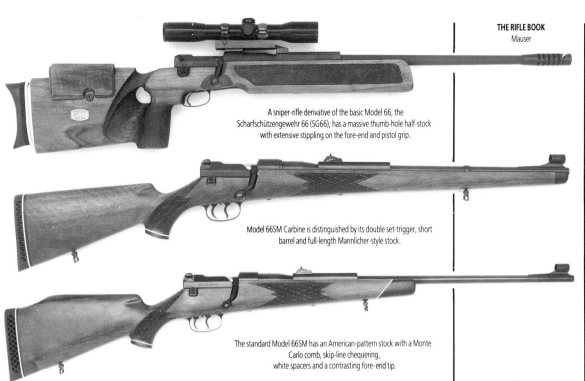

A sniper-rifle derivative of the basic Model 66, the
Scharfschützengewehr 66 (SG66), has a massive thumb-hole half-stock
with extensive stippling on the fore-end and pistol grip.

Model 66SM Carbine is distinguished by its double set-trigger, short
barrel and full-length Mannlicher-style stock.

The standard Model 66SM has an American-pattern stock with a Monte
Carlo comb, skip-line chequering,
white spacers and a contrasting fore-end tip.

Above

Three of the many variants of the
Mauser Model 66 rifle.

Photographs by courtesy of
Mauser-Werke Oberndorf GmbH.

Any of the chamberings from Group I (bolt face
diameter 12·2mm) and Group II (12·65mm) can be used
in a Modell 66 rifle as long as it has the larger bolt;
similarly, all Group III cartridges (13·1mm face) will
operate with the Group IV bolt (13·58mm face), but not
vice-versa. No exchanges are possible between Groups
I/II and III/IV, owing to differences in magazine-body
length.

Group I contains ·243 Winchester, 6·5×57, ·270
Winchester, 7×64, ·30–06 and ·308 Winchester;
Group II is confined to 9·3×64. Group III comprises
6·5×68, 7mm vom Hofe and 8×68S, while Group
IV contains 7mm Remington Magnum, ·300
Winchester Magnum, ·375 H&H Magnum and ·458
Winchester Magnum.

One major shortcoming of the Modell 66 is the
restriction in magazine capacity; otherwise it has no
real faults – apart from expense. It shoots accurately,
has a particularly smooth action owing to the length of
the bearing surfaces, and can be obtained in several
differing variants.

The standard rifle is currently **Modell 66S**, offered
with a walnut half-stock. This has a hog's back comb, a
ventilated rubber butt plate, a rosewood or ebonite
pistol-grip cap, and a rounded rosewood fore-end tip.
Chequering appears on the pistol-grip and fore-end,
while sling swivels lie on the underside of the butt and
on the barrel. A Williams back sight may be slid along
the back sight rail. The rifle is usually supplied with a
double set-trigger, though a single pattern (with a
setting button on the upper tang) and a two-stage
match trigger are optional.

The **Model 66ST** ('Stutzen') shares the basic action
and half-stock, but its barrel measures 53cm compared

with 60cm for the standard guns. It has been marketed
as the '660 Ultra' in the USA. The **Modell 66SM**
amalgamates the standard action, a 60cm barrel and a
double set-trigger; the single set-trigger is an option. In
addition, the half-stock has a Monte Carlo comb,
modified pistol-grip contours and a schnabel tip on the
fore-end. The **Model 66SM Carbine** is a short form of
the 66SM, with a 53cm barrel, a full length Mannlicher
stock with traditional straight comb, a capless pistol-
grip and a Bavarian cheek piece.

Mauser **Modell 66S Magnum** and **66SM Magnum**
rifles are identical with the standard 66S and 66SM
patterns, but have 65cm barrels, larger diameter bolt-
faces and longer magazines.

'Diplomat' variants (66S, 66SM and magnums) offer
engraved game motifs on their specially polished
receivers – red and roe deer, or red deer and wild boar –
plus stocks selected for the beauty of their grain.
Special 'super deluxe' versions, made to order, feature
complex chequering, scroll engraving and typically
baroque stock-carving.

Modell 77

These are conventional bolt-action rifles, made in
Oberndorf to replace the guns made for Mauser by
Heym. The differences are primarily that the '77' guns
are sporters with detachable box magazines while most
of the '83' patterns are competition rifles embodying a
patented match-quality trigger. All embody an action
with three lugs that lock into the receiver behind the
magazine well. The **Modell 77S** (·243 Winchester,
6·5×57, ·270 Winchester, 7×64, ·30–06 or ·308
Winchester) features a rotary safety catch on the
cocking-piece shroud and a setting catch for the single

A

B

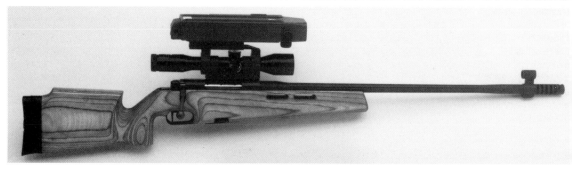

C

set-trigger on the upper tang behind the bolt. The standard sporting rifle displays a walnut half-stock with a hog's back comb, a Bavarian-style cheek piece and a rosewood schnabel tip to the fore-end. It also has a ventilated rubber butt plate accompanied by a black spacer, and a fixed open-notch back sight. However, the **Modell 77S Magnum** (6·5×68, 7mm Remington Magnum, ·300 Winchester Magnum, 8×68S, 9·3×62, 9·3×64, 10·3×60), which has a 65cm barrel, features distinctive white spacers separating the stock wood from the ventilated rubber butt plate, the rosewood pistol-grip cap, and the rounded rosewood fore-end tip. It also has a semi-Monte Carlo comb, and the back sight lies at the front of a distinctive quarter-rib. The rib permits the attachment of large-bell optical sights by means of a clamp-ring. A special big-game Magnum has been offered in ·375 H&H Magnum, while the **Modell 77 Sportsman** is intended for DJV moving target shooting and has a competition-pattern stock with a broad or 'beaver tail' fore-end.

Among the single-shot guns, the standard Wettkampf-Einzellader **Modell 83 Sport UIT** (·308 Winchester only), intended for 300-metre competitions, features a massive action with a stiffening bar above the bolt-way that doubles as a support for aperture sights. The stock has an adjustable butt plate, an elevating comb, stippling on the pistol grip and two lateral slots in the deep slab-side fore-end. Stippling continues under the fore-end until it all but envelopes the tip. The barrel is fluted to conserve weight and strength, and the bolt handle has a large synthetic knob. The **Modell 83 UIT Standardgewehr** is a modification of the single-shot Modell 83 with a detachable ten-round box magazines, while the single-shot **Modell 83 UIT Freigewehr**, intended for Free Rifle shooting, will be encountered with a thumb-hole stock, an adjustable hooked butt plate, and a hand-rest beneath the fore-end.

The magazine-fed Modell 83 has been developed into the **Modell 86SR** sniper rifle, which has a lower rail above the bolt-way, a laminated stock with an adjustable butt plate, and a muzzle-brake/compensator attachment on the fluted barrel.

Mauser-Voere rimfire rifles

The only ex-Voere auto-loader to bear the Mauser banner is the **Modell 105**, made in two variants (Standard and Luxus). The guns are conventional ·22LR rimfire blowbacks, with hardwood half-stocks displaying pistol grips and low Monte Carlo combs. The standard rifle has a plain walnut-finished stock, while the deluxe pattern has skip-line chequering on the pistol grip and fore-end.

The **Modell 107** is a bolt-action ·22LR rimfire repeater feeding from a detachable box magazine containing five, eight or ten rounds. Locking is achieved by turning the bolt handle down into its seat, which is more than adequate for the low pressures involved. The standard gun has a plain hardwood half-stock similar to that of the auto-loading Modell 105; the 107 Luxus displays skip-line chequering on the pistol grip and fore-end; and the 107 Luxus Nussbaum (·22LR or ·22WRM) has a walnut stock with white spacers, plus a rosewood fore-end tip.

The **Modell 201**, made in standard and Luxus variants, is an exceptionally sturdy ·22LR or ·22WMR rifle embodying the Voere 2000 action – a short-throw bolt with two locking lugs on the bolt head. The standard rifle has a walnut-finish beechwood stock with a Bavarian cheek piece, a hog's back comb, and a plain butt plate. Chequering appears on the pistol grip and fore-end. The 201 Luxus is similar, but has a walnut stock with a separate rosewood pistol grip. Both guns have open sights and a safety catch on the rear of the action behind the bolt handle. Though comparatively expensive, they are among the best and strongest bolt-action rimfire rifles.

Mauser-Voere centre-fire rifles

The **Modell 225 Titan II**, Voere's perfected sporter, has a sturdy bolt with three symmetrically-placed lugs and a 60° throw. The 225 and 225 Luxus patterns may be obtained with a shotgun-style single trigger, a double set-trigger (regarded as standard) and a single 'Rückstecher' set by pressing the single trigger-lever

forward before pulling it back to release the sear. 225 and 225 Luxus rifles usually have half-stocks incorporating a semi-Monte Carlo comb and cheek piece; chequering appears on the pistol grip and the fore-end, which has a rounded tip. The Luxusmodell stocks, selected for the beauty of their grain, have contrasting rosewood fore-end tips. Standard chamberings include ·257 Weatherby Magnum, ·270 Weatherby Magnum, 7mm Remington Magnum, ·300 Winchester and Weatherby Magnums, ·30–06, ·308 Norma Magnum, 8×68S, 9·3×64, ·338 Winchester Magnum, and ·375 H&H Magnum.

The **Modell 226 Titan III**, available in standard and deluxe variants, embodies a smaller version of the 225 action chambering ·22–250 Remington, ·243 Winchester, ·25–06, 6·5×55 Mauser, 6·5×57, ·270 Winchester, 7×64, 7·5×55, ·30–06 or ·308 Winchester. Unlike the 225 patterns, a left-hand 226 action is available. The shaping of the rear of the Titan III action, cut away rather than the smooth diagonal of the Titan II, is most distinctive.

· ·

New England Firearms USA
Trading from Industrial Rowe, Gardner, Massachussetts 01440, New England Firearms Company, Inc. is the rump of Harrington & Richardson (q.v.), salvaged after the latter's demise. The current product range includes rimfire revolvers, some single-barrel break-action shotguns and a solitary combination rifle/shotgun known as the **Handi-Gun**. Based on the proven H&R shotgun

Below
Mauser now makes some of the rimfire rifles previously associated with Voere. Shown here are the auto-loading Modell 105 Luxus (A); the bolt-action Modell 107 Luxus (B); and the similar, but much improved Modell 201 Luxus (C).
By courtesy of Mauser-Werke Oberndorf GmbH.

A

B

C

* China Sports, a marketing subsidiary of Norinco, licenses the Chinese-made guns to PTK International – Poly Technologies' parent.

action, this electro-less matt-nickel finish weapon offers exchangeable 20-bore, ·22 Hornet and ·30–30 barrels. It measures about 44in overall and weighs 6·5lb, or 9·5lb with an additional barrel. Butts and fore-ends are walnut-finish hardwood, while the exposed-hammer action incorporates a transfer bar to prevent the firing pin being struck in all but the final stages of a deliberate pull on the trigger lever.

•••••••••••••••••••••••••••••••••

Olympic Arms
USA

Olympic Arms, Inc. (624 Old Pacific Highway SE, Olympia, Washington 98503), specializes in conversion kits for the AR-15/M16 series allowing – for example – the guns to handle 9mm Parabellum or 7·62mm× 39 (Russian M43) ammunition rather than the standard 5·56mm round. The company also offers the **Ultra Match Rifle**, which is a specially selected M16 with a heavyweight broached-rifling stainless steel barrel – 20 or 24in – and match hand-guards. The Ultra has an international-pattern upper receiver, with optical sight mounts replacing the standard hand-guard, and a Williams set-trigger. Operation is essentially similar to the Colt AR-15 (q.v.), but performance is generally much improved. Accuracy bettering 0·5MOA is commonplace.

Norinco CHINA (PRC)

North China Industries Corporation (Norinco) offers a selection of firearms commercially, marketing them aggressively through companies such as Poly Technologies of Atlanta, Georgia, USA.*

SKS-type Simonovs – with a distinctive half-length wood stock – include the standard **Rifle Type 56**, whose internal box magazine is loaded through the top of the open action, plus modified 7·62×39 and 5·56×45 guns feeding from detachable box magazines. Norinco Kalashnikovs include the 7·62×39 '**Submachine-gun Type 56**' with Russian-style folding stocks (Type 56-1), modified butts with a plastic wrist-strengthener (Type 56-2) or an FNC-type tubular pattern; a heavy barrel **NM47** 'National Match' gun; close copies of the Russian 5·45mm AK-74, with fixed or folding stocks; and the 7·62×39 **Type 86** bullpup adaptation.

Kalashnikov derivatives include the **Type 84**, which chambers 5·56×45 rounds; Kalashnikov/Simonov hybrids are marketed in 7·62×39 as **Type 81** (selective fire or semi-automatic), or as **Type EM3611** in 5·56×45.

Factories under Norinco control copy of the US M14 and M16A1 rifles, as well as the Soviet SVD sniper rifle in 7·62×51 NATO ('**NDM86**') and a traditional Browning ·22 semi-automatic with a butt magazine.

Below

A selection of Parker-Hale rifles. The Model 1200 Varmint rifle (A, top), with optical instead of open sights and a heavy barrel, is no longer available; the Model 2100 Midland (A, bottom) features a non-standard Mauser action; the M81 African Rifle (B) has a lightly engraved action; and the M81 Classic (C) is typical of the company's latest products.

By courtesy of Parker-Hale Ltd.

A

B

C

PARKER-HALE

•••

Parker-Hale Ltd, Golden Hillock Road, Birmingham, England B11 2PZ

Britain's premier rifle-maker, with a history dating back to 1880, Parker-Hale Ltd (Golden Hillock Road, Birmingham B11 2PZ) has been making Mauser-action sporting rifles for many years. Operations were enlarged during the 1980s, with a concerted move into target rifles and the adoption of the L81A1 Cadet Rifle by the British Army. It will be interesting to see how business develops in the 1990s.

Product range: bolt-action sporting/target rifles are made on a modified 1898-pattern Mauser action, alongside superb re-creations of Enfield, Whitworth and other percussion-ignition rifle-muskets. A solitary sporter is marketed under the Midland Gun Company banner.

Recently discontinued models: earlier versions of the 1200 series differed mainly in stock configuration and the design of minor fittings. The *M82 sniper rifle*, no longer made in Britain, has been adopted by Canada as the Rifle C3.

Sporting rifles

Excepting the Model 2100 Midland pattern, these feature a classic 1898 Mauser action with two locking lugs on the bolt head and a third lug opposing the bolt-handle base. Unlike many rival manufacturers, who prefer neat-looking (but comparatively weak) extractor/ejectors built into the bolt face, Parker-Hale retains the original, durable and effectual claw. The rifles all have hinged magazine floor plates and radial safety catches protruding from the stock alongside the cocking-piece shroud. Magazine capacity is invariably four rounds.

The **M81 Classic** has an elegant straight-comb walnut stock, hand-cut chequering on the pistol grip and around the fore-end, a rubber recoil pad accompanied by a black spacer, and QD swivels under the butt and fore-end. Available in ·22–250, ·243 Winchester, 6mm Remington, ·270 Winchester, 6·5×55, 7×57, 7×64, 7mm Remington Magnum, ·30–06, ·300 Winchester Magnum, and ·308 Winchester, the M81 Classic measures 44·5in overall and weighs about 7lb 12oz. Its barrel is drilled and tapped for a Williams ramp-pattern back sight, though optical sights are often substituted; set-triggers are also optional.

Stocked similarly to the Classic pattern, **M81 African** rifles have engraved actions, a heavy barrel with folding-leaf 'Express' back sights on a quarter rib, an additional recoil lug, and the front sling swivel on the barrel instead of the stock. They may chamber ·300 H&H Magnum, ·308 Normag, ·375 H&H Magnum or 9·3×62; about 45in long, African Rifles weigh about 9lb without sights.

The current **1200 Super**, sharing the action of the M81 series, has a gold-plated trigger, a half-stock with a roll-over Monte Carlo comb, a contrasting fore-end tip, white spacers and a ventilated rubber recoil pad. A single-leaf folding back sight is standard, as are swivels under the fore-end and butt. The standard 1200 Super (44·5in long, 7lb 8oz) chambers the same nine rounds as the M81 Classic; **1200M** Super Magnum rifles handle 7mm Remington, ·300

Winchester and ·308 Norma magnum cartridges. Otherwise identical **1200C** and **1200CM** Super-Clip rifles, with detachable box magazines restricted to three rounds only, may also be obtained in the regular chamberings.

The **1100L** Lightweight rifle handles the same cartridges as the 1200 Super, but has a 22in barrel instead of 24in,* an overall length of 43in and an unladen weight of 6lb 8oz – achieved by hollowing the bolt handle, substituting an alloy trigger-guard/floor plate assembly and refining the schnabel-tip stock. **1100M** African Magnums (46in long, 9·5lb) have a heavy barrel and a massive weighted stock containing an additional recoil bolt. The stock has a shallow Monte Carlo comb, a rudimentary schnabel tip and a ventilated pad to absorb the recoil of ·375 H&H Magnum, ·404 Jeffrey and ·458 Winchester Magnum ammunition.

Parker-Hale's **1000 Standard** rifle utilizes the standard Mauser action in a plain walnut stock with a low Monte Carlo comb, impressed chequering on pistol grip and fore-end, and a diced nylon butt plate. Obtainable in all nine regular chamberings, the rifles measure 43in overall and weigh about 7lb 4oz. The otherwise similar **Midland 2100** rifle has an 1893-type Mauser action, believed to have been made in Spain, to create an effectual sporter at a highly competitive price.†

Military rifles

The success of the M82 sniper rifle encouraged Parker-Hale to enter Ministry of Defence trials seeking an effectual cadet rifle. The result was the 7·62×51 **M83** NATO Target Rifle, subsequently adopted in Britain as the L81A1 – a sturdy single-shot gun with a short butt and fore-end, a folding leaf sight on top of the strengthened receiver, and a replaceable-element tubular front sight.

The company also featured in British Army sniper-rifle trials, entering the **M85**. With a detachable ten-round box magazine, a length of 1,150mm (without butt spacers) and weighing 6·24kg with a 6×44

* The ·243 Winchester version retains the full 24in barrel.

† Whether this action is refurbished Spanish military, newly made in Spain or acquired elsewhere is not yet known.

optical sight and bipod, the M85 was assessed as 'fit for service' even though the rival Accuracy International PM rifle (q.v.) was preferred. However, Parker-Hale immediately put the M85 into commercial production and it is rapidly attaining an enviable reputation for accuracy.

Target rifles

The success of the M82 and M83 encouraged Parker-Hale to introduce the first of a series of target rifles based on the M83 action. The 7·62×51 **M84 Mk II Canberra** has an ambidexterous walnut stock, extensively stippled on the pistol grip and fore-end, while the otherwise similar **Bisley** can be obtained with plain right- or left-hand stocks. Canberra rifles measure 48–49·5in overall, depending on butt spacers, and weigh 11·5lb with sights and hand-stop. Full-length accessory rails are let into the underside of the fore-end and PH5E aperture back sights are standard.

Derived from the M85 sniper rifle, the 7·62×51 **M86** features a detachable five-round box magazine and can accept optical sight mounts. It is stocked similarly to the M84 Mk II Canberra. **M87** rifles, adapted from the M86 for moving-target shooting, have short heavy barrels and squared fore-ends with less stippling than normal. Optical sights are standard. With a 26in barrel, the M87 measures 45in overall and weighs 10lb; it chambers ·243 Winchester, 6·5×55, ·30–06, ·300 Winchester Magnum or 7·62×51, though others can be supplied to special order.

Perugini-Visini

ITALY

Perugini-Visini e Compania is based in the village of Nuovolera, near Brescia. Its products are mainly double rifles, made to the exacting specifications of design and construction common in Europe. They include Anson & Deeley-pattern box-lock ejectors with monobloc barrels and their back sights on a quarter rib. The standard **Boxlock Express**, with borderline engraving and a colour case-hardened action is available only in 9·3× 74R and ·444 Marlin; the **Boxlock Magnum Express**, with a reinforced action befitting the additional power of the cartridges, may chamber ·270 Winchester, ·375 H&H Magnum and ·458 Winchester.

There is also a **Sidelock Super Express**, which features a Holland & Holland-pattern ejector action with chopper lump barrels and folding-leaf 'Express' back sights on the quarter rib. The standard guns come with English-style pistol grip butts and delicate borderline engraving on the action. However, English Scroll and many other types of engraving are available to order, as is an exchangeable 12-bore barrel set. The guns may be chambered for a variety of cartridges, ranging from 7mm Remington Magnum up to ·470 Nitro.

Perugini's **Over/Under Express** features a box-lock ejector action, with delicate scroll engraving on the action fences, borders and hinge-pin. An English-type pistol grip stock and cheek piece are standard, while a set-trigger is an optional extra. The guns may be obtained for 7mm Remington Magnum, 7× 65R,

Below

The Parker-Hale M85 Sniper Rifle (A), shown here in camouflage finish, performed creditably in British Army trials and is now available commercially; the L81A1 or M83 Cadet Rifle (B) is service issue; and the M84 Mk 2 Canberra (C) is rapidly gaining an impressive reputation on the target range.

By courtesy of Parker-Hale Ltd.

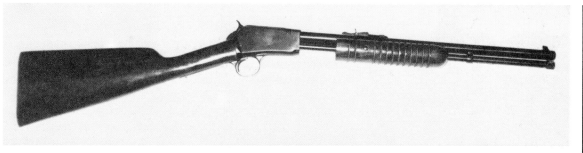

By courtesy of Karl Schäfer.

Above

Rhoener makes a series of rifles and shotguns embodying a break-open action controlled by a trigger-guard lever. The guns make extensive use of precision investment castings and are highly competitively priced.

9·3✕74R, ·270 and ·284 Winchester, ·338 Winchester, ·375 H&H Magnum and ·458 Winchester.

Quality is very good, but the Perugini-Visini double rifles are expensive: they start at about $7,000 (1988 prices) and run upwards of $25,000 for an engraved side-lock. An assortment of brandnames has been applied by the US distributor, William Larkin Moore & Company of Westlake Village, California. The basic gun is known as the 'Victoria', the magnum and the over/under apparently being known as the 'Victoria M' and 'Victoria D' respectively; the side-lock gun, the 'Selous', is regarded as the top of the range.

Rahn USA

The products of the Rahn Gun Works (470 Market Street SW, Grand Rapids, Michigan 49503) – at the time of writing – comprise a series of Mauser-action sporting rifles. Unlike many of the smaller US gunmaking companies, which often invest heavily in specially-developed bolt systems, Rahn bases its work on a conventional 1898-pattern Mauser refined by the removal of the safety from the cocking piece to the tang (allowing a more elegant cocking-piece shroud to be fitted) and substituting a spatulate handle for the knob type. This frees investment for individually-tailored stocks, on the defensible premise that *stock fit* determines whether a firer is comfortable with a gun and not the design of the bolt unit. Rahn's rifles come in four patterns: the **Deer Series**, with 24in barrels in ·25–06, ·270 and ·308 Winchester, and an oakleaf bordered deer's head motif on the floor plate; the 26in barrelled **Elk Series** in 6✕56, 7mm Remington Magnum and ·30–06, with an oakleaf-bordered elk's head; the **Himilayan Series** (sic) with 24in barrels chambering 5·6✕57 or 6·5✕68S, and a yak-head within scroll engraving; and the 26in barrelled **Safari Series**, with an elephant, a rhinoceros or a Cape Buffalo on the floor plate, a gold name plate, and a choice of chamberings ranging from ·308 Normag to 9·3✕64. The walnut stocks

usually feature a Monte Carlo cheek piece and a pistol grip, a rubber recoil pad and a shallow contrasting schnabel-tip to the fore-end. A fibreglass stock is offered as an option on the Himilayan Series only. Prices of these semi-custom guns began at about $800 in 1989.

Rhoener WEST GERMANY

Most of these rifles, shotguns and combination guns embody a break-open action controlled by a trigger-guard lever, but there are also some simple bolt-action patterns – Kleinkalibergewehre **RG69** and **RG69a** – for Flobert and rimfire ammunition. The tipping-barrel rifles include an over/under **RZ70** and the similar, but shorter RZ70L; ·22LR rimfire **RG75** and RG75L; and **RG81**, which apparently handles ·22WMR and ·22 Hornet.

Rossi ARGENTINA

Amadeo Rossi SA, Metalúrgica e Munições (PO Box 28, Saõ Leopoldo-RS, Brazil) makes handguns, shotguns and cartridge rifles.

The lever-action patterns, copied from the 1892 Winchester and often known as the 'Puma' range in North America, include the **Model 65** in ·44 Magnum and **Model 92** in ·357 Magnum/·38 Special. They are about 37in long and weigh 5lb 12oz; an M92 carbine, some four inches shorter, weighs a mere 5lb. Carbine magazines hold seven rounds compared with ten in the standard full-length patterns.

Rossi's traditional pump-action Gallery Guns are based on the 1890-vintage Model 62 Winchester rifle, with straight-wrist butts and cylindrical hardwood pump handles. The **Model 59** (·22 WMR) and **Model 62** (·22LR) measure 39·3in overall and weigh 5·5lb; the carbine form of the M62 is 32·8in long and a mere 4lb 5oz. Under-barrel tube magazines hold ten (M59), twelve (M62 carbine) or thirteen rounds. Octagonal barrels (M62 only) and blue or chrome finish are optional.

Remington. | **REMINGTON**

Remington Arms Company, Inc., Wilmington, Delaware 19898, USA

Founded by Eliphalet Remington in 1816, this gunmaking family produced a range of handguns – including the well-known percussion-ignition revolvers – before running into financial trouble in 1886 and reconstituting as the 'Remington Arms Company'. The best known weapon produced in the nineteenth century was the famed Rolling Block, but substantial numbers of Lee-system military and sporting rifles were also made. Vast quantities of weapons were made during the First World War (including Russian Mosin-Nagant and British P14/US M17 'Enfields'); the first of a series of bolt-action sporting rifles, based on the Enfield action, appeared in the early 1920s and laid the basis for current operations. After enduring several adjustments of ownership, Remington has been owned by E.I. DuPont de Nemours & Company since 1933.

Product range: Remington makes a wide variety of shotguns, rifles and a solitary handgun. The rifles include bolt- and pump-action designs, as well as an auto-loader or two; the most important, however, is the Model 700 bolt-action.

Recently discontinued models: at the beginning of the 1980s, Remington was offering the Model 742 Woodmaster and 760 Gamemaster in several variants; these guns have now been replaced by the Models 7400 and 7600 respectively, by way of the plainer Models 74 and 76. The Model 788 was a simplified bolt-action rifle in ·22– 250 Remington, ·223 Remington, ·243 Winchester, 7mm–08 and ·308 Winchester, its role now being taken by the Model 78 Sportsman and Model 700 Kit Gun. There were three variations of the Nylon 66 ·22LR rimfire auto-loader, suffixes indicating the stock colour: AB signified 'Apache Black', BD was 'Black Diamond' and MB was 'Mohawk Brown'.

Below

Three versions of the obsolescent ·22LR rimfire Remington Nylon 66 auto-loading rifle, differing principally in the design and colour of the stock and fittings.

Photographs by courtesy of Remington Arms Company, Inc.

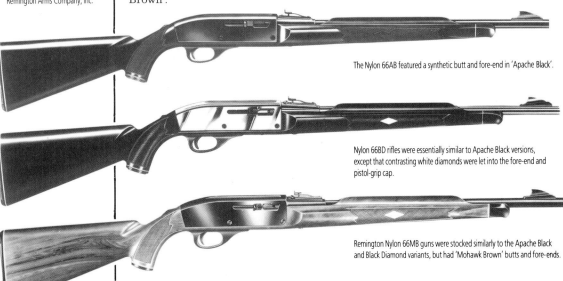

The Nylon 66AB featured a synthetic butt and fore-end in 'Apache Black'.

Nylon 66BD rifles were essentially similar to Apache Black versions, except that contrasting white diamonds were let into the fore-end and pistol-grip cap.

Remington Nylon 66MB guns were stocked similarly to the Apache Black and Black Diamond variants, but had 'Mohawk Brown' butts and fore-ends.

Model 40

These guns are built on a single-shot version of the standard Model 700 action, with a solid-floor receiver to enhance rigidity. The Model 40 is so effectual, and promises such renowned accuracy 'from the box', that it is in great demand among bench-rest aficionados; many trophies have been taken with Model 40 actions over the past decade.

There are currently four major variants: the **Model 40-XB Rangemaster** and **Model 40-XC** in ·308

Winchester; **Model 40-XR** in ·22LR rimfire; and **Model 40-XB BR** ('Bench-Rest'), which can be chambered for virtually any cartridge the purchaser specifies. Excepting the XB BR model, all these guns are now available with optional matt black Kevlar stocks (additional 'KS' suffix) instead of standard walnut. The half-stock profile is common to all, with a straight comb sloping *down* to the pistol grip. Standard guns have no chequering or stippling, but are usually supplied with sturdy rubber butt plates. XB, XC and XR models have

an accessory rail under the fore-end, and the XR pattern – unique to the series – has an extra-deep fore-end level with the base of the trigger guard. The XB BR has a broad flat-bottom fore-end specially for bench-rest work. All Model 40 rifles have massive chrome-plated barrels and jewelled bolts. Mounting blocks for optical sights and short auxiliary rails for aperture sights are supplied as standard. The guns weigh between 9 and 11lb, depending on barrel length and stock material.

Models 541 and 581

Remington's **Model 541-T** (Target) is a neat rimfire sporter with a straight-comb walnut half-stock with chequering on the pistol grip and fore-end. A rocking safety catch lies on the right side of the breech immediately behind the bolt handle, the gun feeds from detachable five-round box magazines (ten-round patterns are optional) and the receiver is suitably drilled and tapped for optical sight mounts. The budget-price **Model 581-S** (Sportsman) shares the action of the 541-T, but its simpler plain-finish stock lacks chequering.

Models 552 and 572

The **Model 552 BDL Autoloader** and **Model 572 BDL Pump Action** are the current versions of guns that have been in production since 1957 and 1955 respectively. The 572 is currently the only pump-action rimfire rifle being made in North America.

Externally similar, apart from the differences in the fore-ends (and the addition of a case deflector behind the Model 552 ejection port), the guns have satin-finish walnut furniture with distinctive fleur-de-lis/strapwork chequering. Under-barrel tube magazines hold fifteen ·22LR rimfire rounds, Williams open back sights are standard, and a cross-bolt safety runs through the back web of the trigger guard.

Model 700

The origins of the Model 700 lie in the first Remington sporting rifle to be introduced after the First World War: the Model 30 of 1920. Credited to Crawford Loomis and Charles Barnes, the Model 30 was based on the M17 Enfield action; indeed, much of the Enfield production line was adapted to make it. Unfortunately, the advent of the Winchester Model 54 completely eclipsed the Model 30; and then deliveries of the Model 30's successor, the Model 720, had hardly commenced when the Second World War interceded.

Once production of M1903A3 Springfield service rifles had ceased in 1945, Remington prepared to re-enter the sporting rifle market with a new gun developed by Michael Walker. The Model 721 appeared in 1947, to be followed within a year by a short-action M722. Mass production of both guns started in 1949.

The Models 721 and 722, though effectual mechanically, lacked the style of the Winchester Model 70. Sales declined gradually after a most promising start, until a remodelled version – designated '700' – appeared in 1962. Apart from small changes in 1968 and 1974, when the sear was modified and a bolt guide-rib system added, the Model 700 remains much as it was nearly thirty years ago. The sturdy Mauser-based action has twin opposed locking lugs, and the extractor and ejector are mounted in the bolt head. Very close manufacturing tolerances ensure that the bolt-body serves as a gas check in the event of a case-head failure, being expanded by the additional pressure to abut the receiver wall.

The trigger is excellent, and accuracy is exemplary; most of the complaints made about the Remington action since its inception have concerned cosmetic features, such as the blind magazine and cheap-looking finish on some early stocks. Over the years, the worst of these has been steadily eliminated and the Model 700 rifle is now undoubtedly one of the world's classic designs.

The current variants include the **Model 700 ADL**, which has the standard action and a walnut half-stock with a low Monte Carlo comb. The cheek piece follows traditional North American practice, the butt plate is plain rubber, the pistol grip has no cap, and the fore-end tip has a reverse-diagonal cut. Chequering graces the pistol grip and fore-end, while sling-swivel eyes are placed conventionally beneath the butt and fore-end. A laminated stock was introduced for the ·30–06 700 ADL at the end of 1987.

Williams back sights are standard fittings on ADLs, and the bolt body is jewelled. Chamberings include ·17, ·22–250, ·222, ·223, 6mm, ·25–06 and 7mm–08

Above

Two versions of the popular Remington Model 40 target rifle, greatly respected by North American target shooters for the rigidity of its action and 'straight from the box' accuracy. The Model 40-XB (A) is favoured for standard full-bore competitions, while the Model 40-XB BR (B) is popular among bench-rest aficionados.

By courtesy of Remington Arms Company, Inc.

Remington. 83

Below

The popular and effectual Remington Model 700 rifle has been made in many differing variants since the early 1960s. The four guns shown here are the standard Model 700 ADL (A), stocked in North American fashion with a Monte Carlo comb; the Model 700 BDL (B), with a better stock; the Model 700 Varmint Special (C), with BDL-type stock and a heavy barrel lacking open sights; and the Sportsman 78 (D), a budget-price gun with a simple straight-comb hardwood stock.

Remington; 7mm Remington Magnum; ·243, ·270 and ·308 Winchester; ·30–06; ·300 and ·338 Winchester Magnum. In addition, 'Safari Grade' guns can be built in ·358 Winchester Magnum, ·375 H&H Magnum and ·458 Winchester Magnum to special order.

The **Model 700 BDL** – available in all the regular chamberings – is essentially an ADL with a better stock. The butt plate, pistol-grip cap and contrasting rounded fore-end tip are all accompanied by white hairline spacers; stock finish is high gloss rather than satin; and skip-line chequering replaces the standard pattern.

Remington has habitually offered a different version of the **Model 700 Classic** each season, the 1988 gun being chambered for the ·35 Whelen cartridge. Classics offer restrained stock styling, with a straight comb and a plain rubber butt plate accompanied by a black spacer, though they are mechanically identical with the standard guns. However, a detachable hinged magazine floor-plate is fitted.

Introduced at the end of 1987, in time for the 1988 season, the **Model 700 FS** features a fibreglass Classic-style stock finished in matt grey or a grey-based camouflage pattern. The contemporary **Model 700 RS** is similar, but the matt black stock is textured DuPont

Rynite; in addition, the RS model has a detachable magazine floor-plate and a distinctive Remington Arms pistol-grip cap.

The **Model 700 Mountain Rifle** (chambering ·243 Winchester, ·270 Winchester, ·280 Remington, 7mm–08, ·30–06 or ·308 Winchester) is a lightweight ADL, with a straight-comb stock, an English-style butt plate, and a contrasting fore-end tip butted directly to the stock wood. No open sights are provided. The **Model 700 Varmint Special** (available in ·22–250 Remington, ·222 and ·223 Remington, 6mm Remington, ·243 Winchester, 7mm–08, and ·308 Winchester) is basically a BDL with a heavy barrel and no iron sights. At 9lb, it is about 1lb 8oz heavier than the standard rifles and 2lb 8oz heavier than the Mountain Rifle.

The **Sportsman Model 78**, a budget-price beginner's gun, is simply a 700-type action in a plain hardwood stock with a plastic butt plate. It lacks chequering, has a simple open back sight, and can be obtained only in ·223 Remington, ·243 or ·308 Winchester, 6mm Remington and 7mm–08. Alternatively, the **Model 700 Kit Gun** – a standard barrelled action with an unfinished ADL-type hardwood stock – may also be obtained cheaply. Kit Guns chamber ·243, ·270 or ·308 Winchester, ·30–06 or 7mm Remington Magnum.

A

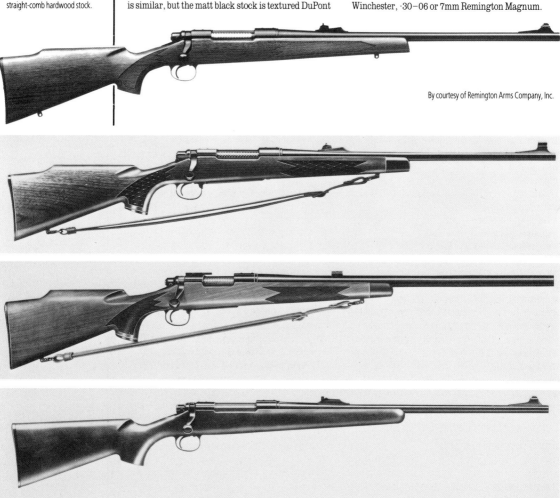

By courtesy of Remington Arms Company, Inc.

B

C

D

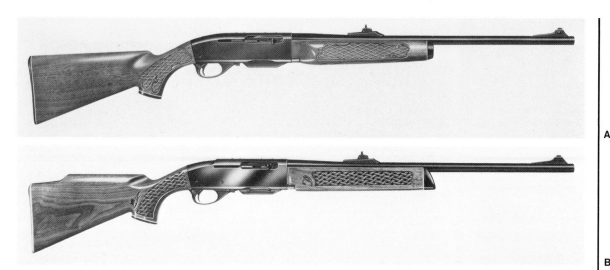

Model Seven

The Model Seven is a small variant of the Model 700, with a short action and an 18·5in barrel chambered similarly to that of the Model 78 Sportsman (q.v.). The Model Seven was to have been a budget-price Model 700 with a plain hardwood stock. However, this niche is now being filled by the Model 78 Sportsman and Model 700 Kit Gun; the current **Model Seven Walnut Stock**, therefore, has a Classic-style stock with a straight comb and extensive chequering on the pistol grip and fore-end. The otherwise similar **Model Seven FS** has a grey or grey-based camouflage fibreglass stock.

Models 7400 and 7600

These guns are essentially similar externally, their pistol-grip butts and fore-ends separated by machined-steel receivers. The woodwork has a high gloss polyurethane finish, and the chequering on the pistol grips and fore-end displays most distinctive fleurs-de-lis and strapwork.

Though the open sights and detachable box magazines are identical, there is a fundamental internal difference: the **Model 7400** is a gas-operated auto-loader, locked by a rotating bolt, while the **Model 7600** is a pump-action embodying Remington's renowned twin-bar support. There is an obvious external difference, as the fore-end of the 7400 runs back as far as the receiver while the 7600 pump-handle exposes several inches of the barrel.

Both rifles are available in ·243 Winchester, ·270 Winchester, ·280 Remington, ·30–06 and ·308 Winchester. Carbine patterns with 18·5in barrels (instead of the regular 22in) are available in ·30–06 only, while a ·35 Whelen 'Classic' variant of the Model 7600 appeared in 1988.

• •

Royal Ordnance BRITAIN

Once a substantial portion of the British Royal Small Arms Factory, Enfield, Royal Ordnance plc (Griffin House, The Strand, London WC2N 5BB) offers what it terms the **Enfield Weapons System**. The cornerstone

of this is the gas-operated 5·56mm Individual Weapon ('IW'), locked by a rotating bolt, which has been adopted by the British Army as the L85A1. Together with the Light Support Weapon ('LSW', L86A1), the IW is supposed to replace the submachine-gun, infantry rifle and light machine-gun in British service.

Development of the IW began in the 1960s, but the project has suffered more than its fair share of teething troubles. Great quantities of taxpayers' money have been poured into the project, but the results have yet to justify the capital investment: the IW has lost out to the Steyr AUG in competitive trials undertaken in Eire, Australia, Malaysia and elsewhere, and has reached service status only in the United Kingdom. It has yet to displace the heavy-but-reliable FN FAL (Rifle L1A1) in the affections of the average British soldier.

The selective-fire IW embodies the fashionable bullpup layout, which prevents the firer making best use of ground cover, and is issued with the 4× Sight Unit, Small Arms, Trilux (SUSAT) on a bracket adjustable for azimuth and elevation. The sight is generally regarded as a success now that internal fogging problems have been corrected, and standards of marksmanship have improved accordingly. The standard thirty-round box magazine is interchangeable with the US M16 pattern.

The **Ensign** is a semi-automatic version of the IW, intended for cadets. The original ten- and twenty-round magazines have now been abandoned in favour of the standard thirty-round version, simplifying logistics. The rifle usually exhibits a combination back sight/carrying handle assembly, has a a front sight carried high above the fore-end, and lacks the grenade launcher found on the IW muzzle.

Though the L1A1 (FN FAL) is no longer to be Britain's service weapon, Royal Ordnance has refurbished guns for sniping. Known as **7·62mm Pearcen**, these have heavy barrels with a sturdy bipod, and the upper receiver has been strengthened to receive heavy optical and image-intensifying

Above

Two variants of the Remington 742, a centre-fire auto-loading rifle now superseded by the Model 74. The standard Woodmaster (A) had a rounded receiver and conventional skip-line chequering; the BDL version (B), however, had basket-weave chequering and a modified upper receiver with a flattened top.

By courtesy of Remington Arms Company, Inc.

* The AK-47, AKM and AK-74 are not
included here: none are marketed
commercially in the West, even though
countless millions have been distributed
to armies, insurgents and nationalist
organisations sympathetic to the Soviet
bloc.

† Prior to the appearance of the current
variants, the TOZ sporters embodied a
differing bolt action which – though
chambering rimfire ammunition – had a
distinct external affinity with the Mosin-
Nagant service rifle. Consequently, it is
believed that they originated as military
trainers.

sights. The Pearcen is claimed to offer the accuracy of
much more sophisticated purpose-built sniper rifles
at considerably less expense.

Russian State Factories USSR

Comparatively little is known about the products of
the factories in Izhevsk and Tula, though several
target rifles and a small series of sporting guns have
been made in addition to millions of Kalashnikov-type
military rifles.* Small quantities of an interesting
autoloading sporting rifle known as 'Medved' ('Bear')
were made in the 1970s, but production seems to have
ceased. Russian guns are marketed in Europe by
Raznoexport (15 Verkhnyaia Krasnoselskaya,
Moskva-107896, USSR).

Standards of manufacture are not what would be
expected in the West; however, the guns are sturdy
and generally shoot acceptably. In addition, as time
passes, the Russians are steadily becoming more
consumer-conscious and the latest target rifles – in
particular – represent extremely good value for
money.

Rimfire target/sporting rifles are made in Tula, the
range being known as 'TOZ' (for Tulskii Oruzheinyi
Zavod', 'Tula ordnance factory') but more popularly in
the West as 'Baikals' or 'Vostok'.† The single-shot ·22
rimfires include the **TOZ 8-01** (approximately 3·9kg
without sights), with a plain half-stock, a capped
boltway, a safety catch immediately behind the bolt-
handle recess, and a tangent-leaf back sight; and the
TOZ 12-01, with a half-length deepened fore-end and
competition-pattern tunnel and aperture sights. The
current **TOZ 16-01** shares the action of the TOZ 8-01,
but has a light barrel and a slender sporting-style
stock contributing to an unladen weight of only
2·6kg. The **TOZ 17-01** and **TOZ 18-01** are practically
identical with the current 16-01, excepting that
both have detachable five-round box magazines; the
18-01 model also has a rail for an optical-sight mount

on the left side of the receiver. They weigh 2·6–2·7kg,
depending on the density of the birchwood stock. **TOZ
78** rifles embody the action of the TOZ 18-01, but have
adjustable-pressure triggers and superior beech or
birch half-stocks, modified open sights (a small block
sight replacing the previous tangent-leaf pattern) and
five- or ten-round magazines.

Soviet-made target rifles come in surprising
variety, though not all are regularly encountered in
the West. The most common is the **SM-2** (often known
as 'CM-2', 'Vostok' or 'Strela'), a single-shot ·22 LR
rimfire 25m or 50m target rifle, popular as a
beginner's gun. The current production variant,
locked by using the bolt-handle base as a lug, has a
hefty birch half-stock – crudely chequered on the
pistol grip and the fore-end sides – and a competition-
pattern diopter back sight. The front sight is a
replaceable-element tunnel, the trigger is adjustable
and the butt plate can be slid vertically in its channel-
plate. One of the most interesting features of the SM-
2, together with most of the current generation of
Soviet target rifles, is the use of a large finger-wheel
to lock the butt-plate: so much more convenient than
the many guns in this class that require a
screwdriver.

The **TOZ 61** was an oddly archaic-looking single-
shot Free Rifle, with a set-trigger, a hooked
adjustable butt plate, a thumbhole half-stock and a
palm-rest beneath the deep square-section fore-end; it
featured a modified TOZ 8 action, but is no longer in
production.

Generally encountered under the Vostok brand, the
BK-3 is intended for Running Boar and moving
target competitions. It embodies an improved single-
shot action with three locking lugs on the bolt head,
and has an adjustable trigger. The most distinctive
feature is the design of the butt, which continues
straight back from the cocking piece without the
wrist found on most other designs. The cheek piece

may be adjusted vertically, as may the butt plate; it must be noted, however, that the standard BK-3 will be encountered with a rubber butt plate that does not meet current UIT regulations. With its sturdy optical sight, the BK-3 weighs a little under 5kg and measures 1,035–1,065mm overall.

The **BK-5** rifle shares the basic action of the BK-3, refined to a point where it is the equal of most Western guns in performance (if not necessarily in finish). Solidly and permanently fixed into the receiver, the barrel is generally fitted with an extension shroud along which three two-piece balancing weights may be adjusted to suit the firer. Unusual features include mounting the receiver on a plastic carrier, with self-adjusting inserts intended to maintain bedding pressure; the cheek piece, butt plate and trigger are all fully adjustable. The half-stock, generally made of beech, has generous stippling on the pistol-grip and fore-end – and, most unusually, a white line border. The sight is a sturdy 6× or 10× fixed-power pattern with a decidedly military appearance. Optical performance is very good, though the sights lack some of the refinements associated with the best European, American and Japanese practice. The BK-5 weighs a little under 5kg with the sight mounted, and measures about 1,170mm overall. It is a most interesting gun.

Intended for 50m Free Rifle and three-position shooting, the **Ural-5-1** features the single-shot three-lug bolt system encountered on the BK-5. The rifle has a thumb-hole half-stock with a fully adjustable hooked butt plate, the cheek piece may be raised, and

a full-length accessory rail beneath the fore-end will accept a palm-rest and a balancing-weight rod. The trigger is fully adjustable, and good quality competition sights are fitted. The tunnel-pattern front sight embodies a spirit level, while, most oddly, the cranked back sight mount sets the sight-line considerably to the left of the bore axis. Though unusual, this makes little difference in fixed-range shooting. The model 5-1 weighs up to 8kg, depending on accessories, and measures 1,265–1,310mm overall.

The **Ural-6-1**, intended for Standard Rifle competitions under UIT rules, amalgamates the basic action of the BK-5 with a conventional half-stock with extensive stippling on the pistol grip and fore-end. The adjustable finger-wheel butt-plate lock, channel plate and spacer system are shared with the SM-2. Micro-adjustable diopter sights are standard, together with an adjustable trigger. In sum, the Ural-6-1, as yet rarely encountered in the West, provides particularly good value for money.

The **Biathlon-6** embodies the action of the BK-3 (q.v.) with a distinctive wristless stock. The principal identifying characteristics include a rubber butt plate with an adjustable rod-type 'hook', a detachable five-shot magazine and a muzzle flap. Four magazines can be carried in the butt, which will also accept the special sling harness used in biathlon competitions. **Biathlon-7-2** is a most interesting rifle locked by a toggle-type bolt comparable with that of the Anschütz-made Fortner system, enabling the

Below

Russian bolt-action rimfires include the TOZ 12-01 target rifle (A), with aperture sights; TOZ 17-01 and TOZ 18-01 sporters (B and C respectively), with box magazines and, in the latter, an optical-sight mounting bracket. None of these rifles is commonly encountered in the West, unlike the single-shot SM-2 target rifle (D). The version shown here is now obsolescent, current production offering a squarer stock.

C

A

B

D

·VOSTOK· 87

By courtesy of Razno & Co. Ltd.

A
B
C

·VOSTOK·

Above

The latest generation of Russian target rifles include BK-3 (A), intended for UIT moving-target competitions; TsVR-2 (B), a full-bore Free Rifle; and Biathlon 7-2 (C), a straight-pull toggle-action rifle intended for cross-country skiers.

marksman to reload with the minimum of effort. The 7-2 has a distinctive stock with a deepened fore-end ahead of the detachable box magazine, while four spare magazines are carried in spring clips on the right side of the butt. Other features include a butt plate hook, conventional diopter sights with hinged covers, and an adjustable trigger. Introduced in the late 1970s, the Biathlon-7-2 helped Soviet marksmen to win the gold medal in the 1980 Olympic Games and the 1983 world team championship.

Soviet factories also offer the **SV-1**, a fullbore Standard Rifle, and **TsVR-2** Free Rifles. These are essentially similar to the Ural-6-1 and Ural-5-1 respectively, with triple-lug bolts, but chamber 7·62mm cartridges and have a noticeably longer loading port in the receiver. A 'mirage band' is generally encountered above the barrel, stretching from the receiver ring to the front sight base. Unlike the rimfire Ural-5-1 Free Rifle, the diopter sight of the SV-1 lies on the centreline of the bore rather than being offset to the left.

The **Los 4** is an angular bolt-action hunting rifle, with an internal box magazine holding five 7·62×51 (·308 Winchester) rounds. Unusual features include a chrome-plate bore – rare on sporting guns – and an under-barrel rib that appears to support a clearing rod. Open and optical sights may be fitted. The Los 4 (which weighs 3·3kg) has an unattractive hardwood stock with a Monte Carlo comb and cheek piece, chequering appearing on the pistol grip and fore-end. The ventilated rubber butt plate and the pistol-grip cap are accompanied by white-line spacers, but the overall effect is ruined by the hideously misshapen trigger guard and crudely stamped magazine floor-plate.

RWS WEST GERMANY

RWS-brand guns are marketed by Dynamit Nobel (D-5210 Troisdorf/Oberlar, Postfach 1261), but are made elsewhere. The most common bolt-action cartridge rifles are made by Mayer & Grammelspacher or Kriegeskorte, or, in the case of combination rifles and Drillinge, in East Germany ('Merkel' and 'Simson' brands). 'Rottweil' combination guns are apparently made in Spain, but suppliers change periodically and generalizations are dangerous. Lever-action carbines come from Rossi, as apparently do basic Mauser-action sporters. The most interesting gun is the RWS-Sicherheits-Repetierbüchse, a Krico-made gun with a distinctive cocking slider on the tang.

SAB/Gamba ITALY

Società Armi Bresciane Srl of I-25063 Gardone Val Trompia, Via Artigiani 93, makes 'Linea Renato Gamba' firearms. These include shotguns, combination weapons, double rifles, a solitary bolt-action pattern, pistols and revolvers. Many of the guns will be encountered with the marks of Mauser (q.v.), with whom first Gamba and now SAB have enjoyed a strong relationship.

The **Bayern 88** offers Gamba's patented box lock in a combination gun with a 12-bore (70mm chamber) smooth-bore barrel above one rifled for 5·6×50R, ·222 Remington, 6·5×57R, 7×57R, 7×65R and ·30–06. It has a walnut butt with a cheek piece and a ventilated rubber butt plate, and a semi-beavertail fore-end. A sliding safety lies on the tang, and the back sight is inlet into a quarter-rib. The action is generally attractively engraved, as the purchaser can specify virtually any decoration he desires.

88

The **Safari Express** double rifle offers excellent quality. Built on a robust Greener-type box-lock, it has a back sight let into a full-length rib, double set-triggers and cocking indicators atop the breech. Swivels lie under the lower barrel ahead of the fore-end, and on the under-edge of the butt. The butt – like the fore-end – is made of specially selected European walnut, with a distinctively beaded cheek piece and a shallowly curved comb. Standard chamberings include 7×65R, 9·3×74R and ·375 H&H Magnum, but others can be obtained to order. As the Safari Express weighs 4·5kg, it is more pleasant to fire than many of the lighter combination guns handling such powerful ammunition.

The **Mustang** is a single barrel rifle with Holland & Holland side lock, elegant and tipping the scales at only a little over 2·6kg without optical sights. Consequently, it chambers cartridges developing moderate power – ·222 Remington, 5·6× 50R, 6·5×57R, ·270 Winchester, 7×65R and ·30–06. The schnabel-tip fore-end and the pistol-gripped butt are made of the finest walnut, swivels lie on the underside of the barrel and butt, and the back sight projects from a traditional quarter rib. Special integral blocks accept the optical-sight mounts. Like many of the SAB/Gamba guns, the Mustang is built and engraved to special order. It is expensive, but quality is exceptional.

The **RGZ 1000** is a conventional sporting rifle with a Mauser-pattern bolt and a pivoting safety catch on the right side of the action behind the bolt handle. Distinguished more by its quality than any quirks of design, the RGZ is made in standard and 'Battue' forms – the latter intended for snap-shooting at driven game. The standard gun has a 60cm barrel, conventional open sights and a double set-trigger, while the RGZ Battue has a 52cm barrel, a fixed back sight at the front of a quarter-rib and a single trigger.

Stocks are of European walnut with contrasting rosewood schnabel tips and pistol-grip caps; Monte Carlo combs, cheek pieces and ventilated rubber butt plates are standard fixtures.

Sabatti ITALY

Fabbrica Italiana Armi Sabatti SpA (FIAS) of I-25063 Gardone Val Trompia, Via Alessandro Volta 90, makes a selection of combination- and double rifles plus a single bolt-action pattern.

The **Forest**, the **MTK** and the **Express 340** all follow the basic pattern, a conventional but well made box-lock action allied with a sliding tang safety and a back sight inlet in a quarter rib. The two combinati – Forest and MTK – are similar, though the latter has more chequering on the fore-end and a cheek piece; the Forest has a plain butt, and also lacks the rubber butt plate found on the MTK. Twin-trigger systems are common, the rear lever firing the upper (smooth-bore) barrel and the front lever firing the lower (rifled) barrel. Forest guns are sold in the USA as 'Kassnar Regent Combos', in a combination of 12-bore (76mm chambers) and ·222 Remington, ·223 Remington, ·243 Winchester, ·270 Winchester, ·30–06 or ·308 Winchester.

The Express double rifle is similar mechanically to the Forest combination weapon, suitably strengthened to handle powerful centre-fire cartridges. Apart from the obvious differences in bore, the guns are difficult to distinguish externally. A special deluxe variant, the Express 340 EDL, offers specially selected woodwork and higher-quality engraving. It also has a squared cheek piece.

FIAS's sporting rifle, the **Carabina Rover 87**, embodies a conventional Mauser bolt action and an internal magazine with a detachable floor plate. The standard pattern has a classic stock profile, with a straight comb; excepting the spatulate bolt handle,

Below
Monochrome does scant justice to the delicate engraving and stock-grain of this SAB-Gamba Mustang, here with a Zeiss optical sight.
By courtesy of Società Armi Bresciane Srl.

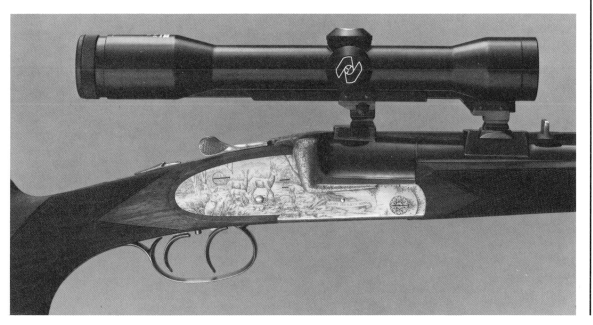

the Rover bears a vague external affinity with the Ruger 77. The stock of the deluxe version, or Rover 87DL, has a pronounced Monte Carlo comb. Consequently, the sight bases are appreciably higher on the 87DL than standard rifles. Rovers are competitively priced and represent good value.

Chamberings in the 22in barrel include ·243 Winchester, ·25–06, 7mm Remington Magnum, ·270 Winchester, ·30–06, ·300 Winchester Magnum and ·308 Winchester.

FIAS/Sabatti rifles are sold in the USA under the Kassnar brandname (q.v.).

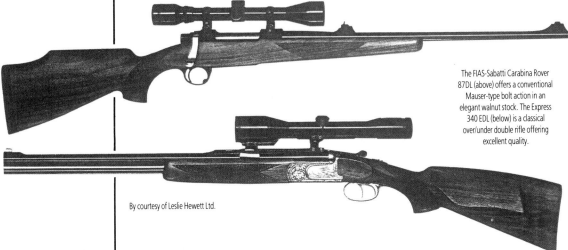

The FIAS-Sabatti Carabina Rover 87DL (above) offers a conventional Mauser-type bolt action in an elegant walnut stock. The Express 340 EDL (below) is a classical over/under double rifle offering excellent quality.

By courtesy of Leslie Hewett Ltd.

RUGER

••

Sturm, Ruger & Company, Lacey Place, Southport, Connecticut 06490, USA

Founded by Alexander Sturm and William ('Bill') Ruger in 1947, this company's is *the* success story of the post-war US firearms industry. Beginning with the well-known Ruger ·22LR rimfire pistol, externally based on the well-known Parabellum (Luger), a series of innovative guns has been produced. Careful attention to design has ensured that each has begun as a market leader; attention to detail has ensured that they have stayed in the limelight.

Product range: the company makes revolvers, pistols and rifles (single-shot, bolt-action and auto-loading), plus the Ruger Red Label shotgun. Though produced on the latest machinery and incorporating up-to-date production techniques, they are all exceptionally well made and have attained an enviable reputation for quality.

Recently discontinued models: Ruger has had a very low incidence of failures, the only rifle of note to disappear being the XGI – an recent enlargement of the Mini-14 to handle ·308 Winchester (7·62×51 NATO) – which failed owing to inherent accuracy problems, even though it was otherwise quite effectual. There were also several versions of the 10/22 carbine (1961-84) chambering ·44 Magnum pistol cartridges.

Mini-14 and Mini-Thirty

Introduced in 1973, the Mini-14 is a small auto-loading rifle chambered for the ·223 Remington cartridge. Though much the same size as the renowned M1 Carbine, from which elements of the gas system are derived, the Mini-14 uses a scaled-down version of the rotating-bolt lock embodied in the original M1 Garand. The gas system incorporates a cupped head over the gas port, which gives a short sharp thrust before the gas is vented to the atmosphere. As a result, the Ruger has a reputation for reliability and is not as susceptible to gas fouling as the M16, where gas impinges directly on the bolt carrier.

The standard Mini-14 has a one-piece hardwood half-stock, steel liners protecting key areas from extremes of stress and temperature. A short fibreglass guard protects the firer's hand from barrel heat and the reciprocating slide on the right side of the action. All fixed-stock Mini-14 rifles have sling swivels, and the safety catch, in the front of the trigger guard, locks hammer and sear.

The standard **Mini-14/5** has blued metalwork and a detachable five-round box magazine; the stainless-steel variant is currently designated **K-Mini-14/5**, while variants with the distinctive Ruger folding stock and are **Mini-14/5F** (blued) or **K-Mini-14/5F** (stainless).

Above

The Mini-14 and its near-relation, the Mini-Thirty, has been one of Ruger's greatest successes. Its many variants include the Mini-14 Ranch Rifle (A), and the stainless-steel K-Mini-14/5F (B) with a folding butt.

By courtesy of Sturm, Ruger & Company.

* An abbreviated form of 'Ruger Sight Mount System'.

Introduced in 1986, the Ruger Ranch Rifle is a Mini-14 with a modified ejector and a patented buffer to reduce the shock of recoil on the optical sight (for which special low mounts are provided). The back sight is a simple open pattern, quite unlike the standard version, and will identify a Ranch Rifle if the optical sight is absent. Ranch rifles come in four patterns – **Mini-14/5R** (blued) and **K-Mini-14/5R** (stainless) with conventional hardwood stocks; **Mini-14/5RF** (blued) and **K-Mini-14/5RF** (stainless) with folding stocks.

The **Mini-Thirty**, announced in 1987, is a modification of the basic Mini-14 chambering the Russian 7·62×39 M43 cartridge. It is practically identical with the Mini-14/5R Ranch Rifle, being intended for an optical sight and having integral mount-blocks. The 7·62mm bullet has advantages over the lighter, faster-moving ·223 for hunting purposes. In addition, though developing less energy than ·30–30 at the muzzle, the pointed 7·62mm retains energy better than most ·30-calibre round-nose bullets.

Model 77

Ruger's first bolt-action rifle created a sensation when it appeared, and rapidly assumed classic status alongside the Winchester Model 70 and Remington 700. The action is based on the M98 Mauser, with twin opposed locking lugs and a long non-rotating extractor that promises better performance than most of the modern spring-loaded claws mounted on the bolt head. The M77 has an excellent trigger, and a sliding safety catch lies on the upper tang behind the cocking-piece shroud. The internal magazine may be unloaded simply by opening the hinged floor plate.

Attention to detail is evident in the front action-retaining bolt, which screws diagonally into the underside of the receiver to combat recoil stresses, and in the use of a one-piece bolt precision-ground from an investment casting.

The standard **Ruger M-77R** has an elegant straight-combed walnut half-stock with chequering on the pistol grip and fore-end; a solid rubber butt plate; and a plastic pistol-grip cap. Sling swivels appear under the butt and fore-end; RSMS* sight bases are integral with the receiver. The **M-77RS** is comparable, but has additional open sights. Short-action 77R guns are made for ·22–250 Remington, ·220 Swift, 6mm Remington, ·243 and ·308 Winchester, while the 77-RS is obtainable only in ·243 and ·308 Winchester. The longer 77R Magnum handles ·25–06, ·257 Roberts, ·270 Winchester, ·280 Remington, 7mm Remington Magnum, 7×57, ·300 Winchester Magnum, ·30–06 and ·338 Winchester Magnum; 77RS Magnums are obtainable in all these excepting ·257 Roberts, 6mm Remington and ·280 Remington. Steel floor plates and trigger guards are only offered as optional extras with the Magnum.

The **M-77RSI**, or International Model, is identical mechanically with the M-77RS, but has a full-length Mannlicher stock. It is only available in ·22–250 Remington, ·243 Winchester, ·250 Savage and ·308 Winchester (Short Action), and ·270 Winchester and ·30–06 (Magnum Action). The **M-77RT**, or Tropical Rifle, is available only in ·458 Winchester Magnum. It has a steel trigger guard and floor plate, and weighs about 8·8lb – too light for a gun of this power, though a heavy optical sight adds to the mass.

Intended for back-packing and mountain shooting, the **M-77RL** or Ruger Ultra-Light weighs a mere 6lb. It is externally similar to the RS variant, excepting that it has a contrasting fore-end tip and lacks open sights. Short Actions are made in ·22–250, ·243 Winchester, ·250 Savage and ·308 Winchester; Magnum Actions in ·257 Roberts, ·270 Winchester and ·30–06. The **M-77RLS** is somewhat similar to the Ultra-Light Rifle, but is really a carbine variant of the 77RS with open sights and an 18·5in barrel. The **M-77V**, or Varmint Rifle, is made only with the Short Action in ·22–250 and 6mm Remington, ·220 Swift, ·243 Winchester, ·25–06 Remington or ·308 Winchester. It has a heavy 24- or 26in barrel and weighs about 9lb; Varmint Rifles lack open sights.

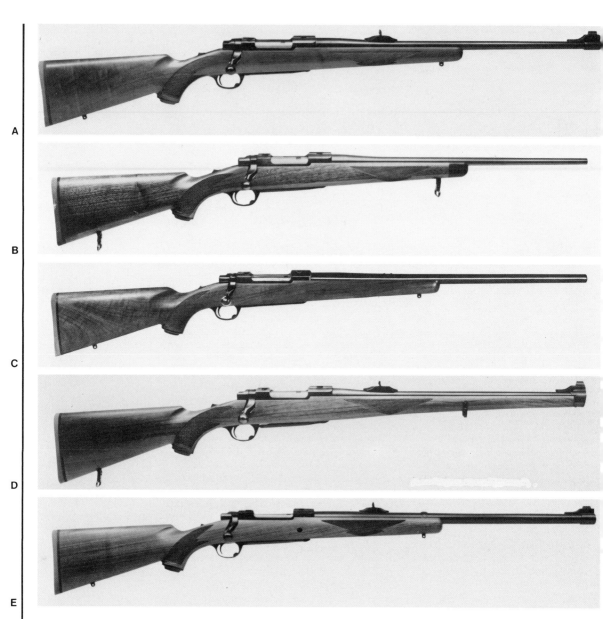

Model 10/22

This auto-loading carbine – the earliest Ruger shoulder
gun – has had a long and glorious career since being
introduced in 1964.† A simple blowback, it accepts ten-
shot detachable rotary or spool magazines and has a
reputation for flawless feeding. The trigger housing
contains the entire hammer-type ignition system, and a
cross-bolt safety appears through the front web of the
trigger guard. The standard **M-10/22RB** has a
hardwood pistol-grip stock, while the deluxe **M-
10/22DSP** features hand-chequered American walnut.
Fixed open sights are standard, though the receiver is
drilled and tapped for a tip-off mount adaptor.

Model 77/22

Ruger's rimfire sporter is another excellent design,
beautifully made of fine materials – but much more

expensive than many of its less effectual rivals. Ruger
has taken the same view as Kimber (q.v.), declining to
compete with bargain-basement imports and instead
satisfy shooters who want the best rimfire rifle and will
pay accordingly. Apart from a nylon butt plate, the
Model 77/22 is stocked similarly to the Model 77R.
Unlike the M-77, which has a tang safety, the 77/22
safety protrudes from the right rear side of the action;
when retracted to its farthest point, it locks the action
closed. Though the crisp single-stage trigger cannot be
adjusted, it remains among the best of its type: lock-
time is an amazing 2·7 milliseconds,‡ which compares
favourably with many of the best target rifles. The
Model 77/22 accepts the proven detachable ten-round
spool magazine introduced with the 10/22 (q.v.).
Consequently, it has a reputation for flawless feeding.
There are three minor variants: **M-77/22R**, a plain-

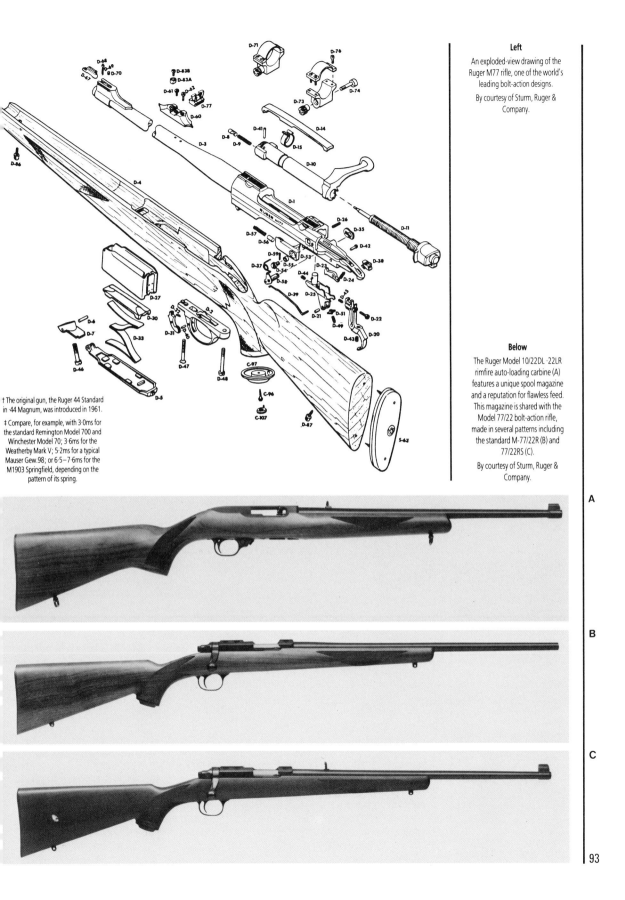

Left

An exploded-view drawing of the Ruger M77 rifle, one of the world's leading bolt-action designs.

By courtesy of Sturm, Ruger & Company.

Below

The Ruger Model 10/22DL ·22LR rimfire auto-loading carbine (A) features a unique spool magazine and a reputation for flawless feed. This magazine is shared with the Model 77/22 bolt-action rifle, made in several patterns including the standard M-77/22R (B) and 77/22RS (C).

By courtesy of Sturm, Ruger & Company.

† The original gun, the Ruger 44 Standard in ·44 Magnum, was introduced in 1961.

‡ Compare, for example, with 3·0ms for the standard Remington Model 700 and Winchester Model 70; 3·6ms for the Weatherby Mark V; 5·2ms for a typical Mauser Gew.98; or 6·5–7·6ms for the M1903 Springfield, depending on the pattern of its spring.

A

B

C

A

B

C

D

barrel model with integral sight-mount bases; **M-77/22RS**, similar but with conventional fixed open sights; and **M-77/22S**, with a folding back sight.

Number One

This is unquestionably the finest modern mass-produced single-shot rifle, a genre currently enjoying a surge in popularity unknown since the end of the nineteenth century. Based somewhat loosely on the old British Farquharson falling-block action, the Ruger No.1 shows the careful attention to detail that characterizes all the company's guns. The massive receiver, which separates the butt and fore-end, contains the breech block and the striker mechanism. The striker is struck by a hammer and transfer block unit when the trigger is pressed.

Though the Ruger No.1 is not as compact as the American de Haas-Miller or the European Blaser, it has had the advantage of being backed by a major manufacturer. Consequently, it has achieved the wide acceptance it richly deserves – but, in so doing, has eclipsed guns of otherwise equal merit. Actions are sold to Heym (q.v.) and used as the basis for guns engraved and stocked to suit European tastes.

The basic **No.1 Standard Rifle** (or No.1-B) features a blued action and walnut furniture, the pistol grip of the straight-comb butt and the sides of the broad fore-end being chequered. A solid rubber butt plate is standard, as are sling swivels on the underside of the butt and fore-end. A sliding safety will be found on the upper tang. The medium-weight 26in barrel is chambered for a wide range of cartridges – ·22–250, ·220 Swift, ·223 Remington, 6mm Remington, ·243 Winchester, ·25–06, ·257 Roberts, ·270 Winchester, ·270 Weatherby Magnum, ·280 Remington, 7mm Remington Magnum ·300 Winchester and Weatherby Magnums, ·30–06 and ·338 Winchester Magnum. Weight averages about 8lb, without accessories. An optical sight can be fitted on the quarter-rib – the latter being the one feature without which, in my opinion at least, the rifle's appearance is greatly enhanced.

Featuring a full-length Mannlicher stock and a lightweight 20in barrel, the **No.1 International Rifle** (No.1-RSI) may be obtained in ·243 and ·270 Winchester, 7×57 Mauser and ·30–06. The **No.1 Medium Sporter** (No.1-S) shares the action and 26in barrel of the No.1-B, but has a distinctive "parrot's beak" fore-end tip, open sights, and a swivel on the barrel rather than the fore-end. The odd shape of the fore-end tip has attracted much adverse comment, but follows its historical precedent faithfully: it was simply that the original British version of a schnabel lost something in translation from German! The guns are available only in 7mm Remington Magnum, ·300 Winchester Magnum, ·338 Winchester Magnum (26in barrels) and ·45–70 (22in barrel only). The **No.1 Light Sporter** (No.1-A) duplicates the No.1-S, but has a lightweight 22in barrel chambering ·243 or ·270 Winchester, 7×57 Mauser and ·30–06.

The Ruger **No.1 Tropical Rifle** (No.1-H), chambered only for ·375 H&H Magnum and ·458 Winchester Magnum, has a 24in heavy barrel and weighs about 9lb. It is otherwise similar to No.1-S, as it is fitted with open sights. **No.1 Special Varminter** rifles (No.1-V), stocked in the same fashion as No.1-B, feature heavy 24in barrels tapped for scope-mounting blocks; there are no open sights, and the absence of the quarter-rib and eccentric parrot's beak fore-end tip lends these guns the neatest appearance in the series. No.1-V Rugers may be obtained in ·22–250 Remington, ·220 Swift, ·223, 6mm Remington and ·25–06, but one of the great attractions of single-shot block-action rifles is the ease with which they can handle wildcat rounds.

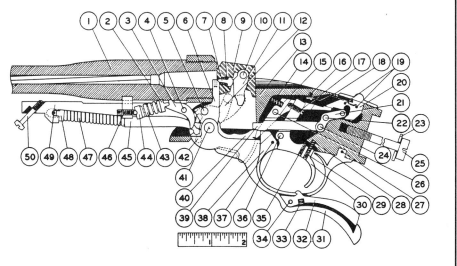

Left

A drawing of the action of the single-shot Ruger No.1 rifle

From the informative *Single Shot Rifles and Actions* by Frank de Haas (Digest Books, 1969).

SAKO

FINLAND sako

Oy Sako Ab, F-11100 Riihimäki 10, Finland

Finland's leading gunmaker has an unusually convoluted history; founded in 1921 to refurbish military firearms, the company was briefly transferred to the Finnish Red Cross in 1944 to prevent it falling into Russian hands. Sako designer Niilo Talvenheimo began work on a bolt-action sporting rifle shortly after the end of the Winter War in 1940, but hostilities prevented the L42 being exploited until after the end of 1945. Enthusiasm in North America then assured Sako's future; production of modified sporters continues today. The company also made m/62 Finnish assault rifles in 1963–9, but no additional orders were forthcoming once the intial contract had been completed; the m/62 and its successors have since been made exclusively by Valmet (q.v.). In the late 1980s, however, Sako and Valmet amalgamated.

Product range: Sako has always preferred to make bolt-action rifles, many of which are currently available. They are all based on the same basic pattern. The rifles are sturdy, well finished and offer good value. That the basic Sako bolt action is used by so many smaller 'manufacturers' – not to mention Browning Arms, Colt and Harrington & Richardson – testifies not only to quality but also to the professionalism with which Sako enters into agreements. The bolt action is very well made, with an absence of stamped parts, and has a reputation for strength.

Discontinued models: excepting older bolt-action guns, the only Sakos to have been discontinued are the lever-action *Finnwolf* and the rimfire *Finnscout*. Rather unusually feeding from a box magazine, allowing spitzer ammunition to be used, the Finnwolf was too expensive and too sophisticated for the North American market; the comparable Winchester Model 88 failed for much the same reason. Also known as the VL63, after the year in which it was introduced, the Finnwolf was developed in 1959–62 and ultimately discontinued in the mid 1970s.

The Finnscout and its derivatives (Finnscout HB, Finnscout Magnum, Finnscout Hornet and M78AH Biathlon rifle) were based on two earlier rifles, the P46 and P54, embodying a simple bolt action fed from a detachable box magazine. They were too well made – and thus expensive – to compete against cheaper, if less effectual rivals. Finnscouts were abandoned in 1984.

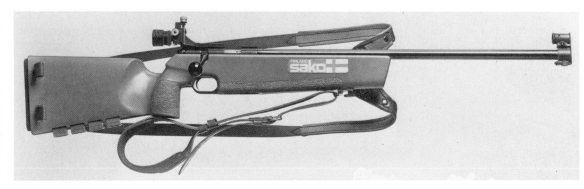

Above
The obsolescent Finnbiathlon 78 was built by Sako on the basic Finnscout action, but was soon outclassed by competing designs and abandoned.
By courtesy of Karl Schäfer.

The basic Sako action is a much modified Mauser. Owing to the interchangeability of designation, the rifles are classified here by their actions: L461 (short), L579 (medium) and L61 (large). There are two versions of the L461, one for use with the standard magazine and the other for single-shot actions. Similarly, there are two L579s – the Super Match pattern has a sturdier receiver pierced only with the ejection port – and three types of L61: regular right-hand (L61R), regular left-hand (L61L) and magnum (L61R Mag).

With the exception of the Varmint, Super Match and Target rifles, which can be supplied with single-shot L461 or L579 actions, all Sako rifles have internal box magazines containing up to six rounds. In addition, the L579 versions of the Hunter, Carbine, Handy and Varmint can be obtained with detachable five-round box magazines. The L579 SM action, unique to the Super Match rifle, accepts a special ten-round detachable box. Hunter, Fiberclass, Laminated, Varmint, Target and Super Match Sako rifles can all be obtained with stainless steel barrels.

The standard trigger unit has a vertically sliding sear, which is more susceptible to binding than radial designs; consequently, few Sako actions stocked in the USA retain the factory trigger system.[*]

Sako Finnbear, L61

The largest of the Sako actions, also made in a true left-handed version, is reserved for the most powerful chamberings. It was developed in 1960–1 – when the demands for 'magnum power' from the North American market became too strong to ignore – and replaced the earlier 'Sako Mauser' or 'USA Mauser' embodied in high-power Sako rifles made in 1950–62.
Known to the factory as 'A V' – i.e., the fifth action –

the L61R can handle long-cased rounds such as ·25–06 Remington, 6·5×55 Mauser, ·270 Winchester, 7×64, ·30–06 and 9·3×62. The strengthened version (A V Mag) is used with the magnum cartridges: 7mm Remington, ·300 Winchester, ·300 Weatherby, ·338 Winchester and ·375 H&H.

The long action is popular, being incorporated in all the Sako rifles excepting Varmint, Super Match and Target. **Hunter** rifles have hand-chequered Circassian walnut stocks, Monte Carlo combs, pistol grips, and solid rubber butt plates; **Deluxe** is similar to the Hunter, with selected stocks graced by skip-line chequering and a contrasting rosewood fore-end tip; the stock of **Super Deluxe** patterns usually features hand-carved oak leaves as well as chequering; **Laminated** models display the colour obtainable from a multi-layer blank; **Fiberclass** rifles feature charcoal-grey synthetic stocks with a straight comb; **Safari**, Sako's big-game rifle, has a straight comb, two transverse recoil bolts and an Express back sight on a quarter-rib; the short-barrelled **Carbine** is stocked to the muzzle; **Handy** is a carbine with a conventional Hunter-type half-stock; and **Handy Fiber** is similar, but with a Fiberclass-type straight-comb stock.

L61R-action guns are available in all six of the standard calibres, ranging from ·25–06 Remington to 9·3×62. In addition, L61R Magnum actions may be incorporated in Hunter, Deluxe, Super Deluxe, Laminated, Fiberclass and Safari rifles. These are available in all five magnum chamberings, apart from the Safari model (·338 Winchester Magnum and ·375 H&H Magnum only).

Sako Forester, L579

The medium action, used for intermediate-length

[*] This was not true of the largest companies, such as Colt and Harrington & Richardson, which imported and sold complete Finnish rifles. Concessions were limited to North American-style stocks.

SAKO RIFLES

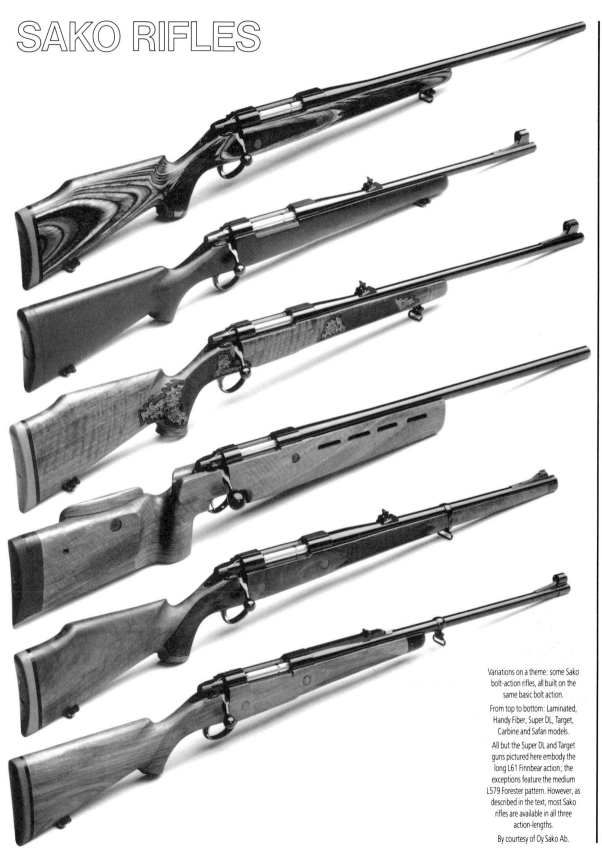

Variations on a theme: some Sako bolt-action rifles, all built on the same basic bolt action.

From top to bottom: Laminated, Handy Fiber, Super DL, Target, Carbine and Safari models.

All but the Super DL and Target guns pictured here embody the long L61 Finnbear action; the exceptions feature the medium L579 Forester pattern. However, as described in the text, most Sako rifles are available in all three action-lengths.

By courtesy of Oy Sako Ab.

cartridges, is the most commonly encountered. Developed in 1957–9 and introduced commercially in 1962, it replaced the short-lived L57. The two basic patterns are designated A IIa for ·22–250 and A IIb for ·243 Winchester, 7mm–08 and ·308 Winchester.

Individual guns making use of this action include **Hunter**, which has a hand-chequered Circassian walnut stock with a Monte Carlo comb, a pistol-grip and a solid rubber butt plate; **Deluxe**, which is similar to the Hunter but features a selected stock with skip-line chequering and a contrasting rosewood fore-end tip; **Super Deluxe**, with a hand-carved and chequered stock; **Laminated**, made from 36-ply stock-blanks; **Carbine**, a short-barrelled gun with a full length stock; **Handy**, basically a carbine with a conventional half-stock; **Varmint**, a Hunter with a special heavy barrel; and **Target** and **Super Match** rifles, which have massive half-stocks with detachable cheek pieces and four slots cut laterally through the fore-ends. These guns are all available in ·22–250, ·243 Winchester, 7mm–08 and ·308 Winchester, excepting the Target (7mm–08, ·308 Winchester) and Super Match (·308).

Sako Vixen, L461

The smallest of the Sako actions, this chambers short-case rounds. Its predecessors included the L42, L46 and L469 (sometimes known as the L459†), development of which had begun in 1941. One version – A I – chambers three proprietary Remington rounds (·17, ·222 and ·223), while A I PPC is specially made for the two highly successful Palmisano-Pindell bench-rest rounds, ·22 and 6mm PPC.

Rifles making use of the L461 action include **Hunter**, with its hand-chequered Circassian walnut stock, Monte Carlo comb, pistol-grip and a solid rubber butt plate; **Deluxe**, similar to the Hunter model but featuring selected stocks with skip-line chequering and a contrasting rosewood fore-end tip; **Super Deluxe**, with a hand-carved and chequered stock; **Laminated**, made from 36-ply stock-blanks, each with a different colour and pattern; **Carbine**, a short-barrelled gun with a full length 'Mannlicher' stock; **Varmint**, a Hunter with a heavy barrel; and **Target**, whose heavy stock has a detachable cheek piece and four slots through the fore-end. Apart from the target models, L461-action guns are all available in ·17 Remington, ·222 Remington and ·223 Remington. The Hunter and Varmint can also be obtained in ·22 PPC and 6mm PPC, while the Target rifle comes in ·222 Remington, ·22 PPC and 6mm PPC only.

SAUER

•••

J.P. Sauer & Sohn GmbH, D-2330 Eckenförde, Sauerstrasse 2–6, West Germany

Founded in Suhl in 1751, the original Sauer company made sporting and military firearms in great numbers prior to 1918. Business was rebuilt again after the First World War, but the company finally disappeared in 1945. The name was resurrected in Eckenförde/Holstein in the 1950s, but the present company has apparently little to do with the original other than perpetuate the name. Sauer was purchased by SIG in the 1970s to overcome restrictions placed on the export of arms by the Swiss government. Consequently, SIG-type assault rifles will sometimes be encountered under the Sauer marketing banner (though never, apparently, so marked) and Sauer bolt-action sniper rifles have been offered as the 'SIG–Sauer SSG 2000'.

Product range: Sauer makes bolt-action rifles, combination guns and Drillinge of the highest quality. None of them is cheap.

Discontinued models: none, excepting older versions of the Model 80/90 series.

Model 90

These sporting rifles share a distinctive bolt action developed in the late 1970s. Eschewing a Mauser-type fixed-lug bolt, Sauer's designers used a cylindrical body into which three symmetrically disposed locking flaps are retracted when the bolt handle is lifted. When the action has been cycled and the bolt handle returned, the final action of turning the handle down into its seat cams the flaps out of the bolt-body to abut the receiver wall. This system has much to commend it, as it permits an unusually smooth bolt – uncluttered by lugs or protrusions – and greatly simplifies the receiver. Owing to the position of the locking flaps behind the magazine well, placing much of the bolt under compressive stress at the moment of firing, many people were sceptical of the Sauer action when it first appeared and predicted head-space problems. However, Sauer rifles soon proved able to handle even the awesome ·458 Winchester Magnum cartridge in perfect safety.

Other unusual features include a cocking indicator in the bottom of the bolt-way, a loaded-chamber indicating pin on the left side of the breech, a detachable box magazine and a sliding shotgun-pattern safety on the upper tang behind the cocking piece shroud. Originally known as the Model 80, the designation was

SAUER ⊛

subsequently advanced by ten with no obvious external changes.*

Eckenförde-made guns include the standard **Sauer 90 Medium** (6·5×57, ·270 Winchester, 7×64, ·30–06 or 9·3×62), with a 60cm barrel. Its stock is selected walnut with a rosewood pistol-grip cap and fore-end tip. The comb and cheek piece follow classical German form; the butt plate is ventilated rubber; sling swivels lie on the barrel ahead of the fore-end tip and on the under-edge of the butt. A wide range of engraving is available to order, which means that some guns are works of art rather than practical hunting tools.

The **Sauer 90 Junior** is essentially similar, but is about 20mm shorter in the butt and available only in ·243 and ·308 Winchester. **Sauer 90 Magnums** chamber an assortment of high-power cartridges, including 6·5×68, 7mm Remington Magnum, ·300 Winchester Magnum, ·300 Weatherby Magnum, 8×68S, ·375 H&H Magnum and 9·3×64

Brenneke. Excepting ·375 H&H examples (60cm), the guns all have 66cm barrels. The **Sauer 90 Safari**, made only in ·458 Winchester Magnum, has a sturdier stock and transverse recoil bolts necessary to handle the increased recoil. It is appreciably heavier than the other guns, weighing 4·8kg.

Sauer 90 Stutzen are shortened forms of the 90 Medium, with a full-length Mannlicher-pattern stock, and may be obtained in the five standard calibres. The **Stutzen Junior** – available only in ·243 and ·308 Winchester – is essentially similar, but has a short butt.

The guns sold by Colt in North America were made in Germany, though a special 'USA pattern' stock offered a Monte Carlo comb. Unmistakable Sauer-action rifles made by Fabrique Nationale (q.v.) had a special receiver separating the butt and fore-end.

Model 200

Though the Sauer 90 has been successful, it has not

Variants of the Sauer Model 90 bolt-action rifle include the Model 90 Medium (A), with a half-stock and a hog's back comb; the Model 90 Stutzen or Short Rifle (B), with a shortened barrel and a full-length Mannlicher stock; and the Scharfschützengewehr 2000 ('SSG2000', C), with a thumb-hole stock, adjustable butt plate and cheek piece, and a muzzle brake/compensator. The drawings show details of the SSG mechanism.

By courtesy of J.P. Sauer & Sohn GmbH.

* At the time of writing, the differences have not been resolved.

achieved universal acclamation. Operation of the flap-lock action is undeniably smooth, but it lacks the effectual primary extraction found in designs where the bolt-body turns as the bolt handle is lifted.

Sauer has now moved on to a turning-bolt action, though it is by no means conventional; indeed, the Sauer 200 rifle is crammed with unorthodox features. The cylindrical bolt carries two banks of three lugs on a reduced-diameter integral head. These lugs lock directly into the barrel extension, isolating the receiver from stress and allowing an optional alloy pattern to be offered without compromising strength or life. The barrel is then clamped into the receiver ring by three large cap-head bolts, facilitating a rapid calibre change assuming the bolt does not also need changed.† The detachable box magazine is comparatively conventional, together with the release catch recessed into the floor plate ahead of the magazine aperture; a cocking indicator protrudes from the rear of the cocking-piece shroud, and the safety catch has been moved to the front web of the trigger guard. Here, it is applied automatically when the action opens. The cleverly packaged standard trigger can be replaced by

an optional set-trigger system in which a small button replaces the second trigger lever.

Perhaps the oddest feature of the Sauer 200 is the separation of butt and fore-end by a narrow shoulder of receiver-metal directly beneath the bolt handle. Both parts of the woodwork slide over the receiver until thin tenons on the leading edges slip beneath the under-cut edges of the shoulder. A massive stock-bolt runs up through the pistol grip and into the receiver, the fore-end being held by a bolt reached by removing the front sling swivel. The system is very sturdy, but requires a special Allen-head screwdriver.

The Sauer 200 is a most distinctive gun, even though its two-piece stock is not obvious until the bolt handle is raised.‡ The standard spatulate handle presents an odd appearance (a rounded version is optional), and screwing the front sling swivel bush horizontally into the fore-end tip is a curious departure from normal practice.

Standard **Sauer 200** rifles have a straight-comb butt without a cheek piece, and a simple fore-end with a plain rounded tip. Chequering appears on the pistol grip and fore-end; the butt plate is solid rubber. The

† There are two types within each calibre group. In Group I, only ·243 Winchester requires a change; in Group II, 6·5x68S and 8x68S share a unique bolt.

‡ Unless, of course, the gun is pictured or viewed from the left side, when the fillet of receiver-metal separating the butt and fore-end is obvious.

Right

The Sauer Model 200 rifle, dismantled into its principal components and fitted into its special carrying case.

The remarkable Sauer 200 incorporates several unorthodox features, including the separate butt and fore-end shown here. Note also the method of retaining the barrel and the design of the bolt-head.
By courtesy of J.P. Sauer & Sohn GmbH.

By courtesy of J.P. Sauer & Sohn GmbH.

The Sauer 200 Carbon-S rifle (top) features a synthetic Carbolite stock in an effort to enhance durability while reducing weight. The BBF-54 Drilling (above) features excellent quality and a butt with a slight-but-perceptible hog's back comb.

Sauer 200 Lux and **Lux E** are identical, featuring specially selected woodwork and (in the Lux E) engraving in any of seven basic styles.

Sauer 200 Europe (sometimes listed as 'Europa') guns are essentially similar to the standard pattern, but have butts with slight hog's back combs and German-style cheek pieces; and, in the case of the Europe Lux and Lux E, rosewood schnabel fore-end tips. Lux rifles also have gold-plated triggers and jewelled bolts. The **Sauer 200 USA** duplicates the Europe-Modell, but has a Monte Carlo comb and a cheek piece more suited to North American tastes. The rosewood fore-end tip is a plain rounded pattern rather than a schnabel, and the woodwork is often stained lighter than the red-brown colour preferred in Europe.

One of the great advantages of the Sauer 200 system is the ease with which chamberings can be changed, assuming the relevant components – barrel, magazine and bolt – are available. Group I contains ·243 Winchester, ·25–06 Remington, 6·5×55 Mauser and 6·5×57, ·270 Winchester, 7×64, ·30–06, ·308 Winchester and 9·3×62; in this the bolts are common to all calibres excepting ·243 Winchester, and the magazine to all but ·243 and ·308 Winchester (which share basic case-head dimensions) plus 9·3×62.[*] In Group II, the magazine is common to all chamberings and there are two types of bolt: bolt IIa will accept 6·5×68 and 8×68S, while bolt IIb handles 7mm Remington Magnum, ·300 Winchester Magnum and ·300 Weatherby Magnum.

In sum, the Sauer 200 is a gun of immense promise in which great attention has been paid to detail. But it is comparatively expensive compared with market leaders such as the Winchester Model 70, and only time will show how much of the market it can capture.

Combination guns

The Sauer over/under box-lock combination gun and Drillinge pre-date the bolt-action rifles by many years. Both offer Greener bolt and double under-lug locks; both are of the highest quality. Sliding safety catches on the tang and adjustable double triggers (the front lever being a set-trigger) are standard features on the combination guns, and the woodwork, though conventionally shaped, reveals excellent grain. This is particularly evident on the Luxusmodelle, which are also often superlatively engraved.

The **Sauer BBF 54** offers a 16-gauge (2¾in case) smooth-bore above a rifled barrel chambering ·222 Remington, ·243 Winchester, 6·5×57R, 7×57R, 7×65R or ·30–06. The **Sauer-Drilling 3000** mates two 16-bore barrels with a central (lower) rifled barrel chambering 6·5×57R, 7×57R, 7×65R or ·30–06. A selector lies on the tang, exposing 'K' (Kugel, ball) instead of 'S' (Schrott, shot) when pushed forward; selecting 'K' automatically elevates the rifle-barrel sight, previously concealed within the top rib, and indicator pins protrude from the top of the action alongside the top lever when the trigger mechanism is cocked. Retracting the selector slide, exposing 'S', automatically disengages the rifle-barrel firing mechanism. A Greener-type safety button will be found on the left side of the stock below the tip of the top lever. Like the BBF 54, the Drilling has a pistol-grip butt with a perceptible hog's back comb; ebonite or rosewood pistol-grip caps, and the rubber butt plate, are accompanied by thin white spacers.

[*] As this barrel has a larger diameter than others in Group I, the fore-end must be relieved to accommodate it.

SAVAGE

•••

Savage Arms Company, Springdale Road, Westfield, Massachussetts 01085, USA

The history of this gunmaker stretches back into the nineteenth century, the Savage Repeating Arms Company being incorporated in Utica in 1893. The best known of the early products are the Model 95 and 99 lever-action rifles patented by Arthur W. Savage in the mid 1890s. Large quantities of sporting guns have been made, many bearing the brand of the Stevens gunmaking company. Savage purchased a substantial interest in the Stevens Arms & Tool Company immediately after the First World War had ended, buying the company entirely in 1936. Unfortunately, like so many North American gunmaking companies, Savage has found the mid-1980s something of a recession; though the company survives, it has done so largely on the basis of cutting back. Virtually all the rimfire rifles have been abandoned and only a single pattern of the legendary Model 99 remains.

The Savage Model 65M featured a simple but unwieldy bolt action, feeding from a detachable box magazine ahead of the trigger guard.

Savage's Model 72 rifle, often encountered under the Stevens brandname, was a single-shot falling-block pattern intended for juniors.

Sharing the lines of the bolt-action 65M, the Savage Model 80 was a blowback auto-loader with a tube magazine beneath the barrel.

Three obsolescent Savage ·22 rimfire rifles.
By courtesy of Karl Schäfer.

Product range: Savage makes shotguns, bolt action rifles and – somewhat unusually for an American manufacturer – a selection of combination guns.

Discontinued models: there have been many recent casualties amongst the Savage rimfires, and the once-lucrative liaison with Anschütz terminated in the mid 1980s. It is not known whether the original licence simply expired or whether the change resulted from competition. Savage-Anschütz rifles often retained their original numerical designation; details will be found in the relevant section.

A wide variety of Savage products was available in 1980. It included the bolt-action Model 340 rifle, with a detachable box magazine and chambered for ·22 Hornet, ·222 Remington, ·223 Remington or ·30–30; the Model 80 auto-loader, a tube-magazine ·22LR rimfire; the Models 34 and 65M, bolt-action rimfires in ·22LR and ·22WRM (respectively) with detachable five-round box magazines; and the Model 89, a single-shot Martini-type junior gun. At the end of 1987, only the Savage-Stevens Model 72 Crackshot, a single-shot falling-block junior gun, remained alongside the tube-magazine ·22LR rimfire Model 987 auto-loader.

Several additional guns were available prior to the recent streamlining of the 110 range.

Combination guns

The **Savage Model 24** is an over/under combination gun with an exposed hammer and the rifled barrel above the shotgun. There are two basic variants of the Model 24 – the 24V with a conventional top-lever lock; and the Models 24 and 24C with an underlever catch ahead of the trigger guard. Excepting the Model 24C, or **Camper's Companion**, the guns have walnut-finish hardwood fore-ends and butts with low Monte Carlo combs; the 24C butt has a straight comb. Grooves are milled in the barrel for optical sight mounts, while adjustable semi-buckhorn back sights (a folding leaf on 24V) are standard fittings.

The standard Model 24 chambers either ·22LR or ·22 WRM, above a 20-bore shotgun barrel; the Model 24C is available only in ·22 LR. Model 24V guns, owing to the sturdier top lever, will handle ·222 Remington, ·223 Remington or ·30–30. Their 20-bore shotgun barrel, like those of the other guns in the series, may be chambered for 2¾ or 3in cartridges; excepting the cylinder-choke 24C, all barrels are fully choked.

Introduced in 1988, the **Model 389** is a conventional over/under box-lock combination gun with the shotgun barrel uppermost. Chequering appears on the walnut pistol-grip butt, and also on the sides of the generously proportioned fore-end; ventilated rubber butt plates are standard. The Model 389 is a 12-bore with exchangeable chokes, its rifled barrel chambering either ·222 Remington or ·308 Winchester.

Model 99 series

Introduced at the turn of the century, this is one of the more interesting lever-action rifles; for many of the last ninety years, the hammerless striker-fired Model 99 has put up a creditable performance against Winchester's sales efforts, and it is a shame that the range should have shrunk to the **Model 99C**. The guns have always featured separate butts and fore-ends, necessary because of the modular full-width construction of the receiver. Original rifles were fitted with a unique rotary magazine, which allowed them to handle spitzer (pointed-nose) centre-fire ammunition which would have been extremely dangerous in rival tube-magazine Winchesters and Marlins. In addition, the bolt of the Savage, despite locking behind the magazine well, was sturdy enough to handle higher-pressure ammunition than its rivals. Beginning with ·303 Savage, comparable in power to ·30–30, the manufacturer soon progressed to ·250–3000 and ·300 Savage.

The current Savage 99C has a walnut butt with a Monte Carlo comb, a cheek piece, chequering on the pistol grip, and a pistol-grip cap with an inlaid Savage Signature medallion. A sliding safety lies on the tang, and a visible cocking indicator lies atop the receiver. The fore-end is chequered, a Williams back sight is standard, and a five-round detachable box magazine is locked by a cross-bolt through the receiver body. The rifles are now available only in ·243 and ·308 Winchester.

Model 110 series

Designed by Nicholas Brewer, Savage's high-power bolt action rifle appeared in 1958 to great acclaim; more than thirty years later, it still has much to commend. Though based on the Mauser – with twin opposed lugs on the bolt-head – the Model 110 embodies some very unusual features. These include a barrel-lock nut, disliked by most customizers; and a combination sear/cocking indicator/bolt stop whose tip protrudes above the line of the stock on the right side of the bridge when the trigger is cocked. Savage has always claimed that the barrel-nut system allows much more positive control of head-space than conventional thread/shoulder attachments, and thus that it is beneficial design feature rather than simply a production expedient.

As the Savage was specifically developed so that right- and left-hand actions could be made with equal facility, custom gunsmiths – not to mention left-handed marksmen – were delighted when barrelled actions became available separately in 1962.

Below
Two of the many variants of the popular and extremely competitively priced Savage 110 bolt-action rifle.

By courtesy of Karl Schäfer.

Now discontinued, the Model 110S was a heavy-barrel 'varmint' derivative, with a plain stock. No open sights were fitted, optical sights being obligatory in this style of shooting. Note the quirky stippling running from the underside of the fore-end to the pistol grip.

The Model 111 'Chieftain' was Savage's short-lived attempt to compete in the luxury market, but failed to challenge its principal rivals.

Though somewhat complicated, the Model 110 action (available as Standard or Magnum) is easily made, operates smoothly, and is as safe as virtually any other available on today's market. Owing to their free-floating barrels, Savages are usually very accurate 'straight from the box'. They are also moderately priced; for example, the Model 110E cost $279 in 1988 compared to $399 for a Winchester Model 70. Even the most expensive of the standard Savages, the 110F at $369 in 1988, was cheaper than a Sako action!

A most distinctive feature of the Model 110, externally at least, is the unusually short cocking-piece head protruding behind the bolt handle. This is quite unlike the bulky pattern associated with derivatives of the Mauser Model 98.

Current variants of the Model 110 include the basic **Model 110E**, with a walnut-finish hardwood half-stock with a Monte Carlo comb, a cheek piece and a sturdy solid rubber butt plate. It is available in ·223 Remington, ·243 Winchester, ·270 Winchester, 7mm Remington Magnum and ·30–06. The **110EX** is identical, but lacks sights. All modern bolt-action Savages have a sliding safety on the upper tang, and their internal magazines are replenished through the open action.

The **Model 110F** is similar to 110E, but has a matt black synthetic DuPont Rynite stock with a straight comb and a ventilated rubber butt plate. Williams back sights are standard, though the receivers of all Savages are drilled and tapped for optical-sight mounts. Similar to 110E, the 1986-vintage **Model 110K** has a laminated warp-resistant hardwood stock without chequering.

....

Shilen USA

Founded by the legendary bench-rest shooter Ed Shilen in 1961, this company – trading from 205 Metro Park Boulevard, Ennis, Texas 75119 – was initially famed for the quality of its barrels. During the 1970s, however, production of complete guns began. A continuing commitment to excellence ensures that the Shilen **DGA** bolt-action rifle lives up to its name . . . an abbreviation of 'Damned Good Accuracy'. Five types of action are offered, all sharing a basic turnbolt action with dual-opposed locking lugs and a pin-type ejector mounted in the recessed bolt face. One of the most obvious characteristics of the Shilen action is its squared contours (on all but the DGA/BP and DGA/BP-S); though the action is otherwise conventional, attention to detail and impeccable manufacturing standards ensure the DGA works unusually smoothly. The lock is also very strong.

In order of declining size, the actions are the **DGA-Magnum** repeater for cartridges up to 3·69in overall; the standard **DGA Repeater** (2·85in); the **DGA Single-shot**, which is particularly rigid and thus most popular for long-range silhouette shooting and Heavy Varmint-class bench-rest competitions; the **DGA/BP**, a single-shot action intended for light rifles and silhouette pistols; and the **DGA/BP-S**, the lightest and shortest of the whole group. The differences in

scale are shown by the weights: 3lb 5oz for the Magnum, but only 1lb 15oz for the DGA/BP-S. Owing to Shilen's long-established barrelsmithing business, DGA rifles may be obtained for an unbelievably wide range of cartridges. The company's 1988 catalogue listed more than seventy rounds from ·17 Remington to ·458 Winchester Magnum.

Standard Shilen rifles are stocked in five styles: Classic Benchrest, Thumbhole Benchrest, Silhouette, Sporter and Varminter. The bench-rest guns have unusually broad fore-ends, generally measuring some 3in; the Silhouette has a very high and sharply pitched comb suited to large optical sights mounted high above the bore; the Sporter has classic straight-comb lines; the Varminter has a wide fore-end, a sharp curved pistol grip and a low semi-rollover comb. The stocks may be obtained in select American walnut or as fibreglass, finished in non-slip textured acrylic enamel (dark brown, silver, black, red, royal blue and green). The fibreglass stocks are particularly suited to the DGA/BP and DGA/BP-S actions, which have rounded undersides.

Rifles may be found with octagonal barrels, which complement the squared action on the larger DGA actions, though cylindrical or tapered-cylinder patterns are more common. The metalwork may be finished in satin-blue or dull nickel. Triggers are usually sturdy multi-lever patterns with a pull adjustable between 2 and 6lb, though purchasers may specify the Shilen Competition Trigger with a pull of 2–6oz. Rocking safety levers are optional on the DGA repeater and DGA-Magnum repeater actions, but are generally omitted from the single-shot patterns.

Shilen rifles are not cheap, as their barrels alone sometimes cost more than other manufacturers' guns. According to the 1987 price list, actions began at $595 and complete guns at about $2,000.

Shiloh USA

This operation began in 1976 as 'Shiloh Products', a division of Drovel Tool Company of Farmingdale, New York. The success of Shiloh's replica Sharps falling-block rifles encouraged the Shiloh Rifle Manufacturing Company, Inc. (as the company had become) to move to Big Timber, Montana 59011, in 1983. Shiloh Sharps come in two basic configurations: percussion-ignition and metal cartridge, patterned after the models of 1863 and 1874 respectively. However, there are several individual models within each group.

The 'Model 1874' rifles are offered in ·32–40, ·38–55, ·40–70 and ·40–90, Shiloh's cartridge guns offer great diversity. The best of the sporters is the **Long Range Express Sporting Rifle**, distinguished by its 34in tapering-octagon barrel, vernier tang sight, globe front sight, and figured American black walnut woodwork. The pistol-grip butt has a cheek piece and a rubber shotgun-type butt plate, while the short fore-end has a schnabel tip. Other sporting patterns include the **Deluxe Sporting Rifle No.1**, with a 30in tapering octagonal barrel, a pistol-grip butt and a schnabel tip on the fore-end; the

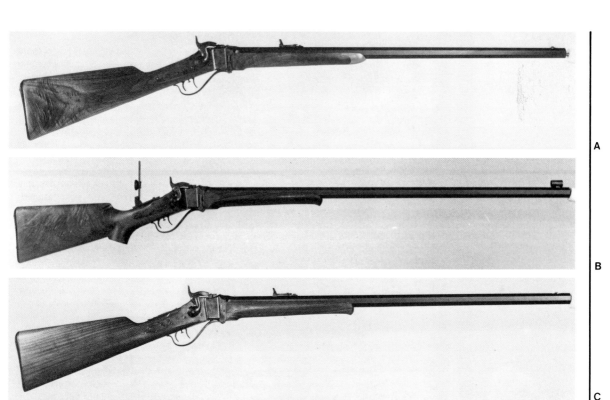

A

B

C

Sporting Rifle No.3, similar to the No.1 but with a straight-wrist military or shotgun-pattern butt; the **Business Rifle**, similar to the No.3 Sporter but with a 28in tapering-cylinder barrel; the **Saddle Rifle**, with a 26in octagonal barrel, a straight-wrist butt and a cheek piece; the lightweight **Jaeger Rifle**, with a half-octagonal 26in barrel and a pistol-grip butt; and, finally, the **Montana Roughrider Rifle**, with a pistol-grip butt, available in half- and full-octagonal barrels measuring 24–34in. The **Hartford Model**, introduced in 1989, features a shotgun-style butt, the so-called 'Hartford Collar' (a short cylindrical section on the barrel immediately ahead of the receiver) and a pewter fore-end tip. All Shiloh Sharps sporters have double set-triggers.

The **Model 1874 Shiloh Sharps** is also made in two single-trigger 'military' configurations – as a rifle, with a three-band stock and a patch box, and a carbine with a plain schnabel tip fore-end. The barrels measure 30 and 24in respectively.

In addition to the standard guns, the prices of which began at about $725 in 1989, Shiloh makes a variety of rifles to special request. The extras include Schützen-style hook butt plates, pewter fore-end tips, chequering, hand-rubbed oil finished woodwork, and choice action-engraving. A particularly interesting variant is the **Gemmer Sharps**, with a half-length fore-end retained by keys and escutcheons, and an under-barrel clearing rod.

The company has also made commemorative rifles, beginning with the Montana Centenary in 1989. Three differing guns are being offered: the ·45–70 Custom Creedmoor Rifle (numbered 1–101), the

·45–70 Hartford Rifle (102–902) and the ·45–70 Bridgeport Rifle (903–2103). The Creedmoor variant, with its vernier-and-globe sights and beautifully figured woodwork, is particularly desirable, but is currently listed at $3,950!

One result of Shiloh's dedication is a peerless re-creation of a gun that played a major role in North American history; another is to persuade the purchaser to part with money, as the customized guns may easily cost $2,500.

Springfield Armory USA

Despite advertising itself as 'The Oldest Name in American Firearms', Springfield Armory of 420 West Main Street, Geneso, Illinois 61254, should not be confused with the US Government ordnance factory of the same name. It is, in fact, a private company that succeeded to the rump when the government operation closed in 1975. Springfield currently offers a series of variations on the US **M1 Garand** and **M14** service rifles, presumably incorporating a mixture of ex-government and new components; when the original Armory was sold, many thousands of parts were still being stored. The Garands are made as standard and 'Match' M1 patterns, the latter with specially bedded barrels, selected actions and competition-grade sights; as the 'M1 Tanker', a re-creation of the abortive short-barrelled T26 developed for jungle warfare towards the end of the Second World War; and an M1D sniper rifle, apparently refurbished from guns used during the Korean War (1950–3) and then mothballed. M1D rifles have optical sights, leather lace-on cheek pads, prong-type

Above

Among the many variants of the Shiloh Sharps rifles are the Custom Saddle Rifle (A); the Long Range Express Rifle (B), with a vernier back sight mounted on the upper tang; and the Sporter No.3 or Buffalo Rifle (C).

By courtesy of Shiloh Rifle Manufacturing Company.

flash suppressors and special heavy barrels.

The Springfield version of the M14 is known as the **M1A**, a rugged and dependable gun now available with a selection of beech, walnut or fibreglass stocks, and a wide range of accessories. The **M1A National Match** and **M1A Super Match** are purpose-built target rifles on the standard M1A (M14) action. The former has a special barrel and gas-piston assembly, a flash suppressor, a fibreglass-bedded walnut stock and a specially honed trigger; the latter has a heavyweight Douglas barrel and a modified stock, enlarged to enhance rigidity, with a deeper pistol grip and sculpted contours immediately behind the action. These target rifles are very popular in Practical Rifle competitions, owing to the effectual action and great attention to detail. However, the chances of success are not bought cheaply: the M1A National Match series begins at about $1,000 and the M1A Super Match at $1,175 (1988 prices).

The **M1A-A1 Bush Rifle** is simply a short-barrelled M1A with either a conventional walnut stock or a folding 'paratrooper' butt and an auxiliary pistol grip behind the trigger guard.

The **SAR-48** rifles are basically FN FALs (q.v.), made under licence in Brazil. These are then supplied to the Brazilian armed forces as well as Springfield Armory, which offers them commercially. There are four basic patterns: the standard wood-stocked SAR-48 and SAR-48 Bush Rifle (the latter with a short barrel); the SAR-48 Para Model with a laterally folding skeleton butt; and the SAR-48 Heavy Barrel 'squad weapon' with a heavy barrel and bipod.

Internally, the guns duplicate their Belgian antecedents.

Springfield Armory also purchased the remaining parts of the 'Italian Garand' or **BM-59**, made under licence by Beretta. These have been assembled in the USA as the BM-59 Ital, BM-59 Nigerian, BM-59 Alpine Para and BM-59 M1. Excepting the M1, which is a conventional clip-loaded Garand, the remainder are basically Garands with M14-type detachable magazines, bipods fitted to the gas-tube assembly, and permanently attached grenade launchers. The Ital model has a standard pistol-grip stock, but the Nigerian and Alpine Para guns have auxiliary pistol-grips behind the trigger guard, and straight-wrist (Nigerian) or skeletal folding (Alpine Para) butts. Quality of these Italo-American guns is very high, but they start at $1,250 (1988 prices).

Swing BRITAIN

Swing Target Rifles Ltd of The Riccarton Complex, Newcastleton, Roxburghshire TD9 0SN, Scotland, makes high-class competition rifles under the guidance of George Swenson. Embodying the finest barrels made by Krieger and Schulz & Larsen, Swing rifles are built largely to order; consequently, as care can be spared for individual guns, they will often out-perform otherwise comparable products of large manufacturers.

By courtesy of Springfield Armory.

A

B

SPRINGFIELD ARMORY

C

Above Springfield Armory's Garand-type rifles include a standard M1 accepting commercial optical sights (A); the M1D sniper rifle (B), refurbished from Korean War guns issued with M84 Weaver telescope sights and special mounts; and the Beretta-made BM59 Alpini (C), which features a folding butt and a grenade launcher integral with the muzzle.

SIG

Schweizerische Industrie-Gesellschaft AG, CH-9212 Neuhausen/Rheinfalls, Switzerland

SIG began life in 1853, making rolling stock for the railway boom until the first percussion-ignition rifles were made in the early 1860s. The company then began to make the Vetterli rifle, laying the foundations of a specialist gunmaking business that has lasted until the present day. SIG-Petter pistols, Schmidt-Rubin and semi-automatic rifles, and machine-guns are among the many products to have borne the 'SIG' trademark.

Product range: SIG currently makes semi-automatic pistols and assault rifles, the bolt-action sniper rifle being a modified Sauer (q.v.) Model 90.

Recently discontinued models: these have included several variations of the SG 510 and SG 530 series. The former group is covered briefly below; the SG 530 was a 5·56mm-calibre adaptation of the SG 510. It worked well enough to sell to armies in Africa, the Far East and South America, but was appreciably more expensive than its rivals. It eventually lost ground to the West German Heckler & Koch HK33 and US M16 – available very cheaply as part of aid programmes – and was replaced by the SG 540.

A

By courtesy of Schweizerische Industrie Gesellschaft AG.

B

SG 510

These guns were developed from the Stgw.57, made by SIG for the Swiss army. The inspiration behind the design was the wartime German MG.42, which also inspired the CETME/Heckler & Koch G3 series. Two rollers on the light bolt-head are forced back into their housing during the firing cycle, then push back on the heavy bolt and the whole unit reciprocates to reload the action for the next shot. However, owing to the precise design of the components, the pressure generated on firing tends to hold the rollers into the receiver walls before dropping to a level at which the breech begins to open. Like many guns in this class, the Stgw.57 operates violently enough to require a fluted chamber;

this prevents the case sticking to the chamber walls during the extraction phase, though it leaves distinctive marks and prevents reloading unless the cartridge cases are re-formed.

The Stgw.57 was a large and comparatively heavy gun, chambering the standard Swiss 7·5×55 Ordonnanzpatrone 11. Manufacturing quality was superlative, though the guns were frighteningly expensive to make. They were sufficiently heavy to mask the rapid breech stroke, and were very accurate. Among the few problems was that the Stgw.57 fired from a closed bolt, even when operating automatically, and the effects of barrel heat on a chambered round had to be monitored carefully.

The earliest of the commercial derivatives, the SIG **SG 510-1**, was little more than an Stgw.57 chambering 7·62×51 NATO. However, the opportunity was taken to improve the design in many minor respects; the most obvious external difference is a short wooden fore-end. The **SG 510-2** was a lightened variant with a wooden butt and a slimmer barrel jacket, but lacking the bipod. Like the SG 510-1, it is now obsolescent. The **SG 510-3** and **SG 510-4**, chambering 7·62×39 (Russian M43) and 7·62×51 NATO cartridges respectively, feature wooden fore-end/hand guard assemblies and wooden butts. Bipods may be fitted *above* the barrel jacket immediately behind the front sight, and a grenade launcher is integral with the muzzle. The SG 510-4 sold well in South America, especially in Chile, but was too expensive to achieve widespread service.

The Swiss saw insufficient merit in the SG 510-4 to abandon the Stgw.57. Trials with the 5·56mm SG 530 were unsuccessful – apparently through no fault of the basic design – and work subsequently concentrated on the simpler gas-operated SG 540.

Small numbers of SG 510 rifles have been modified for sporting purposes, the most notable being the **AMT** in ·308 Winchester (7·62 NATO). Capable of semi-automatic operation only, supplied with five-, ten- or twenty-round magazines, this gun offers some very strange 'sporter' features – including a folding winter trigger and, if required, a bipod! Sales have been minimal owing to a combination of price and ultra-military looks.

SG 540

The failure of the 1969-vintage SG 530 to challenge the then-market leader in 5·56mm calibre, the US M16, forced SIG's designers back to the drawing board. The result was the simplified SG 540, which appeared in the early 1970s. Experience had shown that the 5·56mm cartridge case was not suited to delayed blowback operation, unless a fluted chamber was used. Consequently, like the SG 530, the SG 540 embodies a conventional rotating bolt powered by a piston assembly above the barrel; when the gun is fired, gas is tapped from the barrel and, impinging on the piston-head, drives the piston back against the bolt-carrier to rotate the locking lugs out of engagement. The action then reciprocates, reloading on the forward stroke, and the lugs are rotated back into engagement by the main spring. Externally, guns in the SG 540 series are much plainer than the SG 510. Prototypes had wooden furniture, but this soon became synthetic. A selector lever lies on the left side of the receiver above the pistol grip, displaying its markings through a small circular

aperture, and a CETME/H&K-type drum back sight is fitted. The guns can also accept a detachable three-shot burst firing unit and are remarkably easily dismantled; pressing the release catch on the left side of the receiver, immediately above the magazine-release catch, allows the whole barrel/fore-end/breech assembly to swing open.

Three versions have been made: the standard **SG 540** (7·62×51 NATO), the **SG 542** (5·56mm) and short-barrelled **SG 543** (5·56mm). There was also an SG 541, which formed the basis for the current Stgw.90 described below. The SG 540 is larger and heavier than the SG 542, but both guns will be encountered with tubular skeleton butts that can be folded forward along the right side of the receiver when required.

As it was soon obvious that the SG 542 had considerable potential, a modified variant of the SG 540 – known as the SG 541 – was developed for trials against a rival Eidgenössische Waffenfabrik prototype. Eventually, the SG 542 was licensed to Manurhin (q.v.) so that it could be entered in the French trials with the advantageous backing of a 'French manufacturer'. The **SG 541**, made with short and long barrels, displayed a synthetic skeleton butt, an integral bipod and a modified safety catch in which all the markings were stamped into the outside of the receiver: simpler and more foolproof than the aperture display used on the SG 540.

Switzerland provisionally adopted the SG 541 in 1983, to replace the ageing Stgw.57, but shortage of funds delayed final acceptance. Improvements were made in the interim, advancing the factory designation to SG 550 (q.v.).

SG 550

Little more than an improved SG 541 – practically indistinguishable externally – the **SG 550** and **SG 551** now serve the Swiss Army as the Sturmgewehr Modell 90 (**Stgw.90**). The rifles incorporate the gas-operated rotating bolt action of the SG 540, but the trigger has been modified to include the previously optional three-round burst mechanism. Furniture and magazine bodies are plastic, the butt having a distinctive centre cutaway. A bipod is standard on the long-barrelled SG 550 but not on the shorter SG 551, known to the army as a 'headquarters weapon'. Small quantities of a heavy-barrel sniper rifle are also being made.

As the selective-fire infantry rifle weighs 4·1kg unladen or 6kg with four 30-round magazines, SIG has avoided the trap of sacrificing strength to reduce weight – unlike some rival manufacturers – and the SG 550 is likely to be durable.

SSG 2000

SIG's sniper rifle, the Scharfschützengewehr 2000 ('SSG 2000'), incorporates a standard Sauer Modell 90 bolt action; SIG has had a controlling interest in the West German gunmaker since the 1970s. The SSG features a fully adjustable trigger; a hefty thumb-hole stock, with butt spacers and an adjustable butt plate; an

109

elevating cheek piece; and a heavy barrel with a distinctive muzzle-brake/compensator. The compensator is intended to reduce muzzle jump during firing, so that the sniper can keep his sights on target with minimal disturbance. Left-hand actions are available to order.

Options include Zeiss-Diatal ZA 8×56 or Schmidt & Bender 1·5–6×42 optical sights, a woven mirage band stretching from the breech to the muzzle, and a selection of bipods. Available in ·223 Remington, 7·5×55, ·300 Weatherby Magnum or ·308 Winchester (7·62×51 NATO), the SIG–Sauer sniper rifle is an extremely capable performer.

· ·

Tanner SWITZERLAND

The Swiss rifleman André Tanner's Werkstätte für Präzisionswaffe (CH-4854 Fulenbach), founded in 1960, makes a wide range of excellent target rifles, together with aperture sights and accessories. Many competitions have been won with these rifles during the last two decades,

The single-shot Tanner **Standard UIT-Stutzer** features the company's sturdy bolt action, with three locking lugs and a safety catch on the right rear side of the action to lock the bolt. The action can only be loaded when the catch is set to SAFE. UIT-Stutzer are fitted with mechanical triggers adjustable from 100 to 2,000gm, allowing them to be used as Free Rifles as well as in UIT Standard competitions, where trigger-pull weight is limited to 1,500gm. The walnut

Olympia-Schaft features interchangeable cheek pieces and an adjustable rubber butt plate. The fore-end is distinguished by chequered alloy plates inset in each side to facilitate grip.

A repeating version of the UIT-Stutzer features a nine-round box magazine, running up through the stock ahead of the trigger. A tenth round can be placed directly into the chamber. Excepting the magazine, the two Stutzers are externally identical; internally, however, the bolt head of the repeater has two lugs instead of three.

The Tanner **Super Match 50m** carbine is intended for use as a Free Rifle, as it is fitted with a thumb-hole stock, an adjustable hooked butt plate and a hand-rest beneath the fore-end. It has a heavy large-diameter barrel, contributing to the all-up weight of about 6·3kg, and offers a 'System Tanner' trigger adjustable between 20 and 400gm. The trigger mechanism must be cocked with a lever protruding beneath the guard before the trigger lever can release the sear.

Several patterns of hand-rest may be obtained – ball, cylindrical or universally adjustable – and an extension rod for additional balance weights may be attached under the tip of the fore-end. In common with most of the Tanner series, the sights are offset to the left.

The **Matchstutzer 300m** is essentially similar to the Super Match 50m, but is chambered for 7·5 Swiss or ·308 Winchester centre-fire cartridges. Owing to the more massive action, the gun weighs about 6·8kg compared with 6·3kg for the rimfire version.

Below

Three examples of the work of André Tanner: a bolt-action sporter, the Repetierbüchse Nr.5 (A); a 1989 example of the ·22 rimfire Super Match (B), intended for 50m shooting; and the Matchstutzer 300 (C), destined for full-bore competitions.
By courtesy of Werkstätte für Präzisionswaffe Tanner.

A

B

C

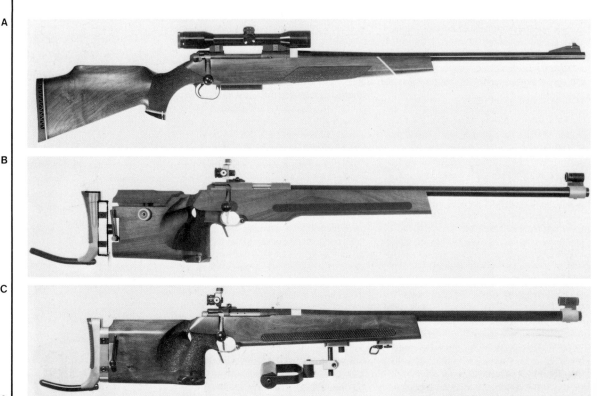

Thompson/Center USA

A Division of the K.W. Thompson Tool Company, Thompson/Center Arms (PO Box 5002, Rochester, New Hampshire 03867) is renowned for the Contender single-shot pistol. However, in addition to a carbine version of this pistol, the company makes a series of break-action rifles, shotguns and black powder guns.

The **Contender Carbine** makes use of the standard falling-block pistol action, allied with a long barrel and black walnut woodwork of the finest quality. The guns look somewhat odd, owing to the lines of the butt, but perform well; the 21in rifle barrel may be chambered for any of nine rounds, from ·22 LR

rimfire to ·44 Magnum, and is readily exchangeable. A ventilated-rib ·410 shotgun barrel can also be substituted.

Unlike the Contender Carbine, the **TCR87** was specifically designed as a longarm. It offers a well-designed break-open action, locked by a shotgun-style top lever, and incorporates the finest materials in action and stock. Measuring about 43·5in overall, with barrels a fraction under 26in and weighing 7lb 4oz (medium barrel version), the TCR87 may be obtained for cartridges as diverse as ·22 Hornet and ·30–06. Several barrel options are available, including 10- and 12-bore shotguns. At a highly competitive $395 (in 1989), the TCR has become justifiably popular.

Below

The Tikka M07 is an interesting variation on the combination-gun theme. Note the exposed hammer, the free-floating rifle barrel, and the muzzle brake.

By courtesy of Karl Schäfer.

TIKKA

•••

Oy Tikkakoski AB, SF-41160 Tikkakoski, Finland

Tikka was founded in 1893, but only began to make firearms after Finland had shaken off Russian clutches in 1917. Best known for m/31 (Suomi) submachine-guns, the company ceased production at the end of the Second World War. In the mid 1950s, however, a modified Mauser-action sporting rifle was developed; this was so successful that, together with a slightly modified successor, it still forms the basis of the Tikka sporters.

Product range: bolt-action sporters, an over/under shotgun and two combination guns.
Discontinued models: none excepting earlier variants of the Models 55 and 65, which differed principally in stock details.

• •

Model 07

This combination gun offers a 12-bore shotgun above a rifled barrel chambering ·222 Remington, 5·6×52R or 5·6×50R Magnum. Though stocked similarly to the more conventional Model 77, excepting that the cheek piece contours are squarer (and white hairline spacers are used), the Tikka 07 has a simplified lock with a single trigger and an exposed hammer spur. A barrel selector lies on the left side of the receiver above the front of the trigger guard. Though comparatively rarely encountered outside Europe, guns of this type are a very useful 'all purpose' compromise.

Model 55

Rifles made on this action are basically Mausers, as two opposed lugs lock into the receiver behind the barrel. The action is unremarkable mechanically, but sturdily made of excellent materials. Distinctive features include a small safety catch on the right side of the breech behind the bolt handle; and a detachable box magazine with a serrated release catch in the trigger guard/magazine floor plate ahead of the trigger lever.

The standard **Tikka 55** has an open back sight (crudely adjustable for azimuth and elevation), and a plain oil-finished hardwood stock with a pistol grip and

111

A

B

C

D

Above

The Tikka 55 (A), with a North American-style stock; the Tikka 55 Sporter (B), with a plain competition stock; the Tikka 65DL (C); and the Tikka 65 Master(D), a specialist sniper rifle usually found with a synthetic stock and a fluted barrel.

By courtesy of Oy Tikkakoski Ab.

a low Monte Carlo comb. Chequering graces the fore-end and the pistol grip; the rubber butt plate is ventilated; and swivels appear beneath the butt and the fore-end. The bolt handle is generally swept slightly backward, and the optional large-diameter bolt-knob is popular in northern countries where the firers' hands are often gloved. Standard chamberings include ·17, ·222, ·22–250 and 6mm Remington, plus ·243 and ·308 Winchester.

Mechanically identical with the standard rifle and available in the same chamberings, the deluxe **Tikka 55 DL** has a better walnut stock with a roll-over comb, a rosewood pistol-grip cap and white-line spacers. The fore-end also has a rosewood tip, cut diagonally and separated from the stock wood by another white spacer.

The current **Tikka 55 Sporter**, intended for hunting and target-shooting, has a 62cm barrel and a heavy stock. The robust pistol grip is almost vertical, assisting control, while the fore-end is deepened until it prolongs the bottom line of the trigger guard. Owing to the depth of the stock, the standard three-round magazine requires a special base-piece extension.

Stippling runs the entire length of the fore-end, past the trigger and onto the pistol grip without interrupton. One sling swivel appears on the right side of the straight-comb butt; the other slides along a rail inlet under the fore-end. No open sights are fitted to the heavy barrel, as the guns are intended for use with optical sights. **Tikka 55 Super Sporters** are similar to the standard version, but their competition-style butt plates slide in vertical channels and special exchangeable cheek pieces are used. They are available only in ·222 Remington, ·22–250, ·243 Winchester and ·308 Winchester.

Model 65

The Tikka 65 is little more than an improved Model 55, many of the parts being strengthened for magnum ammunition. The most obvious external differences lie in the M65 cocking-piece shroud (which is larger than the M55 pattern) and a smoother extension of the bolt-handle base. Standard chamberings include ·25–06 Remington, 6·5×55 Mauser, 7mm Remington Magnum, 7×64, ·270 Winchester, ·30–06, ·300

Winchester Magnum and ·308 Winchester. Free-floating barrels contribute greatly to excellent accuracy.

The stocks of the three standard guns – **Tikka 65, Tikka 65 DL** and **Tikka 65 Sporter** – are similar to corresponding models in the 55 series. However, Tikka 65 Sporters are generally encountered with the solid wooden butt plate prescribed for moving-target competitions. Five-round magazines are standard, except for the seven-round Sporter type available only in 6·5×55 Mauser, ·270 Winchester, ·30–06 and ·308 Winchester.

The **Tikka 65 Master**, which has been used as a sniper rifle, features a synthetic Cycolac stock with an exchangeable cheek piece. It has a fluted barrel, which is light and rigid, and a muzzle weight attached by two cap-head bolts. A large optical sight is generally retained by quick-release clamping mounts and a bipod may be attached to the rail beneath the fore-end.

Model 77

The standard Model 77 is an over/under box-lock shotgun; however, a combination gun, the **Tikka 77K**, offers a 12-gauge smooth-bore above a rifled barrel chambering ·222 Remington, 5·6×52R, 6·5×55 Mauser, 7×57R, 7×65R or ·308 Winchester. The free-floating rifle barrel is isolated from the effects of heat in the shotgun barrel above it; a full-length ventilated barrel rib is standard; detachable rails for optical sight mounts appear above the action; and a distinctively slotted muzzle-brake block lies beneath the muzzle. A sliding safety catch lies on the tang behind the top lever. The butt features a cheek piece with a low Monte Carlo comb, a solid butt plate and a separate rosewood pistol-grip cap. Skip-line chequering appears on the pistol grip, as well as under the broad 'beaver tail' fore-end. Unlike the standard shotgun, the 77K has two triggers; the rear lever fires the rifle barrel.

....

Uberti ITALY

Aldo Uberti & Co. (Via G. Carducci 41, Ponte Zanano, Brescia) offers the **Buckhorn** Revolving Carbine (·44/40 or ·44 Magnum), based on Uberti's Colt Buntline replica, but with a hardwood butt, brass butt plate and spurred trigger guard. The gun measures 34in overall and weighs about 4·5lb. The **1875 Army SA Target** Revolving Carbine (·357 Magnum, ·44/40, ·45 Long Colt) is built on the replica Remington cartridge revolver rather than the Colt Peacemaker. **Rolling Block Baby** carbines, based on the 'New Model No.4' Remington action introduced in 1890, may be obtained in ·22LR, ·22 WMR or ·357 Magnum.

Uberti's most popular longarms are re-creations of the 1860-pattern lever-action **Henry Rifle**, plus the 1866- and 1873-model **Winchesters**. The guns are all available in ·22LR rimfire, ·22 WMR, ·38 Special and ·44/40; 43–44in overall, they weigh 8lb 2oz (Winchesters) or 9lb 5oz (Henry). Carbine forms reduce overall length by 3–5in, and there have been occasional special editions such as the 'Indian Commemoratives' (e.g., Red Cloud Indian Carbine).

Unique FRANCE

Manufacture d'Armes des Pyrénées Françaises (10 Avenue des Allées, F-64700 Hendaye) makes pistols and rifles under the 'Unique' brandname.

The bolt-action rifles share a common mechanism, locked by the combined action of the bolt-handle base in its seat and an opposed lug in the receiver wall. The

Below
Three of the Unique-brand bolt-action rifles. By courtesy of Manufacture d'Armes des Pyrénées Françaises.

The Unique Modèle T Dioptra, a popular ·22LR rimfire sporting rifle.

Made in three versions, the Unique T/SM may be used for target shooting. Note the diopter sights and the free-floating barrel.

Top of the Unique target-rifle range, the Mle T.66 is intended largely for 25m prone shooting. Note the low comb.

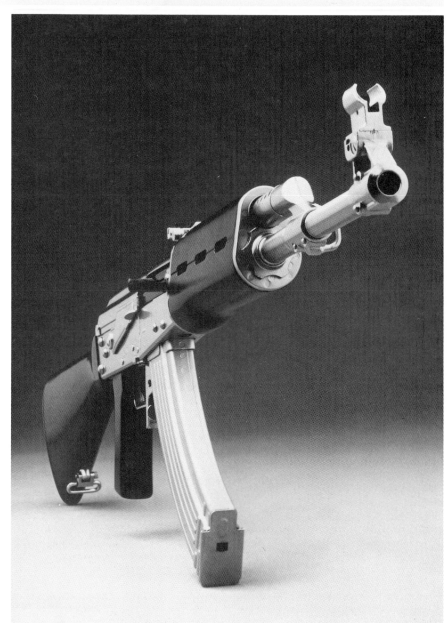

detachable box magazines hold five (·22 Short, ·22LR, ·22 WMR) or ten rounds (·22LR only). **Mle T Audax** sporters (·22 Short or ·22LR rimfire), which have plain hardwood stocks, measure 995mm overall and weigh about 2·9kg. **Mle T Dioptra** (·22LR, ·22 WMR) is essentially similar, but has a better stock with a Monte Carlo comb and chequering on pistol grip and fore-end. It is 1,045mm long and weighs 3·15kg. Models **T/SM** (·22LR, ·22 WMR), T/SM Match Junior (·22LR) and T/SM Biathlon (·22LR) are similar target rifles. The standard gun is intended for moving-target work, having a short heavy barrel and a half-stock stippled on the pistol grip and fore-end; Match Junior has an adjustable butt plate and an accessory rail under the fore-end; and the biathlon variant accepts the shoulder harness unique to this form of shooting. T/SM guns may be encountered with aperture or optical sights.

The single-shot **Mle T.66 Match** (right- or left-hand action), available only in ·22LR, weighs 4·9kg and measures 1,120mm overall. The current version has a walnut stock with an adjustable butt plate, an elevating comb and extensive stippling on the pistol grip and fore-end. The free-floating barrel, adjustable trigger and good quality sights ensure that the competitively priced T.66 is a match for all but the best of its vaunted German rivals. **Mle T.791** (·22LR, 1,020mm, 4·6kg) is a biathlon derivative of the T.66, with a deep fore-end containing a five-round magazine, a muzzle cover, a fixed butt plate, and four spare magazines inlet in the under-edge of the butt.

The company also makes three ·22LR blowback auto-loading rifles. **Mle X-51bis** (1,030mm, 2·7kg), the oldest, has a distinctive cocking plunger protruding from the fore-end beneath the barrel. **Mle G.21** shares a similar action, but is cocked by a handle on the right side of the action; it is about 850mm long and weighs 2·65kg. The magazines, which are shared with the X-51bis, may hold two, five or ten rounds. The most interesting of the trio is **Mle F.11**, a licensed FAMAS lookalike (see GIA section) with a ten-round magazine, an overall length of 840mm and an unladen weight approaching 3·75kg.

Ultra-Light USA

Ultra-Light Arms, Inc. of 214 Price Street, Granville, West Virginia 26534, makes a solitary type of bolt-action rifle. The action features dual opposed locking lugs, a Timney trigger, a unique two-position rocking safety lever, a Douglas barrel (22 or 24in), and a graphite-reinforced Kevlar stock with a straight comb and a rubber recoil pad. Consequently, the guns are unusually light – generally 5–6lb. Their stocks have DuPont Imron epoxy finishes, obtainable in black, brown, green, woodlands, desert or Treebark Camo (or, indeed, in virtually any colour the purchaser specifies).

There are three mechanically identical actions: the **Model 20** is the shortest and lightest, chambering a selection of cartridges from ·222 Remington to 7×57 Mauser and ·358 Winchester; the **Model 24** is appreciably longer, intended for ·270 Winchester, ·25–06, ·30–06 and 7mm Express cartridges; and the **Model 28 Magnum**, offered with the 24in barrel, will handle ·264 Winchester, 7mm Remington, ·300 Winchester and ·338. The actions are all made in right- and left-hand versions. Excepting the Magnum (at least at the time of writing), they are all available separately.

Ultra Light rifles are comparatively expensive – prices began at $1,800 in 1988 – but offer a good combination of strength, quality and weight. Consequently, they are becoming increasingly popular.

US Miniatures USA

Famed for the production of reduced-size commemoratives, such as the Andrew Jackson pistol or the Robert E. Lee revolver, US Miniatures Ltd (PO Box 235, Deep River, Connecticut 06417) has also offered two special Remington Rolling Block rifles reduced to third-scale. The Sporting Rifle No.1, a limited edition of 999 pieces, measures 13·8in overall; it has a plain walnut stock, and is supplied in a velvet lined cherrywood case accompanied by three dummy cartridges – these miniatures function, but cannot fire – and a magnifying glass. Only 25 presentation-grade examples of the miniature Sporting Rifle No.1 were made, patterned after a highly decorative rifle exhibited at the Centennial Exposition in 1876. Elaborately engraved and silver plated, with beautifully figured woodwork, these jewels of the miniaturist's art originally sold for $2,995.

Valmet FINLAND

The products of the former Finnish state rifle factory (Tourula Works, SF-40101 Jyväskylä, PO Box 60) have included a series of Kalashnikov-based assault rifles and a large bolt-action sniper rifle. However, the factory was sold to Sako and there is bound to be some streamlining of the range. The current status of some guns, therefore, is uncertain.

The Valmet auto-loaders are all derived from the Finnish m/62 service rifle, a variant of the Kalashniknov adapted specifically for use in Finland. The m/62 has most distinctive tubular furniture and a detachable 'winter trigger-guard' to suit gloved firers. Valmet then proceeded to the **M76**, touted commercially in 7·62×39 M43 and 5·56×45. Variants have been made with wood or plastic butts, or a tubular butt folding back alongside the receiver. Pistol grips and fore-ends are almost always synthetic, though a wood fore-end may occasionally be encountered on the **M76 Law Enforcement** (semi-automatic only). An extraordinary **Bullpup** has also been touted, seemingly without much success, while a sporting derivative known as the **Petra** has been made in ·243 and ·308 Winchester. This rifle lacks the standard open sights, but has a special mount-base for optical equipment; it displays better finish and has a conventional walnut pistol-grip butt and fore-end, plus chequering and swivels. A detachable ten-round magazine is standard.

The massive Valmet **M86 Sniper Rifle** features a

bolt with three locking lugs, and a heavy barrel with a prominent muzzle brake. The match-type trigger is fully adjustable, as are the elevating comb and sliding butt plate. The half-stock may be wood or fibreglass. A bipod is fitted on the tip of the fore-end, under which there is a full-length accessory rail. The rifle was designed to give a certain hit on a head-size target – 15cm diameter – at a distance of 500 metres. Made in 7·62×51 NATO, though other chamberings can be supplied on request, it measures 121cm overall and weighs about 5·7kg without sights.

Valmet also makes rifles sharing the box-lock action of the **Model 412** shotgun. Changing the barrel group allows the firer to select a double rifle in ·243 Winchester, 7×65R, ·30–06, ·308 Winchester, ·375 Winchester or 9·3×74R; open back sights are carried on quarter ribs, though optical sights can be mounted when required.

Model 412S and 412IM combination guns offer 12-bore shotgun barrels above a rifle; the latter chambers ·243 Winchester (412S and 412IM) or, in Model 412IM only, ·222 and ·223 Remington, 5·6×52R,

7×57R, 7×65R, ·30–06, ·308 Winchester and 9·3×74R. Valmets are sturdy and very well made; though appreciably more expensive than rivals such as the Savages (q.v.), they are much cheaper than comparable German products.

Varner USA

Varner Sporting Arms, Inc. (1044-F Cobb Parkway, Marietta, Georgia 30062) makes a replica of the original Stevens Favorite ·22 rimfire lever-action falling block rifle in three styles – field, sporter and presentation – at prices ranging upwards from about $250. The guns feature half-octagonal, half-cylindrical 21·5in barrels and have attractively colour case-hardened receivers. One unusual feature of the Stevens, perpetuated in this modern version, is the large ring-head bolt beneath the receiver ahead of the action-lever pivot: turning this allows the barrel and fore-end assembly to be detached in a matter of seconds. Although the Stevens design is obsolescent, and by no means as effectual as other falling-block actions, the re-creation is sure to encounter success.

Above

Voere-brand rifles currently being marketed by KGH include the ·22 rimfire auto-loading Models 0014 (A) and 2114S (B), and the Mauser-type bolt action Models 2155/1 (C) and 2165/1 (D).

By courtesy of Kufsteiner Gerätebau- und Handelsgesellschaft mbH.

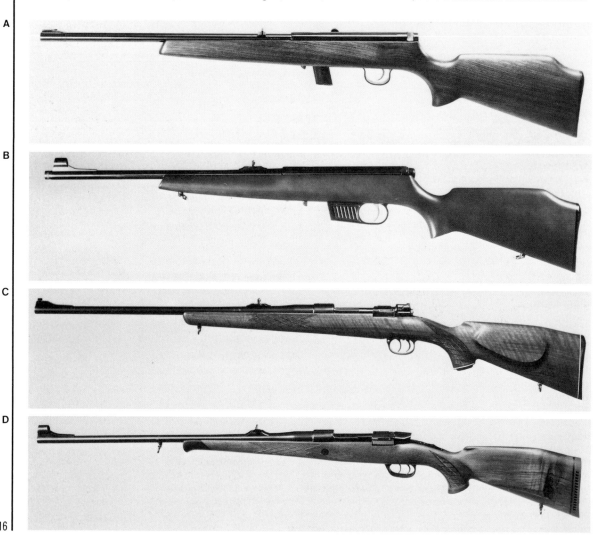

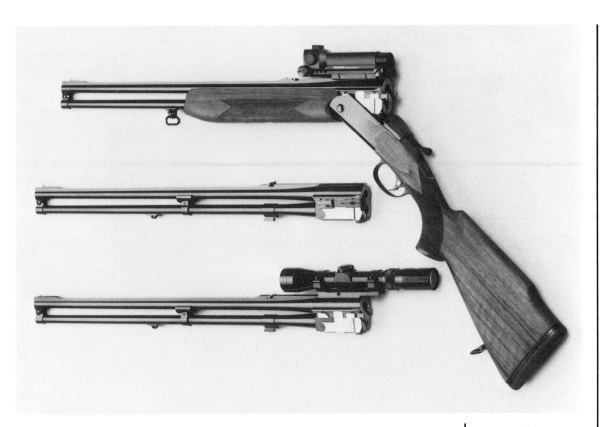

VOERE

●●●

Kufsteiner Gerätebau- und Handelsgesellschaft mbH ('KGH'), A-6333 Kustein/Tirol, Untere Sparchen 56, Austria

Founded as Voetter & Co. in the Schwarzwald district of Germany soon after the end of the Second World War, this company began to make firearms in the 1950s. Until the late 1970s it was trading from Vöhrenbach in Germany, but was subsequently acquired by Tiroler Jagd- und Sportwaffenfabrik GmbH & Co. of Kufstein. This Austrian company then took the trading style 'Voere—Austria' and continued production. In 1987, however, seemingly hit by a recession in the European gunmaking industry, Voere—Austria sold out to Mauser-Werke GmbH and the best Voere rifles are now being made in Oberndorf under the Mauser banner. Substantial stocks of older weapons, and those that had no part in Mauser's plans remained behind after the transaction had been concluded; with effect from 1st March 1988, these weapons and the Voere name passed to KGH.

Product range: Voere makes rimfire rifles – bolt-action and auto-loading – and some high-power sporters. Quality is usually good, particularly in the larger guns, and they offer good value for money.

Recently discontinued models: these have included a range of single-shot ·22LR rimfire bolt-action rifles. The Model 2203 incorporated a small action of a type perpetuated by the 2202 (q.v.), while the Models 2109 and 2110 were similar to the present Model 107. Magazine-feed rimfire rifles included the Models 2107, 2108, 2112 (all ·22LR) and 2113 (·22WMR only). Excepting the Model 2113, which was sturdier and often appeared with a double set-trigger, these guns were built on the standard rimfire

Above

A typical Valmet 412, showing some of the barrel clusters that enable it to be a double rifle, combination gun or shotgun. Note, particularly, the differences in the sights.

By courtesy of Karl Schäfer.

action. The current Model 107 is a minor adaptation of the original 2107. Voere also made the 'Titan Menor', a small version of the Titan II chambering ·222, ·223 and 5·6mm centre-fire cartridges. The Menor, replaced by the Titan III, had a distinctive receiver with an ejection port rather than the entire upper surface cut away. The Models 2135 and 2145 were moving-target rifles built on the Titan II and Titan Menor actions respectively. The Model 2185 was a large auto-loader.

VOERE BARRELLED ACTION INSERT
Calibre .22 l.r. Model 2118

With the Voere Barrelled Action Insert Model 2118 cal. .22 l.r. every rifle with Mauser '98 action in cal. 8 × 57 or in all .30 calibres can be easily converted into Single Shot Bolt Action cal. .22 Rifle.

The handling is very easy:

1. Remove the bolt from the K-98.
2. Clean the barrel of the rifle if it is not tidy.
3. Take the action insert and open the bolt to the left as usual and pull it backward to the stop.
4. Slide the action insert into the K-98 while positioning the bolt handle horizontal to the left (see pict. 1). Now push the action insert with the vertical positioned knurled button forward to the stop (bolt remains backward).

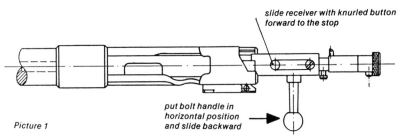

slide receiver with knurled button forward to the stop

Picture 1

put bolt handle in horizontal position and slide backward

5. Turn the bolt handle to the right in an angle of 90 degrees into vertical position up to the catch, push the bolt handle forward and lock by turning to the right as usual.

The inserted action is now operating like all other repeating actions.

• •

Rimfire rifles

The **Modell 0014** is a ·22LR rimfire blowback semi-automatic sporting rifle with a walnut-finish hardwood stock, a plain pistol grip and a low Monte Carlo comb. It has a detachable ten- or fifteen-round box magazine ahead of the trigger group and fixed open sights (an adjustable tangent-leaf back sight is optional).

The **Modell 1014** embodies a similar auto-loading action to the 0014, but has a distinctive military-style stock with a hand guard, a straight-comb butt and the front swivel mounted on a barrel band. Like most of the guns in this series, it can fire single shots merely by locking the cocking handle after reloading. The Modell 1014 has an adjustable aperture back sight on top of the receiver above the trigger, and a wing-pattern safety protrudes from the receiver end-cap.

Voere's **Modelle 2114S** and **2115** are also ·22LR rimfire semi-automatics, distinguished by a prominent trigger-guard extension block filling the gap behind the detachable box magazine. Both guns have adjustable single-stage triggers, and can be converted to fire single shots. Fixed open sights are standard, together with a wing-pattern safety that locks the firing pin. The Modell 2114S has a walnut-finish hardwood stock similar to that of the 0014 (see above), apart from a broader fore-end. The Modell 2115, however, has a hardwood stock with a cheek piece, chequering on the pistol grip and fore-end, and a slight hog's back comb; white spacers accompany the pistol-grip cap and butt plate. Sling swivels are standard on both guns.

The **Modell 1007 Biathlon** is a five-, eight- or fifteen-shot bolt-action rifle with distinctive sliding safety catch at the rear of the receiver and a tangent-leaf sight immediately ahead of the bolt handle. It has a pseudo-military stock similar to that of the Modell 1014 and a single-stage trigger. The **Modell 1013** is

similar, but chambers ·22WRM and comes with a five-
or ten-round magazine. It is also available with a double
set-trigger.

Modell 2202 and Modell 2204 are single-shot bolt-
action guns firing rimfire or primer-propellant
ammunition. They have simple hardwood half-stocks
with pistol grips and low Monte Carlo combs, fixed open
sights, simple triggers and safety catches that lock the
firing pin. Chambering ·22LR and 9mm Flobert
respectively, the 2204 and 2202-pattern rifles measure
99cm and 113cm overall. They weigh 2–2·3kg.

Centre-fire rifles

Before proceeding to the Titan rifles currently being
marketed by Mauser, Voere made sporting guns on the
proven Mauser M98 action. The most basic rifle is the
Repetierbüchse 2155, which mates a classic military-
style Kar.98k action with a spatulate bolt handle and a
sporting half-stock. The Model 2155/1 has a walnut
stock with a German-style cheek piece and a hog's back
comb, with skip-line chequering on the pistol-grip and
fore-end; the plainer 2155/2 has a walnut-finish
beechwood stock with a Monte Carlo comb and cheek
piece. The guns feature double set-triggers, have
adjustable back sights and weigh about 3.2kg with a
61cm barrel. They have been made in 5·6×57, ·22–
250 Remington, ·243 Winchester, ·25–06 Remington,
6·5×55 Mauser, 6·5×57, ·270 Winchester,
7×57, 7×64, 7·5×55 Swiss, ·30–06, ·308
Winchester, 8×57S and 9·3×62.

The Repetierbüchse 2165 is essentially an improved
form of the 2155, distinguished by a double set-trigger
(a shotgun-type single trigger is optional), an elegant
cocking-piece shroud and a streamlined bolt handle.
The safety catch lies on the upper tang rather than the
bolt. Detachable box or internal hinged floor-plate
magazines may be encountered. The 2165 has a shapely
walnut stock with a hog's back comb and a squared
Bavarian cheek piece, skip-line chequering on the pistol
grip and fore-end, and a rosewood schnabel tip. It has
been offered in the same calibres as the 2155 model
(excepting 7·5×55), plus 6·5×68, 7mm
Remington Magnum, ·300 Winchester Magnum,
8×68S and 9·3×64 to special order. The magnums
have barrels measuring 65cm rather than 60cm, and
are about 1,175mm overall compared with only 1,130;
weight varies from 3·2 to 3·4kg, depending on calibre.

Voere's Repetierbüchse 2175 has been made in three
versions (Light, Medium and Special). It shares the
Mauser action and Bavarian-style walnut half-stock
with the preceding guns, but has a short cylindrical
cocking piece shroud and a rocking safety on the right
side of the action behind the bolt handle. Adjustable
single-stage triggers, double set-triggers or a single
French-style set-trigger may all be obtained. The 'L'
action chambers ·222 and ·223 Remington, ·223
Remington Magnum or 5·6×50 Magnum; 'M' guns
are available in the same thirteen chamberings as the
Modell 2165 (q.v.); and the 'S' version handles the usual
five magnum rounds.

WALHER

Carl Walther GmbH, D-7900 Ulm/Donau, Postfach 4325, West Germany

Founded in Zella St Blasii in 1886, Walther rose to prominence during
the Weimar Republic largely on the success of the double-action Polizei-
Pistole. The future seemed assured when the P.38 was adopted to replace
the venerable P.08 (Parabellum) in 1940, but operations collapsed after
the Second World War; years were to elapse before production of
cartridge guns began again in Ulm. However, despite the success of the
target rifles, the handgun business has been based largely on old designs
– the PP, after all, was patented in 1929 – and profitability declined
throughout the 1980s. However, a rationalization process begun in
1988 will restore Walther to the vanguard of German gunmakers.

Left
Developed during the 1980s in a
quest for the ideal sniper rifle, the
Walther WA2000 rejected many
conventional ideas of construction.
A highly unusual bullpup, it had not
been perfected when the project
was abandoned in 1988.
By courtesy of Carl Walther GmbH.

119

Product range: target rifles, auto-loading pistols, and air- and gas-guns, all offering excellent quality and performance.

Recently discontinued models: since the change of ownership, Walther has ceased making the well-known *KKJ-series* sporters (·22LR, ·22 WMR, ·22 Hornet and 5·6×50). The sole remaining centre-fire Walther disappeared ten years ago; and the promising *WA2000* ·300 Winchester Magnum and ·308 Winchester), specially developed in the 1980s as a sniper rifle, has also now been abandoned.

Bolt-action rifles

Like the Anschütz Match 54 (q.v.), Walther's rimfire action dates from the early 1950s, but is none the worst for its age: countless international championships are still being won with it. The basic action locks by using the base of the bolt handle and an opposed lug engaging the receiver wall – copied by many other manufacturers, but rarely with Walther's attention to detail. Special attention has been paid to the mechanical triggers, resulting in very fast lock times and a smoothness shared only by similar Anschütz and Feinwerkbau rifles.

Six ·22LR target rifles survive. The **UIT-Spezial** – now the basic pattern – offers a fixed-comb walnut half-stock with an adjustable butt plate, and a deep fore-end with an accessory rail. A conventional aperture back sight is paired with a replaceable-

element front tunnel. Measuring 1,120mm overall, with a 650mm barrel, the rifle weighs about 4·7kg and can be supplied with an optional five-round box magazine. Apart from the shape of the slab-side fore-end, the UIT-Spezial can be distinguished by a trigger aperture noticeably longer than other bolt-action Walthers.

UIT-Match (1,110mm, 5kg) and **UIT-Match Universal** (1,120mm, 5kg) rifles share identical actions. Their walnut stocks have distinctive tapering fore-ends, extensively stippled, but the Universals have an adjustable four-position comb adjusted by removing the retaining bolt, inserting the elevator pillars in the desired holes (each pillar has two positions) and then replacing the retaining bolt. The system is quirky, but the selected position cannot be knocked out of position as easily as some screw-elevated combs.

Below

Typical rimfire bolt-action target rifles. All photographs by courtesy of Carl Walther GmbH.

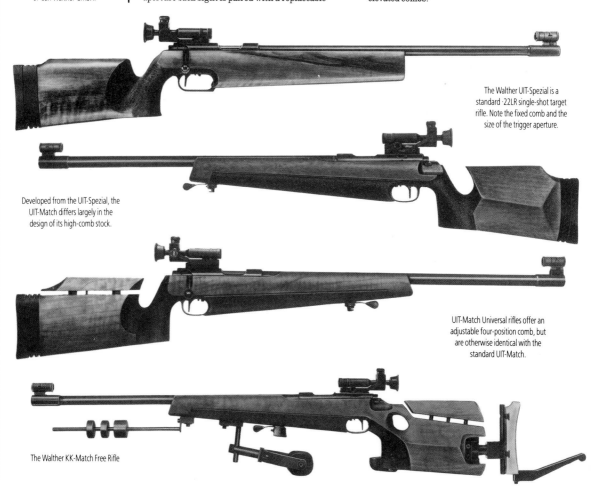

The Walther UIT-Spezial is a standard ·22LR single-shot target rifle. Note the fixed comb and the size of the trigger aperture.

Developed from the UIT-Spezial, the UIT-Match differs largely in the design of its high-comb stock.

UIT-Match Universal rifles offer an adjustable four-position comb, but are otherwise identical with the standard UIT-Match.

The Walther KK-Match Free Rifle

The Walther KK Silhouette rifle, distinguished by its thumb-hole stock and fixed rubber butt plate, is intended for the rapidly growing sport of metallic-target shooting.

Intended for moving target competitions, the Walther UIT-LS has a thumb-hole stock with an elevating comb and an adjustable wooden butt plate.

Unlike the other Walther target rifles pictured here, the UIT-E-Universal features a block action and an electronic trigger.

Above

Specialist target rifles. Pictures by courtesy of Carl Walther GmbH.

Rifles intended for specialist competitions are designated **UIT-LS** (Laufende Scheibe, 'moving target') and **KK-Silhouette**, for increasingly popular metallic-target shooting. These guns share the standard bolt action, but their thumb-hole stocks differ radically from the standard Walthers. The UIT-LS model is 1,085mm overall, has a 60cm barrel and weighs 3·9kg without its optical sight. The stock has a short rounded fore-end, extensively stippled, and the adjustable comb relies on elevating rods and screw-clamps; the rifles also have a 220gm muzzle weight and adjustable wooden butt plates prescribed by UIT rules. The trigger is pre-set to 500gm. Silhouette rifles (1,060mm, 3·8kg) have a fixed-comb stock and a ventilated rubber butt plate. Both rifles have enlarged bolt-handle knobs and accept optical rather than aperture sights.

The acme of the Walther bolt-action rifles is the **KK-Match**, which helped gain a gold medal in the 1984 Olympic Free Rifle competition. Though the action remains the standard Walther bolt, the KK-Match has a selected walnut stock with every conceivable accessory – a screw-elevating comb; a butt plate adjustable for length, cant and height; a palm rest on the pistol grip; a hand rest sliding along the accessory rail under the fore-end; and a balance-weight rod running forward from the fore-end tip. The rifle weighs 7·4kg without the fore-end rest or balance weights, and measures 1,210mm overall.

Block-action rifles

Introduced in 1985, these rifles feature a block action locked by a lever on the receiver-side.* The goal was a simpler mechanism that could be made more easily than the traditional, but complicated Walther bolt unit. The **UIT-BV-Universal** (Blockverschluss, 'block action') shares the adjustable-comb stock of the UIT-Universal, but has a distinctive squared receiver with the operating lever on the right side.† When the gun has been fired, pulling the lever out of the receiver unlocks the breech and draws the breech-block back until the spent case is ejected. A new round is placed in the chamber and the operating lever returned to its original position in the receiver wall, shutting the breech as it does so. The system is elegantly designed, well made and reliable; however, it has yet to challenge the bolt action Walthers in the affections of marksmen.

UIT-E-Universal (sometimes known as UIT-BV-E-Universal) is a variation of the standard BV pattern with an electronic trigger, substituted for the standard mechanical one in an attempt to reduce lock time. It measures 1,120mm overall and weighs about 4·7kg. Like the standard rifle, the electronic-trigger gun has a squared trigger guard and a longer trigger aperture than all the bolt actions excepting UIT-Spezial.

* This could almost be described as a straight-pull non-rotating bolt action.

† An alternative left-hand action is available from stock.

WINCHESTER

●●

US Repeating Arms Company, Inc., 275 Winchester Avenue, New Haven, Connecticut 06511, USA

The Winchester Arms Company was formed in New Haven, Connecticut, in 1866, being an outgrowth of the New Haven Arms Co. and, by extension, of the Volcanic Repeating Arms Co. of Norwich. The Volcanic company had been formed to make a lever-action repeater firing primer-propellant ammunition, but this early attempt at an entirely self-contained cartridge was doomed to fail by low power. However, the Volcanic became the Henry Rifle (designed in 1859−60), which fired a more powerful rimfire cartridge; and then the Henry, suitably improved, became the Winchester Model 1866 − the first of a long line of lever-action rifles now represented by the Winchester Model 94. The tremendous success of the Model 1873 and strengthened guns patented by John Browning (beginning with the Model 1886) enabled Winchester to move into the military market, eventually making great quantities of munitions during the First World War. Production of sporting guns continued in the period between the wars, creating the Model 54 and Model 70 bolt-action rifles, until the company went to war again in 1941. The ·30 US M1 Carbine was a Winchester development. Work concentrated on sporting guns after 1945, but fortunes declined appreciably in the 1970s − scarcely helped by radical changes in production methods and ever-increasing competition. Finally, the owners of Winchester, Olin Corporation, sold the gunmaking business to the US Repeating Rifle Company; the new management immediately passed the remaining commemoratives on to the appropriately named Commemorative Firearms (q.v.) of Omaha, rationalized production and recommenced production with vigour sufficient to take the Winchester name proudly into the 21st century.

Product range: a variety of bolt- and lever-action rifles, plus the Model 1300 pump and Model 1400 autoloading shotguns are being made under the Winchester banner.

Recently discontinued models: excepting commemoratives and variations of the Models 70 and 94, generally with differing stocks and finishes, few guns have been discontinued since 1980.

Below

The many variants of the popular Winchester Model 70 bolt-action rifle include the M70 Featherweight (A), with its distinctive chequering and schnabel fore-end tip, and the plainer M70 Lightweight (B).

By courtesy of US Repeating Arms Co., Inc.

A

B

A

B

C

D

Model 70

The Winchester Model 70 is one of the world's truly classic rifles. It owes its origins to the first Winchester bolt-action sporting rifle to be introduced after the end of the First World War, the Model 54 of 1925. Designed by a team headed by Thomas Johnson, then Winchester's premier designer, the Model 25 made an immediate impact in a market dominated by variations on war-surplus themes. The Model 54, based on the US Army M1903 Springfield service rifle, had twin opposed locking lugs and a Mauser collar-pattern extractor. A special guide-lug ensured a smooth bolt stroke, a three-position safety appeared on the cocking-piece shroud and an internal box magazine was fitted.

The success of the Model 54 permitted Winchester the luxury of designing its successor at leisure, with the result that the Model 70 was not introduced until 1936. Credited to a team led by Edwin Pugsley, in which Leroy Crockett and Albert Laudensack were prominent, the Model 70 retained the basic operating system of the older gun. It had a cone-breech, a partially shrouded bolt head and a modified bedding system in which the front trigger-guard bolt ran up into the underside of the receiver rather than, as on the Model 54, into the recoil lug. The bolt handle was swept downward and back, a graceful and practical feature that allowed it to clear most optical sights, and the safety catch on the cocking-piece shroud was

changed to work laterally rather than longitudinally. It could be set to fire, to retract the firing-pin (but allowing the bolt to open) or to lock the bolt in the action.

Production of the Model 70 resumed after the end of the Second World War, continuing in a wide variety of chamberings until 1960. However, Winchesters were expensive to produce, and the company's profitability declined until it was bought by the giant Olin Corporation in 1961. Work immediately began to modernize the Model 70 – with the primary goal of simplifying production – but the new management misjudged matters badly. When the modified rifles appeared in 1964, they were greeted with howls of protest. Though some changes were for the better, the Winchesters were poorly finished and unattractive; within four years, therefore, another pattern appeared. It had several distinguishing characteristics, not least being a return to the smoothness of the pre-1964 bolt-stroke and an 'anti-bind feature' in the form of a slot in the bolt-head engaging a narrow rib in the right side of the receiver. The magazine follower was improved; considerably more attention was paid to finish; the extractor became a small sprung claw inlet in the right-hand locking lug; and a plunger-type ejector was set into the shrouded bolt-face.

These improvements were such that the Model 70 regained much of its former position as the market

Above

Other versions of the Model 70 include the M70 Winlite (A), with a synthetic stock; the M70 Win-Cam (B), with a laminated camouflage stock; the M70 XTR Super Express (C), with additional recoil bolts; and the M70 HB Varmint (D), with a plain heavy barrel.

By courtesy of US Repeating Arms Co., Inc.

WINCHESTER ®

123

leader, though now challenged in North America by the Ruger M77.

The basic rifle is currently the **Model 70 Sporter**, available in a bewildering variety of calibres – for the 1990 season, ·22–250 Remington, ·223 Remington, ·243 Winchester, ·25–06, ·264 Winchester Magnum, ·270 Winchester, ·270 Weatherby Magnum, 7mm Remington Magnum, ·30–06, ·300 H&H Magnum, ·300 Weatherby Magnum, ·300 Winchester Magnum and ·338 Winchester Magnum. Guns may be obtained with open sights, or bases and rings for optical sights. The M70 Sporter has an elegant American walnut half-stock with a low Monte Carlo comb, a cheek piece, and chequering on the pistol gip and fore-end. The solid rubber butt plate is accompanied by a black spacer and a nylon pistol-grip cap. Sling swivels will be found on the underside of the butt and fore-end.

The **Model 70 Sporter Winlite** features a textured black McMillan fibreglass stock carrying a lifetime guarantee. These stocks – waterproof, scratch-resistant and appreciably stronger than wood – are gaining increasing favour with professional shooters, though not with purists. Winlite stocks have straight combs and pistol grips, but lack chequering. Those fitted to 22in-barrelled Featherweight actions generally have a shallow schnabel tip on the fore-end, while 24in-barrelled Sporter patterns are rounded. Chamberings include 7mm Remington Magnum, ·300 Weatherby or Winchester Magnums, and ·338 Winchester Magnum. Guns have also been made in ·270 Winchester, ·280 Remington and ·30–06, but these chamberings have recently – perhaps temporarily – been discontinued.

Announced at the end of 1989, for delivery in time for the 1990 season, the **Model 70 Super Grade** is a deluxe version of the standard Sporter available with a 24in barrel in 7mm Remington Magnum, ·300 and ·338 Winchester Magnums. It weighs about 7·8lb unladen. The classic straight-comb stock, patterned on that of the Featherwight (q.v.), has swivel eyes beneath the butt and the fore-end, and the hand-cut chequering lacks the strapwork of its prototype. The most distinctive feature of the Super Grade rifles, however, is the non-rotating collar-type extractor (what the manufacturer calls 'claw controlled feed').

The **Model 70 Varmint Rifle**, introduced in 1989, features a standard Sporter stock – with Monte Carlo comb and cheek piece – plus a 26in heavyweight barrel with a counter-bored muzzle. The receiver is drilled and tapped for optical sight mounts, open sights being absent. Weighing about 9lb, the Model 70 Varmint may be obtained in ·22–250 or ·223 Remington, ·243 Winchester and ·308 Winchester.

The **Model 70 Featherweight** is essentially an M70 Sporter, but has an elegant American walnut straight-comb half-stock with a schnabel fore-end tip. The chequering – on current guns at least – features floral strapwork that mars otherwise classic lines. Weighing a mere 6¼–6¾lb, depending on calibre, the Featherweight is available in ·22–250 or ·223 Remington; ·243, ·270 or ·308 Winchester; ·280 Remington and ·30–06. The **Model 70 Featherweight Winlite** (·270 Winchester, ·280 Remington and ·30–06 only) features a MacMillan fibreglass stock and weighs 6¼lb.

Model 70 Lightweight guns may be obtained with walnut, Win-Tuff or Win-Cam half-stocks, all of which feature straight combs and a rounded fore-end tip. Win-Tuff (brown) and Win-Cam (green/brown camouflage) are laminated hardwood, combining strength and durability with warp resistance. The rifles weigh 6¼-7lb, depending on calibre, and have 22in barrels. They may be chambered for ·22–250 (walnut-stock version only), ·223 Remington (walnut and Win-Tuff only), ·243 Winchester (walnut and Win-Tuff only), ·270 Winchester (all), ·280 Remington (walnut only), ·30–06 (all) or ·308 Winchester (walnut and Win-Tuff only).

Intended for big-game shooting, **Model 70 Super Express Walnut Magnum** Winchesters are distinguished by two steel recoil bolts in the stock, thermoplastic bedding, matt-black finish, open sights, and the front sling-swivel on the barrel instead of the fore-end. Chambered only for ·375 H&H Magnum and ·458 Winchester Magnum, they weigh about 8½lb apiece and have three-round magazines.

Ranger rifles are a basic budget-price version of the Model 70, embodying the standard action in a plain hardwood stock with a straight comb. They lack chequering, but are otherwise comparable with the standard guns; chamberings are ·270 Winchester and ·30–06. The **Ranger Youth Rifle** is similar to the Ranger, excepting that the butt has been shortened and the radius of the pistol grip tightened to suit small hands. The Youth Rifle, only available in ·243 Winchester, has a 22in barrel and weighs a little under 6lb.

Model 94

This lever-action rifle traces its ancestry back to the Winchester Model 1886 rifle, designed by John Browning, which used vertically sliding bolts to lock the breech block securely in the receiver – a much

A

B

C

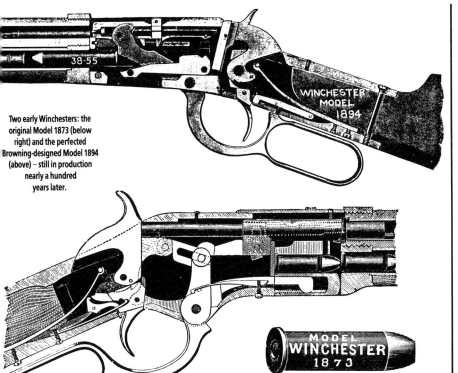

Two early Winchesters: the original Model 1873 (below right) and the perfected Browning-designed Model 1894 (above) – still in production nearly a hundred years later.

38-55

WINCHESTER MODEL 1894

MODEL WINCHESTER 1873

Above

Rapidly approaching its centenary, Winchester's Model 94 is the most famous of all modern lever-action rifles. Shown here are the M94 Win-Tuff (A), featuring a laminated butt and fore-end; the budget-price M94 Ranger (B), with a Bushnell Sportview optical sight and See-Thru mounts; and the M94 Big Bore (C), strengthened for the new ·307 and ·356 Winchester cartridges.

By courtesy of US Repeating Arms Co., Inc.

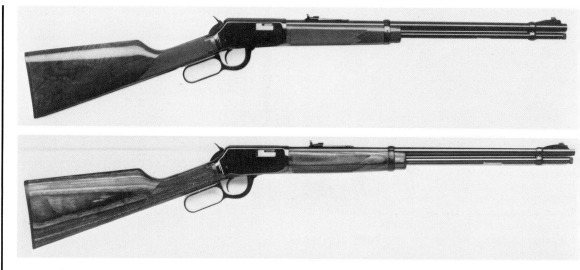

Above

The Model 9422 is currently the only Winchester rimfire lever-action rifle. These guns are the M9422 Walnut (A), with a deluxe stock, and the M9422 Win-Cam (B) with brown/green camouflage laminate woodwork.

By courtesy of US Repeating Arms Co., Inc.

stronger method than had been used on previous guns. A link was subsequently added in the action to lengthen the breech block stroke in relation to the receiver, permitting longer cartridges to be used. The Model 1894 and a box-magazine military version, the Model 1895, were very successful; their influence lasts to the present time, though substantial machining changes have been made in the current Model 94. In common with most Winchesters – and the myriad copies of them – the first post-war M94 guns ejected upward. This was no handicap when open sights were fitted, but was a considerable disadvantage with optical sights: either they had to be offset to the left, or carried high enough to enable ejected cases to bounce off a deflector. Early in the 1970s, Winchester revised the M94 action so that the cases were thrown up and out diagonally (M94 Angle Eject) and then, in 1978, so that the trajectory was lateral (the current M94 Side Eject).

The **Model 94 Side Eject** Winchester may be obtained in several variants. The standard 20in-barrelled gun has a plain walnut straight-grip butt and fore-end, a rubber butt plate and open sights (the back sight being a variation on the traditional elevating 'semi-buckhorn'). It has an automatic hammer-block safety and a lateral hammer-spur extension facilitating thumb-cocking when an optical sight is fitted. The rifle is currently available only in 7–30 Waters and ·30–30, its capabilities blighted by the unsuitability of tube-magazine guns for pointed bullets. The **M94 Checkered** (·30–30 only) is simply a standard gun with hand-cut chequering in the wrist and fore-end, while the **Model 94 Side Eject Win-Tuff** (·30–30 only) features a durable laminated stock. This looks better on the lever-action guns than it does on the bolt-action Model 70.

Model 94 Side Eject Trapper Carbines (·30–30, ·44 S&W Special, ·44 Remington Magnum or ·45 Colt) are simply variants of the standard rifle with a 16in barrel, though the reduction in length restricts magazine capacity to five (rather than six) ·30–30 rounds and the front sight has been moved back

behind the barrel/magazine tube retaining collar.

The **Model 94 Side Eject Big Bore** is a modification of the basic M94 action for the comparatively new ·307 and ·356 Winchester cartridges. It is immediately identifiable by the reinforced receiver, machined from a solid billet of ordnance steel rather than forged from bar-stock. It also has a folding-leaf back sight and chequered walnut furniture.

For those who seek a cheaper lever-action Winchester, the **Model 94 Ranger** (·30–30 only) offers plain hardwood furniture that is no less durable than walnut. The rifle is otherwise identical with the standard M94.

Model 9422

This is a rimfire M94 lookalike, though internally quite different befitting the lesser power of ·22LR and ·22WMR. The most obvious external features are the squared ejection port – on the right or left side of the receiver, depending on pattern – and the loading gate lies under the receiver rather that simply let into the right side. Most of the lockwork is carried on a sub-frame, rather than in the receiver forging. The guns are made in three versions: Model 9422 Walnut, Win-Tuff (both ·22LR and ·22WRM) and Win-Cam (·22 WRM only), their stocks being walnut, brown laminate and brown/green camouflage laminate respectively. They weigh about 6¼lb and measure 37·2in overall.

The 9422 is among the very best of rimfire rifles in its class, but at $330 or more (1988–9 prices) is by no means the cheapest. It sells simply because it *is* a Winchester and bears the famous trademark.

• •

Weatherby USA

The name of Roy Weatherby – the 'Magnum King' – is written large in the annals of modern gun history, being the first man to promote a matched range of powerful belted-case magnum cartridges to the North American sporting public. Beginning in the early 1940s, Weatherby produced several new rounds by

necking and re-forming Holland & Holland Magnum cartridge cases. When hostilities ended, Weatherby began to make rifles based on FN Mauser and Schultz & Larsen actions. Advocates of power were impressed; the Weatherby Magnums shot far and flat, and had ample reserves of energy provided they were matched to the task. Success bred success; the Weatherby name was soon established for all time.

However, Weatherby had always wanted to make his own rifles to ensure that action-strength was commensurate with the power of cartridges whose muzzle energy – in the ·460 Weatherby Magnum at least – exceeded four foot-tons. Roy Weatherby and Fred Jennie began work in 1954, patents were sought in 1958, and production of components began. Though parts were originally investment-cast in San Francisco, an agreement was signed with J.P. Sauer & Sohn (q.v.) in 1959 and production was diverted to Germany. The Mark V action was made in Germany until about 1972, though a contract had been signed with Howa (q.v.) in Japan in 1969; the first Japanese-made actions appeared in 1971. The two actions are practically identical, though the German and Japanese triggers differ.

The Mark V features a counter-bored breech that enables the bolt-head to be partly shrouded by the barrel, and nine locking lugs disposed at 120° in three rows of three. This allows the lugs to share the external diameter of the bolt body, but has little bearing on the strength of the action as some conventional two-lug systems (e.g., Remington 700) possess equal theoretical durability.

The **Weatherby Mark V** is a most distinctive rifle, largely owing to the fluted bolt and the shape of the cocking-piece shroud. Current variants include the Mark V **Deluxe**, with a gloss-finished Claro walnut stock, skip-line chequering, white-line spacers and diamond pistol-grip cap inlay. The **Euromark** has a more restrained satin-finish stock lacking the white-line spacers; instead, it features conventional chequering, an ebony pistol-grip cap with a maplewood diamond inlay, an ebony fore-end tip and a plain black spacer ahead of a solid rubber butt plate. **Lazermark** guns are similar to the standard deluxe Mark V, but have intricate carving on pistol-grip cap and fore-end; **Fibermark** rifles feature a matt black fibreglass stock with a black recoil pad and pistol grip (the latter complete with white diamond inlay and obligatory white-line spacer). The rifles are available in virtually all the standard chamberings from ·22–250 Remington up through the various Weatherby Magnums to the awesome ·378 and ·460.

The now discontinued **Weatherby Mark V Varmintmaster** embodied a short action with only six lugs (three rows of two), developed by Sauer and introduced in 1964 to suit cartridges shorter than the standard Weatherby Magnums. The **Vanguard**, incorporating a Mauser-type Howa action, is offered to those who want to use a 'Weatherby' without the expense of a Mark V rifle. The Vanguards chamber a

By courtesy of Weatherby, Inc.

Three Weatherby rifles: the standard Mark V (A), with a variable-power telescope sight; the Mark V Crown Custom (B), with a highly decorative stock; and the Mark V Lazermark (C), with laser-cut foliate bordering on the pistol grip and fore-end.

Below
The Weatherby Vanguard VGX (A) utilizes a conventional bolt action made in Japan by Howa, while the Mark XXII Clip (B) has a blowback semi-automatic action made by Beretta.
By courtesy of Weatherby, Inc.

Bottom
The HW52J is a single-shot target/sporting rifle incorporating a falling block actuated by the trigger guard lever. The quality of the woodwork and attention to detail on Weihruauch rifles is generally exemplary.
By courtesy of Hermann Weihrauch

selection of cartridges from ·22–250 and ·223 Remington up to 7mm Remington Magnum, ·30–06 and ·308 Winchester. They cannot be obtained for the Weatherby Magnums. Variants include the **VGX**, which is stocked similarly to the Mark V deluxe; the **VGS**, similar to the Euromark but lacking the separate fore-end tip; the **VGL**, a walnut-stocked lightweight VGS with a 20in barrel; and the **Fiberguard**, a VGL with a textured fibreglass stock.

There are also two selectable single-shot/auto-loading rimfire rifles, using actions made in Italy by Beretta: the **Mark XXII Tubular** and **Mark XXII Clip**, which feed from under-barrel tube and detachable box magazines respectively. The guns are stocked similarly to the Mark V deluxe. Compared with other guns in this class, the Weatherby rimfire auto-loaders are hefty, beautifully made and very expensive.

Weihrauch WEST GERMANY

Hermann Weihrauch KG (D-8744 Mellrichstadt/Bayern, Postfach 20) has a lengthy pedigree, being founded in Zella St Blasii in 1899. Re-established in western Germany after the end of the Second World War, Weihrauch is best known for its

high-quality sporting airguns. However, small numbers of sporting/target rifles are also made. The **HW52J** (·22LR rimfire, ·22 Hornet, ·222 Remington or 5·6× 50R) is a single-shot rifle in which the breech-block is dropped by pressing down on the trigger-guard spur. The HW52J has an elegant walnut butt with a Monte Carlo comb, a cheek piece, skip-line chequering on the pistol grip, and a ventilated rubber butt plate; the half-length fore-end has a chequer panel and a contrasting rosewood tip. Thin white spacers separate the tip from the fore-end, the nylon pistol-grip cap from the butt, and the butt plate from the stock-wood. The action usually displays scroll engraving, the two-stage trigger is adjustable, and a push-button safety will be found on the right side of the receiver.

The HW60 series comprises a number of rifles built on a good-quality bolt action with an auxiliary locking lug supplementing the bolt-handle base. Chambered for ·22LR rimfire, ·22WMR or ·22 Hornet, the **HW60J** is the standard sporting version: it has an excellent quality half-stock with a hog's back comb and an ovoid cheek piece, chequering on the pistol grip and fore-end, a ventilated rubber butt plate, a schnabel tip and swivels on the underside of the butt and fore-end.

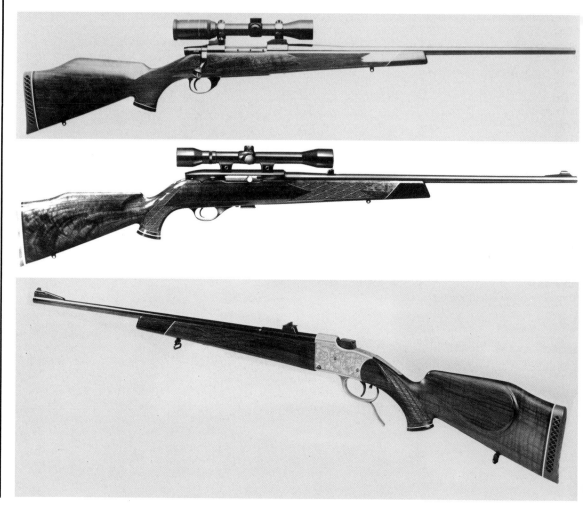

A

B

C

Open sights are supplied, though the HW60J will also accept optical sight mounts. The guns are about 108cm overall, have 58cm barrels and weigh 3kg.

The **HW60 Match** (·22LR only) is intended for 25-metre UIT competition shooting. Built on the standard 60-series action, it has a heavyweight 66cm barrel and aperture sights. The stock features a deep fore-end, extensively stippled, and a near-vertical pistol grip improves control. The cheek piece is a conventional slab-sided pattern and the adjustable butt plate slides vertically in its channel. Like virtually all Weihrauch guns, the HW60 Match (115cm overall, 4·85kg) has an excellent adjustable trigger and offers good performance at a reasonable price. **HW66** rifles, intended for DJV moving target competitions, have a short barrel, a half-stock with extensive stippling on the underside of the shallow fore-end, and a fixed rubber butt plate. The **HW660 Match** is a variant of the HW60 Match, differing primarily in the design of the stock. Its features include an adjustable-height comb and two slots cut laterally through the fore-end.

Wichita USA

The rifles built by Wichita Arms of 444 Ellis, Wichita,

Kansas 67211, embody a bolt system with triple lugs and a 60° bolt-throw. Available separately, the action is neat, sturdy and effectual. Complete rifles may be obtained from Wichita in three styles – Classic, Varmint and Silhouette – differing principally in stock design and barrel weight. The Classic and Varmint rifles have neatly chequered straight-comb walnut stocks, together with Canjar triggers. Some guns are single shot, but others carry internal 'blind' two-round magazines within the stock. The Varmint rifle has a heavy barrel, which gives it a weight of about 8lb; the Classic is about a pound lighter. The Silhouette rifle, with a grey Fiberthane stock, has a high Monte Carlo comb and a deepened near-vertical pistol grip. With a heavyweight 24in barrel, it weighs about 9lb. Fluting on the bolt is used to conserve weight within NRA rules and the trigger is a Canjar pattern with a 2oz release. Wichita rifles will accept the MRQS – 'Multi-Range Quick-change Sighting system' – of a pre-set four-position back sight and an adjustable front sight. They can chamber virtually any standard cartridge measuring less than 2·8in overall, and may also be obtained in left-hand versions. Prices (in 1987) began in the region of $2,000.

Above

The ·22 rimfire auto-loading Weihrauch HW60J (A) and the HW660 Match target rifle (B), the latter showing its distinctive adjustable comb and butt profile to advantage.

By courtesy of Hermann Weihrauch

Below

An ornate Würthrich falling-block rifle, featuring an unusually compact action opened by pivoting the trigger guard downward around a pivot at the rear.

By courtesy of Würthrich Jagd- und Sportwaffen.

Above

Würthrich SWITZERLAND

Only a single pattern of falling-block rifle is made by
W. Würthrich Jagd- und Sportwaffen of CH-3432
Lützelflüh, a small company that has specialized in
die-forming and vacuum-moulding since 1965. The
Würthrich rifle was introduced in 1977, but only a
little over a hundred guns has been made: each is
made to special order, in virtually any calibre the user
specifies. The compact action is a modernized
'Heeren', patented in France and elsewhere in the
1880s, which was very popular in Switzerland prior
to 1939. The most distinctive feature of the system is
the use of the trigger-guard to drop the breech;
however, the guard is hinged at the rear rather than
the front – as in most other dropping-block designs –
and is locked by a catch partially inlet in the front
trigger-guard web. The Würthrich rifle also has an
unusual trigger mechanism, the subject of Swiss
Patent 458,126 but based on traditional practice. The
guard contains what appears to be two triggers,
though the back lever is actually the hammer spur. To
cock the rifle it is necessary to pull the hammer spur
back until the front (trigger) lever is engaged; when
the trigger is pressed, the hammer is released to hit a
'striking piece' and, ultimately, the firing pin. This
provides a means of isolating the ignition system
from the trigger, but also avoids cutting the upper
surface of the breech-block to receive a hammer. A
separate safety catch lies on the right side of the
receiver-top, where it may be applied to prevent the
striking piece reaching the firing pin. Heeren-system
rifles were notorious for their weak extraction,
largely due to the lack of mechanical advantage and
the short trigger guard; the Würthrich embodies a
special extractor (Swiss Patent 458,125) claimed to
overcome this weakness.

Most rifles will be encountered with round barels
(octagon or half-octagon will be made to order) and
engraved receivers, the standard patterns being
deer/stag, chamois/stag or chamois/ibex. Half- or
Mannlicher-style stocks generally have distinctively
squared cheek pieces with fluted under-edges, but
stock carving is also common. Compact design allows
much tighter pistol-grip radii than possible, for
example, with the Ruger No.1. A typical Würthrich
rifle measures about 101cm overall, has a 65cm barrel
and weighs 2·8 – 3·3kg.

Zastava YUGOSLAVIA

The Yugoslav government firearms factory – Zavodi
Crvena Zastava, 'ZCZ' – in Kraguyevač makes a series
of rifles based on the Kalashnikov. Offered for sale
commercially, these include the M70B1 and M70AB2
in 7·62× 39 M43, with fixed and folding butts
respectively, Russian-style spatulate compensators and
standard Yugoslav selector markings ('U' for safe, 'R'
for automatic and 'J' for single shots). The M76 is a
special sniper rifle chambering the ubiquitous 7·9× 57
Mauser, while the M77B1 is a fixed-butt gun chambered
for 7·62× 51 NATO; the M78B1 and M78AB2 chamber
the 5·56× 45mm round. Most Yugoslavian
Kalashnikov derivatives feature ribbed wooden pistol
grips and grenade launchers; the standards of
manufacture are noticeably better than on
Kalashnikov-type rifles produced in some of the other
Eastern bloc countries.

Prior to adopting Russian auto-loaders, the Yugoslav
army used Mauser-action guns similar to the Kar.98k.

As much of the production line still existed in the 1960s, ZCZ began to make M98-type Mauser actions for commercial sale. Distributed in the USA by Interarms, from 1968–9 onward, the ZCZ Mausers have offered unpredictable quality; many of those made prior to 1980 were roughly finished compared with American products in similar price groups, but there has never been any doubt about their strength. Finish has improved appreciably in recent years, and the ZCZ-action rifles now offer good performance at a competitive price.

Interarms currently offers the basic gun as the **Mark X** in the 'American Field Series'. Available in ·22– 250 Remington, ·243 Winchester, ·25–06, ·270 Winchester, 7×57, 7mm Remington Magnum, ·30–06, ·300 Winchester Magnum and ·308 Winchester, the guns have classic straight-comb stocks with

chequering on the pistol grip and fore-end, contrasting fore-end tips, and swivels on the underside of the butt and barrel. A Williams open back sight is standard, though the receivers are drilled and tapped for sight-mount bases. The **Mark X LTW**, or Lightweight (·270 Winchester, 7mm Remington Magnum and ·30–06 only), features a 20in barrel and a CarboLite stock.

The **Mini Mark X** has a short action accepting ·223 Remington only, a 20in barrel, a trim Monte Carlo-type stock and weighs 6·4lb; the **Viscount**, with a 24in barrel, has a Monte Carlo comb and a cheek piece on its walnut stock. It lacks open sights and the front sling swivel lies under the fore-end (cf., Mark X). Viscounts can be obtained in all the standard Mark X chamberings.

The **Whitworth** is the 'Safari Grade' gun in the ZCZ Mauser series, chambering ·375 H&H Magnum and

Left

The standard ZCZ-made Mauser, taken from a recent Interarms catalogue. The American company has been stocking and distributing Yugoslav-made actions for many years, under a selection of proprietary names.

By courtesy of Interarms.

MARK X

WHITWORTH
EXPRESS RIFLES
A F R I C A N   S E R I E S

MARK X Whitworth rifles reflect the dedication to the gunmakers' art expected of the great English arms houses. The African Series is produced in four potent Safari calibers: 7mm Rem. Magnum, .300 Win. Magnum, .375 H & H Magnum and .458 Win. Magnum. Their precise Mauser System actions have been fitted with premium steel barrels - all profiled, bored, chambered and rifled for high density, heavy bullets. A traditional hand-checkered, oil finished, English style European walnut stock is fitted with a solid steel recoil bearing cross block and bedded in steel reinforced epoxy resin. Three leaf Express Sights, rubber recoil pad and quick detachable sling swivels are but a few of its many custom appointments.
CALIBERS: 7mm Rem. Mag., 300 Win. Mag., .375 H & H Mag., .458 Win. Mag.

·458 Winchester Magnum; its large diameter 24in
barrel and folding-leaf Express Sight are most
distinctive, though it is stocked in the same fashion as
the Mark X (q.v.). However, at only 7·6lb, the
Whitworth is too light for its purpose and asks the
firer to absorb far too much recoil.

Zoli ITALY

Antonio Zoli SpA of I-25063 Gardone Val Trompia, 39
via Zanardelli, makes a wide range of shotguns,
combination guns (Combinati), double- and bolt-
action rifles.

The Zoli Combinati are almost all over/under
patterns with box locks. Special features include a
patented safety system, which locks the hammers as
well as the trigger levers, and a set-trigger for the
lower or rifled barrel. The standard gun is designated
Combinato SP, the 'SP2' being a similar gun with
exchangeable shotgun barrels; the **Safari** is the
deluxe pattern, the 'Safari 2' being accompanied by
shotgun barrels, while the **Safari de Luxe** has
specially selected woodwork and side plates to allow
extra engraving. A single-trigger system is available
on all models, but generally in conjunction with 60cm
rather than 65cm barrels. Shotgun barrels are
invariably 12-bore, though 16- and 20-bore are
available to order; the rifles may chamber a wide
range of cartridges from ·22 Hornet to 9·3× 74R.

The double rifles, known as the **Express** series, are
similar to the Combinati and, like their near-
relations, have back sights on a quarter rib. The
Express E is an auto-ejecting variant of the basic
design in which a single-trigger system may be
substituted to order. The Express 2 is accompanied by
a shotgun barrel-group of similar length to the rifle

pattern, while the Express 3 is supplied with a
standard length combination barrel-group and a
longer shotgun pattern. The Express de Luxe features
specially selected woodwork and side plates
displaying additional engraving. Smooth-bore
Express barrels almost always accept 20-bore
cartridges with 70 or 76mm cases, while the rifles
chamber 7× 65R, ·30−06 or 9·3× 74R.

The Zoli **Savana** is a side-by-side box-lock double
rifle, generally made with an automatic ejector
('Savana E'), and can only be obtained in 7× 65R or
9·3× 74R. The Savana de Luxe is identical, apart from
specially selected woodwork and additional engraving.
Unlike the de luxe Combinati and Express guns, the
Savana de Luxe retains the standard box lock.

In addition to shotgun-style rifles and combination
guns, Zoli makes the bolt-action **AZ1900**. Inexpensive
yet effectual enough for most purposes, this is an
elegant Mauser-type sporter with twin opposed lugs
on the bolt head and a fully recessed bolt-face. The
cocking-piece shroud is neatly contoured, and a
rocking safety catch will be found on the right side of
the stock immediately behind the bolt handle. A
conventional detachable magazine floor plate is
released by a catch in the front of the trigger guard.
Woodwork is generally European walnut, with
chequering on the pistol grip and the fore-end, while
quick-detachable swivels lie under the fore-end and
the butt.

At the time of writing, the AZ1900 is only available
in a single barrel length, though specially engraved
deluxe versions are made to special order. The
standard chamberings are ·243 Winchester, 6·5× 55
Mauser, 6·5× 57, ·270 Winchester, 7× 64, ·30− 06 and
·308 Winchester.

COMBINATI

Rifle-shotgun combinations for big game hunting.

Ammunition

There seems every likelihood that a caseless cartridge will ultimately be adopted for military purposes, ammunition of this type having distinct advantages over conventional patterns if the teething troubles can be overcome. Caseless cartridges need neither an extractor nor an ejector (two of the parts most easily damaged in conventional weapons), and the gun-body can be completely sealed against the ingress of dirt or mud. On the debit side, the caseless cartridges still generate rather more chamber fouling than the promoters would wish and are still apparently suffering from excessive chamber heating during burst-firing. Currently, Heckler & Koch's G11, under development since the mid 1970s, looks most likely to succeed.

The simplest rifle cartridges are *rimmed*, with straight or straight-tapered cases; these extract efficiently, as the rim gives the extractor more to bite against than in rimless rivals. The rim also enables head-space* to be regulated properly. However, rimmed cartridges rarely feed as well from box magazines unless interruptors are included (e.g., in the Russian Mosin-Nagant rifle) or the magazine is very carefully shaped internally. Straight-case rimmed cartridges range in size from minuscule ·22 Short up to the mighty ·45–120 Sharps. Rimmed necked cartridges share similar characteristics, but are more difficult to make than straight patterns – even though they can contain more propellant in a given length. Excepting military rounds such as 7·62 × 54R Russian and ·303 British, necked rimmed cartridges are now common only in European double rifles and Drillinge.

Rimless cartridges – both straight and necked – are most common, being made in a bewildering profusion of calibres and styles. They feed effectually from box magazines, particularly when the case-body is approximately parallel.† Their major disadvantage is that the extractor is more likely to pull out of the shallow extraction groove than over a sturdy rim. In addition, rimless cartridges have to locate in the chamber on the shoulder or case-mouth, either of which may create head-space problems unless manufacturing tolerances are very fine.

Belted cartridges are basically rimless, but have a sturdy reinforcing ring around the base immediately ahead of the extractor groove. Though they share the extraction shortcomings of rimless cases and the belt may cause occasional difficulties in box magazines, head-space problems are resolved: the cartridges simply locate on the leading edge of the belt. In addition, as belted cases are stronger than rimless patterns of comparable size, they are almost always very powerful.

The rifles made since the end of the Second World War have chambered an incredible variety of cartridges from the tiny ·17 Ackley Bee up to the ·458 Winchester Magnum and the ·600 Nitro Express. Many cartridges (including many in the ·17 series) were unsuccessful commercially, though legions of wildcats‡ have satisfied their inventors' whims . . . if no-one else.

Cartridges usually begin life as private or corporate experiments, but the latter group has a much better chance of success. In the lists that follow, complete data cannot be given: there are too many permutations of bullet weight and propellant charge – and so many manufacturers involved – to list them individually.

The utility of individual cartridges is difficult to assess in general terms, as variations in propellant charge and bullet pattern can modify performance characteristics substantially; a small-calibre cartridge loaded with a comparatively heavy bullet, therefore, may be as useful on medium game as a large-bore cartridge deliberately under-loaded to reduce its power.

Despite the collosal efforts expended in the development of factory-loaded and wildcat ammunition since the end of the Second World War, many of the most useful cartridges appeared decades ago: one has only to look to the continued success of the ·22 Hornet, ·220 Swift, ·30–30 Winchester, ·30–06 and ·375 H&H Magnum. Indeed, many of these old-timers have provided the basis for many of today's 'innovations'.

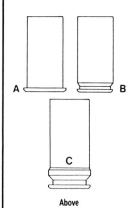

Above

Three of the major types of cartridge case – rimmed (A), rimless (B) and belted (C). In addition to the straight patterns drawn here, all three may be necked.

* Head-space is the distance between the bolt face and whatever part of the breech or chamber stops the cartridge moving too far forward – a step in the chamber or the edge of the breech. It is a critical dimension. If head-space is too small, the action will not shut; if it is too great, case-head separations and extraction failures will result.

† Conversely, parallel-side cases may cause extraction problems in automatic rifles, particularly delayed blowbacks. Slightly tapered cases often perform better in auto-loaders.

‡ A term originally coined in North America. A 'wildcat' cartridge is generally produced by an enthusiast or custom gunsmith, though the best may be marketed commercially by large manufacturers such as Remington or Dynamit Nobel. Wildcats often originate by modifying existing production cartridges (e.g., ·35 Whelen was made by expanding the neck of ·30–06 to take larger projectiles).

Left

Manufacturing cartridges is an exacting process, now highly automated and extremely reliable.

By courtesy of Dynamit Nobel AG.

Below

Six types of bullet: full jacket (A), TUG-Brenneke (B), H-Mantel (C), TIG Brenneke (D), soft point (E) and cone point (F).

By courtesy of Dynamit Nobel AG.

If the advances in cartridge design have been comparatively minor in the twentieth century, great strides have been made in propellant technology and bullet design. Few of today's major ammunition manufacturers are as satisfied with one type of bullet per load as they were fifty years ago. To keep one step ahead of competitors, it is necessary to come up with continual 'advances'; many may be little more than gimmickry within a few years, but some improvements, genuinely advantageous, have long-lasting effects on production.

Dynamit Nobel, to highlight one particular manufacturer as an example, currently offers several projectiles in its RWS-brand sporting cartridges. The SG or *Scheiben Geschoss* (target bullet) has a thin tombak-plated jacket over a lead/antimony core and a hollow nose to encourage disintegration. The ST or *Standard Teilmantel* (soft point) is similar to the SG, but has a soft lead point to minimize fragmentation and improve expansion on thin-skinned game. *T-Mantel* (Teilmantel) soft-points are similar, but have round noses and greater core-exposure than the ST pattern. Full-jacketed *V-Mantel* (Vollmantel) are designed to penetrate, offering cleaner wounds, less tissue damage and smaller exit holes than the soft points. These projectiles are designed primarily for shooting for food in smaller sizes, or for big-game hunting in larger ones. Large-calibre V-Mantel bullets have a reinforced jacket at the tip.

KS-Geschosse, with cone-points (Kegelspitze), are generally jacketed with only a tip of the core protruding at the nose. The intention is to combine low air resistance with controlled expansion to prevent excessive tissue damage. The *H-Mantel* is potentially very destructive. Its annular mid-body construction is designed to retain the after-core during the early part of a strike on the target. The hollow nose crumples on impact; the short fore-core then also disintegrates, releasing much of its energy to shock or stun, and then the medial constriction releases the undamaged cylindrical after-core to penetrate.

Dynamit Nobel also offers two versions of the patented Brenneke bullets, known as the *TIG-Brenneke* (Torpedo-Ideal-Geschoss) and *TUG-Brenneke* (Torpedo-Universal-Geschoss). Both projectiles have an annular 'wadcutting ring' designed primarily to signify entrance wounds, and their twin interlocking cores are intended to promote rapid expansion. The front portion of the TIG-pattern core protrudes back into the after-core, while TUG is reversed. Consequently, though both are designed to expand, TIG does so appreciably quicker.

Dynamit Nobel currently loads its ·308 Winchester cartridge (7·62× 51 NATO) with no less than nine differing bullets: 147-grain SG; 150-grain KS; 150-grain TS (Teilmantel-Spitz, 'partly-jacketed pointed'); 150-grain TIG-Brenneke; 165-grain KS; 168-grain match (SG); 180-grain H-Mantel; 180-grain TUG-Brenneke; and 190-grain match (SG).

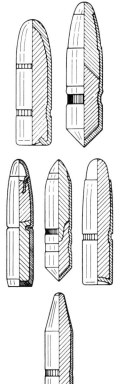

A
B

C
D
E

F

135

Typical of other manufacturers' efforts is the Remington ·22 Accelerator, dating from 1978-81, which embodies a discarding sabot to increase velocity of otherwise conventional ·308 Winchester, ·30−30 and ·30−06 cartridge cases. Sectional density and velocity are greatly improved by using a sub-calibre projectile. However, owing to the somewhat unpredictable discard of the 'carrier' at the muzzle, accuracy is rarely as good as standard ammunition. In very general terms, Accelerator cartridges will rarely better 2MOA. Loaded with standard 55-grain bullets, they will generate velocities ranging from 3,400fs (·30−30) to 4,080fs (·30−06). The great advantage is the ease with which the role of a rifle can be changed merely by substituting Accelerator cartridges for the full-bore types; at short range, of course, 2MOA may be an acceptable price to pay for enhanced velocity that reduces flight-time.

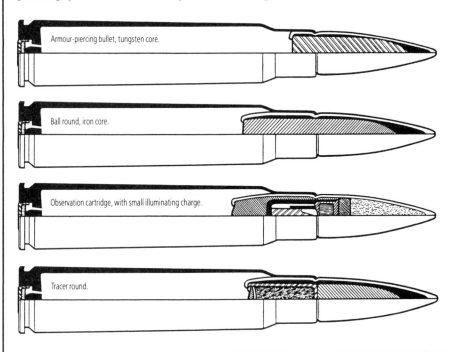

Right

Four typical German 7·9mm (7·9×57) military cartridges, showing the complexity of some of the bullet designs.

Armour-piercing bullet, tungsten core.

Ball round, iron core.

Observation cartridge, with small illuminating charge.

Tracer round.

Above

Typical low-power ammunition comprises nothing but a larger-than-normal charge of priming compound. These cartridges – their calibres ranging from 4mm to 9mm – are still dangerous at point-blank range.

By courtesy of Dynamit Nobel AG.

CARTRIDGE REGISTER

There are several excellent sources of information about the hundreds of cartridges used for sporting purposes. Frank C. Barnes's *Cartridges of the World* (DBI, fifth edition, 1985) is particularly useful as an identification guide, while the manuals provided by ammunition manufacturers (especially Speer) supply indispensable hand-loading details.

With the exception of bullet diameter, which is held to the finest tolerances, all cartridge dimensions are given to the nearest five thousandths of an inch, being adapted from *Cartridges of the World* and Ian Hogg's *The Cartridge Guide* (Arms & Armour Press, 1982). Some dimensional fluctuations are to be expected, particularly if measurements have been taken from fired cases. Performance details can be nothing more than a guide: differing barrel lengths or bullet weights can modify them greatly. Muzzle energies have been calculated on the assumption that gravitational acceleration is $32·16\mathrm{fs}^{-2}$.

Cartridges marked with a star (★) are named in accordance with the recommendations of the Commission Internationale Permanente pour l'Épreuve des Armes à Feu Portatives (CIP) and accepted for classification purposes by the International Standards Organisation. Those marked with a dagger (†) were originally loaded with black powder and are often, therefore, much weaker than similar cartridges designed for smokeless propellant.

INDIVIDUAL ROUNDS

·17 Remington

Case type: necked, rimless. Ignition: centre-fire. Case length: 1795. Diameters: rim 380, shoulder 355, neck 200, bullet 172. Typical performance: 4,020fs with a 25-grain bullet (897 ft-lb). Developed by Remington in the late 1960s, this cartridge was introduced in 1971 to accompany the 700-series bolt-action rifles and has since been adapted to others (e.g., Harrington & Richardson Model 317). Owing to the light bullet, ·17 Remington is suited only to long-range varmint shooting and should not be used on even moderate-size game.

4mm Übungsmunition M20

Case type: straight, rimmed. Ignition: primer propelled. Case length: 275. Diameters: rim 225, neck 190, bullet 174. This tiny practice cartridge, generally used in sub-calibre inserts, was designed by Karl Weiss of Rheinisch–Westfälische Sprengstoff AG ('RWS') in 1921 and has since achieved widespread distribution. Though it generates very little power, the minuscule bullet can inflict a nasty flesh wound at close range and should be treated with appropriate care.

·22 BB Cap RF★

Case type: straight, rimmed. Ignition: primer propelled. Case length: 270. Diameters: rim 280, shoulder, neck and bullet 225. The propellant in this tiny cartridge can consist either entirely of priming compound or priming compound with a small black powder charge. Widely (but somewhat mistakenly) believed to be useless, the BB Cap often provides ultra low-power practice in circumstances where even the ·22 Short cannot be used.

·22 Short RF★

Case type: straight, rimmed. Ignition: rimfire. Case length: 420. Diameters: rim 280, shoulder, neck and bullet 225. Typical performance: 1,050fs with a 29-grain bullet (71 ft-lb). Introduced by Smith & Wesson in 1857, this survives principally for rapid-fire competition use, where its ultra-low power enables the firer to return his sights to the target in the shortest possible time.

·22 Long Rifle RF★

Synonyms: ·22LR, 5·6mm lang für Büchsen, 5·6mm lfb. Case type: straight, rimmed. Ignition: rimfire. Case length: 615. Diameters: rim 280, shoulder, neck and bullet 225. Typical performance: 1,150fs with a 40-grain bullet (117 ft-lb). Apparently developed for or by the Stevens Tool & Arms Company in 1887, this has become very popular in recent years – practically every manufacturer now offers at least one loading, from cheap low-grade plinkers up to the finest competition ammunition.

·22 Winchester Magnum RF★

Synonym: ·22WMR. Case type: straight, rimmed. Ignition: rimfire. Case length: 1055. Diameters: rim 295, neck 240, bullet 224. Typical performance: 2,000fs with a 40-grain bullet (355 ft-lb). This cartridge replaced the old ·22 Winchester Rim Fire (·22 WRF) in 1959 and is among the most powerful of all rimfire cartridges; it is also a popular-if-expensive substitute for the Long Rifle variety.

·22 Hornet★

Case type: necked, rimmed. Ignition: centre-fire. Case length: 1405. Diameters: rim 350, shoulder 300, neck 245, bullet 224. Typical performance: 2,680fs with a 45-grain bullet (718 ft-lb). Developed at Springfield Armory in the late 1920s from the obsolescent ·22 WCF, the ·22 Hornet – the first small high-velocity cartridge to be sold commercially in the USA – was loaded by Winchester from 1932. Used exclusively in bolt-action and dropping-block rifles, the Hornet achieved phenomenal popularity. Though now partly superseded by ·222 and ·223 Remington (q.v.), it may still be fired in rifles such as the Savage 340, Anschütz 1432 and Kimber M82.

·22 PPC

Case type: necked, rimless. Ignition: centre-fire. Case length: 1510. Diameters: bullet 225. Typical performance: 3,475fs with a 52-grain bullet (1,395 ft-lb). Developed in 1974 by Louis Palmisano and Ferris Pindel from the ·220 Russian, a wildcat based on the 7·62× 39 case, rifles chambering this cartridge are currently being made commercially by Sako on the L461 Vixen action. Conceived for bench-rest shooting, the ·22 PPC may ultimately find a far wider application in varmint rifles.

·22– 250 Remington

Case type: necked, rimless. Ignition: centre-fire. Case length: 1910. Diameters: rim 475, shoulder 415, neck 255, bullet 220. Typical performance: 3,730fs with a 55-grain bullet (1,700 ft-lb). Though introduced by Remington in 1965, this popular cartridge – currently chambering in most major bolt-action rifles – has a parentage dating back before the Second World War, when a prototype was produced by necking ·250 Savage cases down to ·22. The ·22– 250, which has a noticeably stubbier case than the ·223 Remington, offers many of the advantages of ·220 Swift without the drawback of short barrel life. It is generally regarded as the best all-round cartridge in the ·220– ·225 group, as it is accurate enough for target-shooting and sufficiently powerful to take game up to the size of small deer.

·220 Swift

Case type: necked, rimless. Ignition: centre-fire. Case length: 2205. Diameters: rim 475, shoulder 400, neck 260, bullet 220. Typical performance: 4,110fs with a 45-grain bullet (1,688 ft-lb). Developed by Winchester and introduced in 1935 with a variant of the Model 54 bolt-action rifle, this cartridge still develops the highest velocity of any factory load and has always had a reputation for exemplary accuracy. Its popularity has been eroded in recent years with the advent of ·222 and ·223 Remington; scarcity of ammunition and comparatively short barrel-life militate against it, even though the Swift has no real peer against small game at long range.

5·6× 50 Magnum

Case type: necked, rimless. Ignition: centre-fire. Case length: 1970. Diameters: rim 380, neck 255, bullet 244. Typical performance: 3,590fs with a 50-grain

Above
The three most popular rimfire cartridges are ·22 Short (A), ·22 Long Rifle (B) and ·22 Winchester Magnum Rimfire (C).
By courtesy of Dynamit Nobel AG.

Above
Dating from the early 1930s, ·22 Hornet is one of the smallest centre-fire rifle rounds, but still retains much of its popularity.
By courtesy of Dynamit Nobel AG.

Above
Three small-calibre centre-fire sporting rifle cartridges: ·222 Remington (A), 5·6×50 Magnum (B) and 5·6×52R (C).
By courtesy of Dynamit Nobel AG.

bullet (1,431 ft-lb). Produced by DWM in co-operation with Heym in 1968–9, this is basically a long-case version of the ·222 Remington developing slightly more power. A rimmed version – 5·6× 50R Magnum – is made for single-loaders, double rifles and Drillinge. It is slightly less powerful than its rimless near-relation.

5·6× 52R

Case type: necked, rimmed. Ignition: centre-fire. Case length: 2045. Diameters: rim 490, neck 250, bullet 226. Typical performance: 2,850fs with a 71-grain bullet (1,281 ft-lb). Introduced as the ·22 Savage High-Power shortly before 1913, designed by Charles Newton and chambered in the Savage M99 lever-action rifle, this varmint and small-game cartridge enjoyed widespread popularity in the USA prior to the Second World War. No longer made in North America, it is still produced in Europe for double rifles and Drillinge.

5·6× 57 RWS

Case type: necked, rimless. Ignition: centre-fire. Case length: 2230. Diameters: rim 470, neck 255, bullet 224. Typical performance: 3,410fs with a 74-grain bullet (1,911 ft-lb). This cartridge was developed in the 1960s, after a law had been passed in Germany specifying the minimum residual 200m energy permissible for deer hunting. Few existing 5·6mm cartridges were acceptable, so RWS simply necked down the 7× 57 Mauser. The 5·6× 57, also made in rimmed guise (5·6× 57R), has a very distinctive thick-walled neck. It is at its best against small game but, despite the law, a marginal performer against deer.

5·6× 61 vom Hofe Super Express

Case type: necked, rimless. Ignition: centre-fire. Case length: 2400. Diameters: rim 480, neck 265, bullet 227. Typical performance: 3,705fs with a 77-grain bullet (2,348 ft-lb). Introduced commercially in 1937 with vom Hofe Mauser-action sporters, this is a European equivalent of ·220 Swift (q.v.). An ideal long-range varmint round, though often touted as suitable for deer or boar, it is also made in a rimmed version (5·6× 61R) for double rifles and Drillinge.

·222 Remington

Case type: necked, rimless. Ignition: centre-fire. Case length: 1700. Diameters: rim 380, shoulder 355, neck 255, bullet 223. Typical performance: 3,215fs with a 50-grain bullet (1,148 ft-lb). Developed for the Remington Model 722 bolt-action rifle, this cartridge made its début in 1950. It has a reputation for excellent accuracy and has taken many bench-rest prizes. Unlike some of the others in this calibre-group, the ·222 Remington is suitable for both target-shooting and against small game.

·222 Remington Magnum

Case type: necked, rimless. Ignition: centre-fire. Case length: 1850. Diameters: rim 380, shoulder 355, neck 255, bullet 223. Typical performance: 3,305fs with a 55-grain bullet (1,334 ft-lb). Introduced commercially in 1958 to accompany the Model 722 rifle, this had been developed by Remington and Springfield Armory as a combat round. Currently, owing to ground lost to ·223 (see below), it is available only in the Remington 700 series and some European double rifles. The ·222 Remington Magnum is very similar to ·223 Remington, with which it is all too easily confused – ·223 cartridges, which are marginally too short, will chamber in ·222 Remington Magnum rifles. Unfortunately, case ruptures will occur should these be fired.

·223 Remington

Synonym: 5·56× 45. Case type: necked, rimless. Ignition: centre-fire. Case length: 1760. Diameters: rim 380, shoulder 355, neck 255, bullet 223. Typical performance: 3,185fs with a 55-grain bullet (1,239 ft-lb). Originally an experimental design chambered in the AR-15, this was developed in 1956–7 and now serves worldwide. There are two principal loadings, one with the US Army-type M193 Ball and the other with the Belgian developed SS109; the former is less stable and potentially more destructive, while the latter offers better long-range performance.

·224 Weatherby Magnum

Case type: necked, rimless. Ignition: centre-fire. Case length: 1920. Diameters: rim 430, shoulder 395, neck 250, bullet 224. Typical performance: 3,600fs with a 55-grain bullet (1,583 ft-lb). Developed in the mid 1950s, this distinctive belted cartridge appeared on the commercial market in 1963. The belt provides a excellent means of locating the cartridge in the chamber, reducing head-space problems, and is generally reckoned to prolong case life. However, Weatherby guns and ammunition are expensive, and the ·224 does nothing ·22– 250 Remington cannot do at half the cost.

·240 Weatherby Magnum

Case type: necked, rimless. Ignition: centre-fire. Case length: 2500. Diameters: rim 475, shoulder 430, neck 270, bullet 240. Typical performance: 3,500fs with a 90-grain bullet (2,449 ft-lb). Introduced commercially in 1968, this distinctive belted-case cartridge is the most powerful in its class. However, despite its advantages, the ·240 Weatherby is comparatively rare: only the Weatherby Mark V bolt-action rifle chambers it, apart from a handful of custom guns. As gun and ammunition are expensive, the admittedly less effectual ·243 Winchester and ·244/6mm Remington are preferred by the cost-conscious.

·243 Winchester

Case type: necked, rimless. Ignition: centre-fire. Case length: 2045. Diameters: rim 475, shoulder 455, neck 275, bullet 243. Typical performance: 3,500fs with an 80-grain bullet (2,177 ft-lb). Perhaps the most popular modern sporting rifle cartridge, excepting ·308 Winchester (q.v.), this appeared commercially in 1955 to accompany the Model 70 bolt- and Model 88 lever-action rifles. Most manufacturers now chamber

Above

Two versions of the 5·6×57 cartridge, confined largely to European markets. The rimless version (A) is generally chambered in bolt-action rifles, while the rimmed pattern (B) is popular in combination guns.

By courtesy of Dynamit Nobel AG.

a   b

Above

Introduced commercially in 1955, ·243 Winchester is among the world's most popular (and best distributed) sporting rifle cartridges.

By courtesy of Dynamit Nobel AG.

bolt-action rifles for this cartridge. The ·243 is simply a necked-down ·308, generally credited to Warren Page. It was developed to satisfy the needs of varmint shooters favouring ·220 Swift, while simultaneously extending capabilities up to deer. Though ·243 is ideal for this type of shooting at medium range, the 6mm Remington (q.v.) is generally reckoned to be better at long distances.

·244 Holland & Holland Magnum★

Synonym: ·244 Belted Rimless Magnum. Case type: necked, rimless. Ignition: centre-fire. Case length: 2790. Diameters: rim 530, neck 280, bullet 245. Typical performance: 3,350fs with a 100-grain bullet (2,493 ft-lb). Introduced in 1955, this was the last of Holland & Holland's proprietary cartridges. Basically a ·375 H&H Magnum necked to ·244, it is powerful – but not outstandingly so. Adequate for most types of medium game, it is at its best as a long-range varmint round.

6mm PPC

Case type: necked, rimless. Ignition: centre-fire. Case length: 1510. Diameters: bullet 243. Typical performance: 3,085fs with a 75-grain bullet (1,585 ft-lb). Developed by Louis Palmisano and Ferris Pindel from the ·22 PPC, and thus indirectly from the 7·62× 39 Russian round, this wildcat is now being made commercially by Sako. Conceived for bench-rest shooting, a discipline where its accuracy reigns supreme, it will probably find a far wider application in small game rifles.

6mm Remington

Case type: necked, rimless. Ignition: centre-fire. Case length: 2235. Diameters: rim 470, shoulder 430, neck 275, bullet 244. Typical performance: 3,130fs with a 100-grain bullet (2,176 ft-lb). Derived from the ·244 Remington of 1955, which shared the same case, this cartridge was renamed in 1963 when it was realised that the rifling of the guns for which the ·244 was designed – making a turn in 12in – could not stabilize bullets weighing more than 100 grains at long range. A change to a turn in 9in was made, but rounds marked '·244 Remington' will obviously also chamber in 6mm Remington rifles. 6mm Remington has a slight edge on ·243 Winchester when loaded with bullets weighing more than 100 grains, and its longer neck is appreciated by hand-loaders.

·25 ACP★

Synonym: 6·35 Auto Pistol. Case type: straight, rimless. Ignition: centre-fire. Case length: 610. Diameters – rim 300, shoulder and neck 275, bullet 251. Typical performance: 810fs with a 50-grain bullet (73 ft-lb). Developed in Europe, this was introduced commercially with the Baby Browning in 1906. Chambered only in some small semi-automatic rifles, otherwise exclusively a handgun cartridge, 6·35mm Auto develops a high velocity for so small a case. However, its jacketed bullet is notoriously ineffectual: it has been remarked quite frequently (with more

than a hint of truth) that the lead bulletted ·22LR rimfire is a better man-stopper.

·25–06 Remington

Case type: necked, rimless. Ignition: centre-fire. Case length: 2495. Diameters: rim 475, shoulder 440, neck 290, bullet 250. Typical performance: 3,120fs with a 120-grain bullet (2,594 ft-lb). Originally made in the 1920s by necking ·30–06 cases to ·25, this wildcat reappeared in 1969. Now chambered in many bolt-action rifles, the Ruger No.1 and some European double rifles, ·25–06 is a useful all-purpose cartridge. Loaded with the standard 87-grain bullet, developing 3,500fs, it is an ideal long-range varmint round; loaded with the 120-grain patterns, it is suitable for game up to deer size.

·25–20 Winchester★

Synonym: ·25–20 WCF. Case type: necked, rimmed. Ignition: centre-fire. Case length: 1330. Diameters: rim 410, shoulder 335, neck 275, bullet 251. Typical performance: 1,460fs with an 86-grain bullet (407 ft-lb). Introduced for the short-action Winchester Model 1892 rifle in the mid 1890s, this obsolescent cartridge was popular against small game until the advent of the ·218 Bee and ·22 Hornet. Its comparatively low power minimizes tissue damage, but restricts effective range to 100–125yd.

·250 Savage

Synonym: ·250–3000. Case type: necked, rimless. Ignition: centre-fire. Case length: 1910. Diameters: rim 475, shoulder 415, neck 285, bullet 250. Typical performance: 2,820fs with a 100-grain bullet (1,766 ft-lb). Designed by Charles Newton for the Savage Model 99 rifle in the 1920s, the ·250 Savage is outstandingly accurate and effectual on small- and medium-size game at distances up to 300yd. Though now eclipsed by ·243 Winchester and 6mm Remington, it still has its champions and may chamber in rifles such as the Ruger M-77.

6·5× 54

Synonyms: 6·5mm MS, 6·5× 54 Mannlicher-Schönauer, 6·5mm Greek. Case type: necked, rimless. Ignition: centre-fire. Case length: 2110. Diameters: rim 455, neck 295, bullet 264. Typical performance: 2,200fs with a 159-grain bullet (1,709 ft-lb). Developed in the early years of the twentieth century and adopted by the Greek army in 1903, this is a classical military rifle cartridge. By the standards of the day it was not especially powerful, but had a light recoil and a comparatively soft report. Modern sporting loads are entirely adequate for medium game at anything other than extreme range, as the 6·5× 54 is substantially more powerful than the vaunted ·30–30.

6·5× 55

Synonyms: 6·5mm Swedish Mauser, 6·5mm Norwegian Krag. Case type: necked, rimless. Ignition: centre-fire. Case length: 2165. Diameters: rim 480, neck 280, bullet 263. Typical performance:

Above

Although comparatively ineffectual, even for a pistol cartridge, ·25 ACP is occasionally chambered in small rifles.

By courtesy of Dynamit Nobel AG.

Below
Four mid-power sporting rifle cartridges: 6·5×57 (A), based on the 57mm Mauser case; 6·5×68 Schuler (B); the popular ·270 Winchester (C); and 7mm Remington Magnum (D).
By courtesy of Dynamit Nobel AG.

a   b

c   d

2,720fs with a 139-grain bullet (2,284 ft-lb). Developed for the Swedish army and adopted in 1894, this is among the best all-purpose cartridges when loaded with modern sporting bullets. 6·5× 55 can do anything ·30–30 can do, being more powerful, and has a reputation for accuracy combined with pleasant shooting characteristics. However, it remains almost exclusively European and is particularly favoured in Scandinavia owing to the proliferation of suitably chambered military surplus rifles.

6·5× 57

Case type: necked, rimless. Ignition: centre-fire. Case length: 2230. Diameters: rim 470, neck 300, bullet 264. Typical performance: 2,850fs with a 127-grain bullet (2,291 ft-lb). Developed in the early 1890s simply by necking the 7× 57, this cartridge soon proved popular in European bolt-action sporters. The result is a good all-purpose cartridge comparable with the 6·5× 55 (see above). A rimmed version (6·5× 57R) is also made for double rifles and Drillinge.

6·5× 68 Schuler

Synonym: 6·5× 68S. Case type: necked, rimless. Ignition: centre-fire. Case length: 2660. Diameters: rim 510, neck 480, bullet 265. Typical performance: 3,770fs with a 93-grain bullet (2,936 ft-lb). Introduced commercially by RWS shortly before the Second World War began, this is basically a necked-down 8× 68S. Only Mauser and Mannlicher rifles were to be encountered in this chambering prior to 1970, but there is now greater variety. Trajectory with the lightest bullets is extremely flat, which makes 6·5× 68 an excellent long-range varmint cartridge, while the heavier patterns are suitable for medium game. A rimmed version, 6·5× 68R, is made for double rifles and Drillinge.

·257 Roberts

Case type: necked, rimless. Ignition: centre-fire. Case length: 2235. Diameters: rim 475, shoulder 430, neck 290, bullet 258. Typical performance: 2,650fs with a 117-grain bullet (1,825 ft-lb). Designed by N.H. Roberts in the 1920s and introduced with the Remington Model 30 bolt-action rifle in 1934, this is one of the best 'all-purpose' cartridges, particularly when hand-loaded to give greater power than conservative factory loads. ·257 is suited to a wide range of sporting/hunting applications and can be used on deer, antelope or bear. It does not have the power of ·270 Winchester or ·30–06, but is much more easily controlled in a light rifle.

·257 Weatherby Magnum

Case type: necked, rimless. Ignition: centre-fire. Case length: 2545. Diameters: rim 530, shoulder 490, neck 280, bullet 257. Typical performance: 3,555fs with a 100-grain bullet (2,807 ft-lb). Another of the belted Weatherby magnums, this powerful 1944-vintage cartridge is a useful all-purpose design, robust enough, when loaded with 120-grain bullets, for deer, antelope or bear. Though much larger game has been taken, the ·257 Weatherby – like most cartridges with comparatively light bullets – is not suited to wooded terrain; the projectiles are deflected too easily.

·264 Winchester Magnum

Case type: necked, rimless. Ignition: centre-fire. Case length: 2500. Diameters: rim 530, shoulder 480, neck 295, bullet 264. Typical performance: 3,200fs with 140-grain bullet (3,184 ft-lb). Announced in 1958, doubtless inspired by the Weatherby Magnums, this high-velocity cartridge offers marginally better performance than ·270 Winchester (q.v.) and the advantages of a belted case. It is currently obtainable only with the Winchester Model 70 bolt-action rifle.

·270 Winchester

Case type: necked, rimless. Ignition: centre-fire. Case length: 2540. Diameters: rim 475, shoulder 440, neck 310, bullet 270. Typical performance: 3,140fs with a 130-grain bullet (2,847 ft-lb). One of the older examples in its class, introduced with the Winchester Model 54 bolt-action rifle in 1925, this is basically ·30–06 necked to ·270. It is far better than its parent on small game, possessing a flatter trajectory and less recoil, and is at least on a par on medium game; as a big-game load, however, in brush or wooded terrain, the heavier ·30–06 bullets have a distinct advantage. ·270 Winchester remains one of world's most popular and effectual cartridges.

·270 Weatherby Magnum

Case type: necked, rimless. Ignition: centre-fire. Case length: 2545. Diameters: rim 530, shoulder 490, neck 310, bullet 270. Typical performance: 3,375fs with a 130-grain bullet (3,289 ft-lb). Another of the powerful belted-case Weatherby magnums, the ·270 dates from 1943. Though best when loaded to full power, when it makes an excellent long-range game cartridge, it is also a passable small game cartridge when loaded with 100-grain bullets.

·275 Holland & Holland Magnum★

Synonym: ·275 Belted Rimless Magnum. Case type: necked, rimless. Ignition: centre-fire. Case length: 2500. Diameters: rim 530, neck 325, bullet 287. Typical performance: 2,680fs with a 175-grain bullet (2,792 ft-lb). Developed by F.W. Jones shortly before the First World War, inspired by the success of the ·280 Ross (on which the ·275 H&H was regarded as an improvement), this belted cartridge is an adequate all-purpose design. However, it is is comparatively rarely seen – particularly in North America – and the shorter ·280 Remington is a good substitute. A rimmed version of the basic design was known as the ·275 Flanged Magnum.

7mm Remington Magnum

Case type: necked, rimless. Ignition: centre-fire. Case length: 2500. Diameters: rim 530, shoulder 490, neck 315, bullet 284. Typical performance: 3,260fs with a 150-grain bullet (3,541 ft-lb). Introduced in 1962 to accompany the Remington Model 700 bolt-action rifle, this is an effectual long-range hunting cartridge that can also serve for varmint shooting with sympathetic hand-loading. The Remington cartridge has no real advantages over the similar Weatherby pattern, but the Remington Model 700 rifle is appreciably cheaper than its Weatherby equivalent.

7mm Weatherby Magnum
Case type: necked, rimless. Ignition: centre-fire. Case length: 2545. Diameters: rim 530, shoulder 490, neck 315, bullet 284. Typical performance: 3,300fs with a 139-grain bullet (3,362 ft-lb). Developed in 1944, this belted-case magnum is another of the powerful Weatherby series. Best when loaded to full power, for use on medium game, the 7mm Weatherby Magnum has a slight advantage over the otherwise similar ·270 pattern excepting as a long-range varmint cartridge. However, the 7mm Remington Magnum, described above, is a cheaper option than either.

7mm–08 Remington
Case type: necked, rimless. Ignition: centre-fire. Case length: 2035. Diameters: rim 475, shoulder 455, neck 315, bullet 284. Typical performance: 2,860fs with a 140-grain bullet (2,543 ft-lb). Introduced in 1980, this is simply a ·308 Winchester case necked to take a ·284 projectile. Apparently intended largely for metallic-silhouette target shooting, a role to which it is well suited, 7mm–08 makes an excellent all-purpose game cartridge when hand-loaded to its full potential. It is currently handicapped only by the solitary factory loading.

7–30 Waters
Case type: necked, rimmed. Ignition: centre-fire. Case length: 2040. Diameters: rim 505, shoulder 400, neck 305, bullet 284. Typical performance: 2,700fs with a 120-grain bullet (1,943 ft-lb). Developed for compact lever-action rifles, to overcome limitations imposed by tube magazines, this distinctive cartridge was introduced commercially for the Winchester 94XTR Angle Eject guns in 1984. It has also been chambered in Thompson/Center Contender and similar single-shot pistols intended for long-range metallic silhouette shooting. 7–30 is effectual enough, but lacks the power of the ·30–30 (q.v.) in short-barrelled guns and its exploitable range does not extend much beyond 200yd; however, its recoil is mild and it is proving to be very accurate.

7× 57
Synonyms: 7mm Mauser, 7mm Spanish. Case type: necked, rimless. Ignition: centre-fire. Case length: 1895. Diameters: rim 475, shoulder 430, neck 320, bullet 284. Typical performance: 2,620fs with a 162-grain bullet (2,470 ft-lb). Developed by Mauser and DWM about 1890, this military cartridge was adopted by the Spanish Army in 1892. Widely used for sporting purposes prior to 1939, 7× 57 subsequently lost most of its popularity. Influx of war-surplus 7mm rifles into North America in the 1950s reversed the

trend, and now Winchester, Ruger and others make rifles in this calibre. In many respects 7× 57 is an ideal 'all-purpose' round, though not at its best against big game. A rimmed version (7× 57R) is popular in European double rifles and Drillinge.

7× 64 Brenneke
Case type: necked, rimless. Ignition: centre-fire. Case length: 2520. Diameters: rim 495, neck 305, bullet 284. Typical performance: 2,890fs with a 162-grain bullet (3,005 ft-lb). Developed by Wilhelm Brenneke during the First World War and introduced by RWS in 1917, specifically for hunting, this was originally loaded with Brenneke Torpedo bullets. Presaging the ·280 Remington by forty years, the modern loadings make a fine all-purpose game cartridge. A rimmed version for double rifles and Drilling is known as 7× 65R Brenneke.

7mm vom Hofe Super Express
Case type: necked, rimless. Ignition: centre-fire. Case length: 2600. Diameters: rim 505, head 545, bullet 284. Typical performance: 3,300fs with a 169-grain bullet (4,088ft-lb). A descendant of the pre-war 7× 66 vom Hofe, this cartridge reappeared in the late 1950s with sporting rifles built on the Swedish Husqvarna-Mauser action. It is now chambered in some European sporting rifles, though generally only to special order. The 7mm vom Hofe SE, distinguished by a noticeably reduced-diameter rim compared with the case head, is a good general-purpose cartridge. However, the 7mm Remington Magnum – albeit less powerful – is far easier to obtain.

·280 Remington
Synonym: 7mm Remington Express. Case type: necked, rimless. Ignition: centre-fire. Case length: 2540. Diameters: rim 475, shoulder 440, neck 315, bullet 284. Typical performance: 2,890fs with a 150-grain bullet (2,783 ft-lb). Introduced for the Model 740 auto-loading rifle in 1957, this is really little more than another necked-down ·30–06. Comparable to ·270 Winchester though more versatile, it makes an adequate varmint cartridge. When loaded with the heaviest bullet options, however, it is at its best against thin-skinned game at long range.

7·5× 55
Synonyms: 7·5mm Schmidt-Rubin, 7·5mm Swiss M11. Case type: necked, rimless. Ignition: centre-fire. Case length: 2180. Diameters: rim 495, neck 335, bullet 305. Typical performance: 2,533fs with a 174-grain bullet (2,710 ft-lb). This cartridge was adopted by the Swiss Army in 1889 and extensively revised in 1911. Popular in central Europe, particularly where modified Schmidt-Rubin sporters are still seen in considerable numbers, 7·5× 55 cartridges can be loaded to duplicate the performance of ·308 Winchester or any military cartridge in the same calibre group.

7·62× 39
Synonym: 7·62mm Russian M43. Case type: necked,

a

b   c

Above

7mm is a popular, but by no means universal choice for 'all-purpose' cartridges. The long-established 7×57 (A), has enjoyed fluctuating fortunes since the 1890s; 7×64 Brenneke (B) and its rimmed near-relation, 7×65R (C), are common only in some parts of central Europe.

By courtesy of Dynamit Nobel AG.

Above

Above

rimless. Ignition: centre-fire. Case length: 1510. Diameters: rim 445, neck 340, bullet 308. Typical muzzle velocity: 2,330fs with a 122-grain bullet (1,471 ft-lb). Developed during the Second World War, this is an 'intermediate' round apparently based – whatever the Russians may claim – on the German 7·9mm Kurzpatrone. Being somewhat longer, the Russian M43 can be hand-loaded to give greater power than its German prototype and can even duplicate cartridges such as 7–30 Waters or ·30–30. Owing to its compact dimensions and ability to handle bullets weighing up to 150 grains, the M43 could prove a popular multi-purpose round. The Ruger Mini-Thirty and the Heckler & Koch HK32 series are some of the guns adapted for it.

7·62× 54R

Synonyms: 7·62mm Russian M91, 7·62mm Russian Rimmed, 7·62mm Mosin-Nagant. Case type: necked, rimmed. Ignition: centre-fire. Case length: 2110. Diameters: rim 565, neck 335, bullet 308. Typical muzzle velocity: 2,820fs with a 150-grain bullet (2,649 ft-lb). Adopted in 1891, but since revised several times, the old Tsarist rifle cartridge is now used only in military-surplus Mosin-Nagant rifles, the current Dragunov (SVD) sniper rifle and some machine-guns. Comparable to 8× 57 Mauser or ·30–06, it is powerful enough for most medium game. Unfortunately, the awkward rimmed case feeds poorly from box magazines unless fitted with the standard Mosin-Nagant interruptor.

·30 M1 Carbine

Case type: straight tapered, rimless. Ignition: centre-fire. Case length: 1290. Diameters: rim 360, base 355, neck 335, bullet 304. Typical muzzle velocity: 1,975fs with a 110-grain bullet (953 ft-lb). Developed by Winchester in 1940–1, this was chambered in the popular US ·30 M1 Carbine. A poor man-stopper by military standards, the cartridge has nonetheless remained popular on the sporting market – not least because of the undying appeal of the war-surplus and modern replica M1 Carbines.

·30–06 Springfield

Case type: necked, rimless. Ignition: centre-fire. Case length: 2495. Diameters: rim 475, shoulder 440, neck 340, bullet 300. Typical performance: 2,800fs with a 165-grain bullet (2,873 ft-lb). Adopted by the US Army in 1906, replacing the earlier Model 1903, this cartridge soon proved popular among sportsmen. Huge amounts of cheap war-surplus ammunition assured its popularity after 1945. Though now regarded as too powerful for a military rifle and less than ideal for varmint shooting, even when loaded with 93-grain bullets, ·30–06 is an excellent choice for medium game when loaded with 180- or 220-grain bullets.

·30–30 Winchester★

Synonym: ·30 WCF. Case type: necked, rimmed. Ignition: centre-fire. Case length: 2010. Diameters:

rim 505, shoulder 420, neck 330, bullet 309. Typical muzzle velocity: 2,415fs with a 150-grain bullet (1,943 ft-lb). Designed by Winchester and introduced commercially in 1895, this remains one of the best-known US sporting rifle cartridges; lever-action ·30–30 rifles are still made by Winchester and Marlin, while several bolt-action rifles may also be obtained. Widely regarded in North America as the bench-mark for deer hunting, ·30–30 is by no means the best cartridge for the job; generally loaded with round-nose bullets suited to tube magazines, it is not particularly powerful and its effective range does not extend much beyond 250yd.

·30–40 Krag

Case type: necked, rimmed. Ignition: centre-fire. Case length: 2315. Diameters: rim 545, shoulder 425, neck 340, bullet 300. Typical performance: 2,470fs with a 180-grain bullet (2,439 ft-lb). The US Army's first small-bore cartridge, adopted in 1892, the Krag has a lasting reputation even though no rifles were chambered for it commercially between 1936 and 1973. Since then, however, Ruger No.1 and other single-shot rifles have rekindled interest. The ·30–40 has a reputation for accuracy, but only when loaded to moderate pressures; though inferior in virtually every respect to ·30–06, it is considerably better than ·30–30.

·300 Holland & Holland Magnum★

Synonym: ·300 Belted Rimless Magnum. Case type: necked, rimless. Ignition: centre-fire. Case length: 2850. Diameters: rim 530, shoulder 455, neck 340, bullet 300. Typical performance: 3,190fs with a 150-grain bullet (3,390 ft-lb). Developed by Holland & Holland of London and introduced commercially in 1925, this cartridge is still chambered in US and European rifles. Though it has lost ground to ·300 Weatherby Magnum and a selection of ·300 wildcats – almost all based on the ·300 H&H case – the cartridge remains a good choice for medium game. In Africa, particularly, it is still regarded as an optimum all-purpose plains rifle round.

·300 Weatherby Magnum

Case type: necked, rimless. Ignition: centre-fire. Case length: 2820. Diameters: rim 530, shoulder 490, neck 330, bullet 300. Typical performance: 3,245fs with a 180-grain bullet (4,210 ft-lb). Developed in 1944 from ·300 H&H Magnum, the long-range accuracy and great striking power of this belted cartridge combine to make one of the best all-purpose game cartridges currently available. It is basically a ·300 H&H with a sharper shoulder and a larger-diameter case-body that increases propellant capacity.

·300 Winchester Magnum

Case type: necked, rimless. Ignition: centre-fire. Case length: 2620. Diameters: rim 530, shoulder 475, neck 335, bullet 300. Typical performance: 3,400fs with a 150-grain bullet (3,851 ft-lb). Introduced for the Winchester Model 70 bolt-action rifle in 1963, to an expectant (but subsequently somewhat disappointed) shooting public, this is a belted-case magnum with an unusually short neck that restricts bullet length. However, the ·300 Winchester Magnum remains an excellent game cartridge.

·303 Lee-Enfield

Synonyms: ·303 British, 7·7×56R. Case type: necked, rimmed. Ignition: centre-fire. Case length: 2220. Diameters: rim 540, body 400, neck 340, bullet 303. Typical performance: 2,540fs with a 180-grain bullet (2,579 ft-lb). Developed for the British Army, this cartridge dates from 1888. Few new rifles are being chambered for it, but the ready availability of ex-military Lee-Enfields assures supplies of factory loads for many years. Apart from the Lee-action rifles, the ·303 is best suited to single-shot rifles as its rimmed case feeds comparatively poorly from box magazines.* In addition, the cartridge can be hand-loaded to higher pressures than the comparatively weak Lee action can withstand. Though not unduly powerful by current standards, ·303 is more than a match for ·30−40 Krag.

·307 Winchester

Case type: necked, rimmed. Ignition: centre-fire. Case length: 2015. Diameters: rim 505, body 455, neck 345, bullet 308. Typical performance: 2,360fs with a 180-grain bullet (2,227 ft-lb). Introduced in 1980 for the Winchester Model 94XTR Angle Eject rifle, and now also chambered in the Marlin 336ER, this is basically a rimmed ·308 Winchester specifically developed for lever-action guns, though Shiloh Sharps Montana Roughrider and Hartford Model

single-shot rifles also chamber it. ·307 Winchester deserves to replace the less effectual ·30−30 as the North American bench-mark for deer hunting, but the public esteem in which the latter is held may prevent such a radical change.

·308 Norma Magnum

Synonym: ·308 Normag. Case type: necked, rimless. Ignition: centre-fire. Case length: 2560. Diameters: head 530, body 490, neck 340, bullet 308. Typical performance: 3,100fs with a 180-grain bullet (3,842 ft-lb). Announced in 1960, no commercial rifles were chambered for this cartridge until 1962. The cartridge is basically a ·338 Winchester Magnum necked down to ·308. Powerful enough for African plains game, in addition to anything encountered in the Americas, the Norma Magnum is an acceptable substitute for ·300 H&H or Weatherby Magnums.

·308 Winchester

Synonym: 7·62×51 NATO. Case type: necked, rimless. Ignition: centre-fire. Case length: 2015. Diameters: head 475, body 455, neck 345, bullet 308. Typical performance: 2,610fs with a 180-grain bullet (2,723 ft-lb). Developed by the US Army as the T65 this was ultimately adopted as the standard NATO rifle and machine-gun cartridge. In 1954, however, Winchester astutely introduced the T65 to the sporting fraternity as '·308 Winchester' and the designation became commonplace in North America; worldwide, virtually every manufacturer now chambers rifles for it. The ·308 is a useful all-purpose cartridge, short enough to fit most medium-length rifle actions but with a

* With the exception of the British Lee-Enfield rifles, the magazines of which were refined to handle the ·303 cartridge over many years.

Below
A selection of the military cartridges in vogue prior to the First World War. From left to right: two versions of the German 8×57 pattern, loaded with roundnose and spitzer bullets; the Greek 6·5×54, for the Mannlicher-Schönauer; the Dutch 6·5×53R Mannlicher; the Italian 6·5×52 Mannlicher-Carcano; the Japanese 6·5×50 semi-rim round, for the Arisaka; and the obsolescent Portuguese 8×60R for the Guedes and Kropatschek rifles.

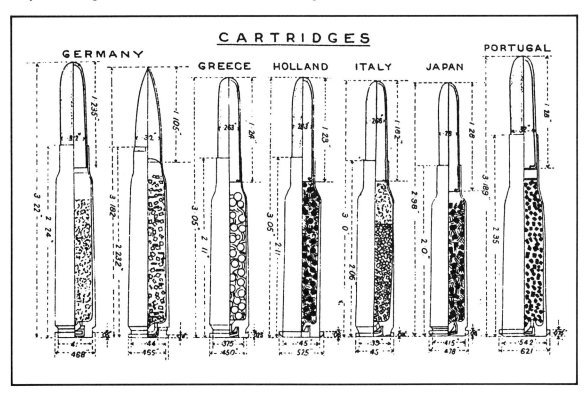

CARTRIDGES

GERMANY   GREECE   HOLLAND   ITALY   JAPAN   PORTUGAL

a   b

c

Above

Three German sporting cartridges:
8×57 Mauser (A), 8×68
Schuler (B) and 8·15×46R
Fröhn (C).

By courtesy of Dynamit Nobel AG.

Above

The ineffectual 7·65mm Short (·32
ACP) round may be chambered in
light rifles, but is generally
associated with handguns.

By courtesy of Dynamit Nobel AG.

satisfactory powder capacity. Though inferior to some of the smaller rounds for varmint shooting (cf., ·22–250 or ·25–06), ·308 is a good choice against medium game.

8mm Remington Magnum

Case type: necked, rimless. Ignition: centre-fire. Case length: 2850. Diameters: head 530, body 485, neck 355, bullet 323. Typical performance: 2,830fs with a 220-grain bullet (3,913 ft-lb). This powerful belted-case round appeared in 1978 for the Remington Model 700 BDL rifle, but has thus far failed to find widespread favour. This is partly because it requires a longer action than ·30–06, but also because the Remington Magnum has little extra to offer compared with the shorter ·338 Winchester pattern.

8×57

Synonyms: 7·9×57, 7·92×57, 8mm German Mauser. Case type: necked, rimless. Ignition: centre-fire. Case length: 2240. Diameters: head 475, body 435, neck 350, bullet 323. Typical performance: 2,625fs with a 198-grain bullet (3,030 ft-lb). Introduced as the service cartridge of the German army in 1888, when it was loaded with a ·318-diameter bullet, this is primarily a European cartridge. It chambers in many European sporting rifles – bolt-action, double and Drilling alike. Under-loaded in the USA, where it is often comparable with ·30–40 Krag, the full-power 8mm Mauser is in much the same class as ·30–06. The low power of the US-made factory ammunition is undoubtedly due to the potentially dangerous confusion between the original ·318 'I' (or 'J') loads and the later ·323 'S' type; firing a ·323-diameter bullet in the older guns may raise chamber pressures above the safety limit. A rimmed version of the basic cartridge (8×57R) is made for double rifles and Drillinge.

8×60 Schuler

Synonym: 8×60S Mauser. Case type: necked, rimless. Ignition: centre-fire. Case length: 2360. Diameters: bullet 323. Typical performance: 2,770fs with a 187-grain bullet (3,187 ft-lb). This is a typical European sporting rifle cartridge, originating before the Second World War but rarely encountered in North America even today. It does little that the ·30–06 or ·308 Winchester cannot.

8×68S Magnum★

Case type: necked, rimless. Ignition: centre-fire. Case length: 2655. Diameters: head 510, neck 360, bullet 324. Typical performance: 3,050fs with a 196-grain bullet (4,050 ft-lb). Introduced commercially at the beginning of the Second World War, this is believed to have been a vom Hofe design. Made only with ·323-diameter bullets, it is a powerful game cartridge comparable with ·338 Winchester or the ·300 Magnums. It is still confined almost exclusively to Europe.

·32 ACP

Synonym: 7·65mm Auto Pistol. Case type: straight,

rimless. Ignition: centre-fire. Case length: 680. Diameters: rim 350, body and neck 335, bullet 309. Typical performance: 960fs with a 71-grain bullet (145 ft-lb). Developed by John Browning and Fabrique Nationale and introduced in 1899, this is widely used in automatic pistols and – less commonly – semi-automatic carbines. However, it is a poor man-stopper and marginally effective against even the smallest game.

·32–20 Winchester★ †

Synonym: ·32–20 WCF. Case type: necked, rimmed. Ignition: centre-fire. Case length: 1315. Diameters: rim 410, body 355, neck 325, bullet 313. Typical muzzle velocity: 1,700fs with a 100-grain bullet (642 ft-lb). Winchester introduced this venerable cartridge for the Model 73 lever-action rifle in 1882. Now comparatively uncommon, it will chamber in some of the commemorative Winchesters produced in the last twenty years – as well as some single-shot pistols and even a revolver or two. Its virtues lie in its low power, useful in urban districts, and the ease with which it can be reloaded.

·32–40 Ballard†

Synonyms: ·32–40 WCF, ·32–40 Winchester. Case type: straight tapered, rimmed. Ignition: centre-fire. Case length: 2130. Diameters: rim 505, neck 340, bullet 320. Typical performance: 1,440fs with a 165-grain bullet (760 ft-lb). Developed for a Ballard single-shot target rifle and introduced commercially in 1884, this was subsequently appropriated for Winchester and Marlin lever-action rifles. It was discontinued at the outbreak of the Second World War and has only recently been resurrected for guns such as the Shiloh Sharps. Modern ·32–40 loads can develop energies as high as 1,440 ft-lb and approach ·30–30 performance, but only at the expense of appreciable chamber pressures; care should be taken not to strain old guns. Comparatively low-power factory loads are generally best against small game at medium distances.

8·15×46R Fröhn★ †

Case type: necked, rimmed. Ignition: centre-fire. Case length: 1830. Diameters: rim 485, neck 350, bullet 330. Typical performance: 1,805fs with a 151-grain bullet (1,093 ft-lb). Said to have been developed by a Suhl gunsmith in the early 1890s, this low-power rimmed cartridge was intended primarily for 200m target shooting. It was rarely seen outside central Europe until after the Second World War, when Allied servicemen took large quantities of Mauser-action Wehrmann-Büchsen – single-shot training rifles – and falling-block target rifles as souvenirs. Modern cartridges are loaded with semi-wadcutter bullets, but are as useful on small game at moderate ranges as they are on the target range.

·338 Winchester Magnum

Case type: necked, rimless. Ignition: centre-fire. Case length: 2500. Diameters: head 530, body 480, neck

360, bullet 338. Typical performance: 2,700fs with a 250-grain bullet (4,048 ft-lb). Introduced commercially in 1958 for the Winchester Model 70 Alaskan rifle, this is a necked-down ·458 Winchester Magnum. It is extremely powerful, but appreciably shorter than most comparable ·300 and 8mm magnums. The consensus is that ·338 has an advantage on ·300 H&H Magnum out on the African plains, as it can handle a wider range of heavy bullets.

·338/416 Barrett

Currently chambered only in AMAC and Barrett long-range sniping rifles, this cartridge is believed to be a ·416 Rigby case necked down to accept the ·338 Winchester bullet. Performance is likely to be impressive.

·340 Weatherby Magnum

Case type: necked, rimless. Ignition: centre-fire. Case length: 2820. Diameters: head 530, body 490, neck 360, bullet 340. Typical performance: 3,165fs with a 210-grain bullet (4,672 ft-lb). Longer and more powerful than the ·338 Winchester pattern, but sharing a belted case, this cartridge appeared commercially in 1962. Ideal against big game, ·340 Weatherby has a fearsome recoil and is scarcely suited to the faint-hearted flincher. In addition, as accuracy deteriorates with excessive power, rifles chambering ·340 Weatherby Magnum are rarely capable of bettering 2MOA. If accuracy is paramount, the ·300 version is preferable.

·35 Remington★

Case type: necked, rimless. Ignition: centre-fire. Case length: 1920. Diameters: rim 460, neck 385, bullet 359. Typical muzzle velocity: 2,100fs with a 200-grain bullet (1,959 ft-lb). This once-popular cartridge – now only chambered in the Marlin 336 lever-action rifle and the Thompson/Center Contender pistol – dates from 1908. It offers a good combination of stopping power and cross-sectional area, but is handicapped by a blunt bullet. ·35 Remington is unquestionably superior to ·30–30 on medium game.

·35 Whelen

Case type: necked, rimless. Ignition: centre-fire. Case length: 2500. Diameters: rim 475, neck 380, bullet 358. Typical performance: 2,505fs with a 250-grain bullet (3,484 ft-lb). Chambered in the Remington Model 700 Classic bolt-action and Model 7600 pump-action rifles (1988 season only), this was developed by the gunsmith James Howe in the early 1920s simply by expanding the neck of ·30–06 cases. Though a good all-purpose cartridge, useful on medium game, the popularity of the Whelen round was speedily eroded by ·375 H&H Magnum and ·338 Winchester. However, the ready availability of ·30–06 cases and a wide range of suitable ·35 bullets still makes Whelen ammunition attractive for hand-loaders.

·356 Winchester

Case type: necked, rimmed. Ignition: centre-fire. Case

length: 2015. Diameters: head 505, body 455, neck 390, bullet 356. Typical performance: 2,320fs with a 200-grain bullet (2,391 ft-lb). Developed in 1980 and introduced commercially in 1982–3 with the Model 94XTR Angle Eject, this is one of the new cartridges introduced for the latest range of Winchester lever-action rifles. No sooner had ·356 appeared than Marlin chambered a version of the Model 336ER for it. The designation has been chosen to avoid confusion with the rimless ·358 Winchester, which shares similar dimensions. As ·356 Winchester is more powerful than ·30–30 or ·35 Remington, it represents an ideal short-range brush cartridge and is eminently acceptable against deer.

9×19

Synonyms: 9mm Luger, 9mm Parabellum. Case type: straight, rimless. Ignition: centre-fire. Case length: 760. Diameters: rim and body 390, neck 380, bullet 357. Typical performance: 1,140fs with a 115-grain bullet (332 ft-lb).‡ Developed by Georg Luger and DWM in 1902, this is now the world's most popular and widely distributed pistol and submachine-gun cartridge. It is also encountered in semi-automatic carbines, particularly those that have been derived from submachine-guns. When loaded with the right bullets, 9×19 has a good all-purpose compromise, though its virtues on game or as a man-stopper, particularly when loaded with jacketed bullets, may be legitimately questioned.

·357 Magnum★

Case type: straight, rimmed. Ignition: centre-fire. Case length: 1290. Diameters: rim 440, body and neck 380, bullet diameter 359. Typical performance: 1,825fs with a 158-grain bullet (1,169 ft-lb). Developed in the mid 1930s by Smith & Wesson in collusion with Philip Sharpe, this is basically a lengthened ·38 Special – but infinitely more powerful and a better man-stopper. Some of the rifle loads are much too hot for pistols, though the latter loads are quite satisfactory in the longarms. The ·357 Magnum round is chambered in the lever-action Rossi and Uberti Baby Rolling Block Carbines, together with the Marlin Model 94 and Savage 24-V rifles.

·358 Norma Magnum

Synonym: ·358 Normag. Case type: necked, rimless. Ignition: centre-fire. Case length: 2520. Diameters: head 595, body 490, neck 390, bullet 358. Typical performance: 2,790fs with a 250-grain bullet (4,322 ft-lb). Another of the powerful European-style belted-case magnums, this cartridge was announced in 1959 – though some years elapsed before Schulz & Larsen and Husqvarna chambered suitable rifles. Best suited to big game hunting, it is comparatively rarely encountered. It does little that the popular ·375 H&H cannot equal.

·358 Winchester

Case type: necked, rimless. Ignition: centre-fire. Case length: 2015. Diameters: head 475, body 455, neck

Above

Better known as '9mm Luger' or '9mm Parabellum', 9×19 is popular in handguns and submachine-guns. It is also occasionally associated with carbines and light automatic rifles.

By courtesy of Dynamit Nobel AG.

Above

Conceived as a revolver cartridge, ·357 Magnum has since found a wider application in replica Winchesters and some types of carbine. Rifle loads are generally much too powerful for handguns, however.

By courtesy of Dynamit Nobel AG.

390, bullet 358. Typical performance: 2,250fs with 250-grain bullet (2,811 ft-lb). Introduced in 1955 for the Winchester Model 70 and 88 rifles, this is a good all-purpose cartridge for medium or large thin-skinned game at ranges below 250yd. Though appreciably less powerful than the super-magnums, the compact ·358 has the merits of excellent accuracy and moderate recoil.

9·3×62 Mauser★

Case type: necked, rimless. Ignition: centre-fire. Case length: 2440. Diameters: head 470, neck 390, bullet 366. Typical performance: 2,325fs with a 258-grain bullet (3,098 ft-lb). This big-game cartridge, originally chambered in Mauser-action sporting rifles and introduced commercially in 1905–6, was once very popular in Africa as an all-purpose round. It has now lost much of its former eminence to ·338 Winchester and ·340 Weatherby Magnums, and is still largely confined to Europe.

9·3×64 Brenneke

Case type: necked, rimless. Ignition: centre-fire. Case length: 2520. Diameters: head 495, neck 395, bullet 366. Typical performance: 2,690fs with a 285-grain bullet (4,580 ft-lb). The largest of the Brenneke Torpedo-Geschosse cartridges developed before the First World War, 9·3×64 is really suited only to big-game hunting: it generates too much power for lesser tasks, unless deliberately under-loaded. Currently offered by RWS, the Brenneke rounds are generally restricted to double rifles.

9·3×72R†

Case type: straight tapered, rimmed. Ignition: centre-fire. Case length: 2830. Diameters: rim 520, neck 390, bullet 365. Typical performance: 2,020fs with a 193-grain bullet (1,749 ft-lb). An old design, dating back to the 1890s and the days of black powder, this cartridge is popular in Drillinge: the long slender case is ideally suited to the lack of space in the breech of combination guns. However, 9·3×72R cartridges lack power and should not be used on anything larger than medium game.

9·3×74R

Case type: necked, rimmed. Ignition: centre-fire. Case length: 2930. Diameters: rim 525, neck 385, bullet 365. Typical performance: 2,280fs with a 285-grain bullet (3,291 ft-lb). Despite originating in the early part of the twentieth century, this cartridge remains popular in the double rifles and Drillinge to which its slender case is well suited. It is powerful enough to be used against all but the most dangerous game.

·375 Holland & Holland Magnum★

Synonym: ·375 Belted Rimless Magnum. Case type: necked, rimless. Ignition: centre-fire. Case length: 2850. Diameters: head 530, body 450, neck 405, bullet 375. Typical performance: 2,590fs with a 300-grain bullet (4,470 ft-lb). Introduced by Holland & Holland in 1912, this cartridge remains popular despite the legions of 'improvements' derived from it. It is much too powerful for anything but big-game hunting, and the cartridge is long enough to require a special bolt-action; originally, many of the rifles chambering it were side-by-side doubles. Modern cartridges such as ·358 Winchester are preferable for most purposes.

·375 Winchester

Case type: straight tapered, rimmed. Ignition: centre-fire. Case length: 2020. Diameters: rim 495, body 395, bullet 375. Typical performance: 2,200fs with a 200-grain bullet (2,150 ft-lb). Introduced for the Model 94 Winchester Big Bore lever-action rifle in 1978, this is basically a shortened ·38–55 (q.v.). Unfortunately, ·375 rounds will chamber in most ·38–55 rifles and, owing to higher pressure, can easily wreck them. The substantial rim suits ·375 Winchester cartridges to single-shot rifles such as the Ruger No.3, but not to box-magazine designs. Owing to the flat-nose bullets, a safety feature necessary in tube magazines, ·375 Winchester does not perform particularly well at long ranges and is generally reckoned to be inferior ballistically to ·444 Marlin. However, it is an excellent short-range brush or hunting cartridge.

·378 Weatherby Magnum

Case type: necked, rimless. Ignition: centre-fire. Case length: 2910. Diameters: head 580, body 560, neck 400, bullet 378. Typical performance: 3,180fs with a 270-grain bullet (6,064 ft-lb). The comments made about ·375 H&H Magnum are even more relevant to this belted-case super-magnum, introduced in 1953. Useful only against the largest of big game, it has a fearsome recoil and requires a firer of great experience to place shots accurately. Cartridges of this power should only be selected if extreme hitting power is essential.

·38 Special★

Case type: straight, rimmed. Ignition: centre-fire. Case length: 1155. Diameters: rim 440, body and neck 380, bullet 360. Typical velocity: 730fs with a 200-grain bullet (237 ft-lb). Developed by Smith & Wesson in 1902, this is widely regarded as the most accurate handgun cartridge – but by no means the best choice for personal defence, being incomparably superior to the 6·35mm and 7·65mm Auto pistol cartridges and the ·32 S&W Long. Once universally used in police revolvers, it has been losing ground steadily to the ·357 Magnum despite the advent of high-pressure loadings. The standard ·38 Special cartridge may chamber in pseudo-replica rifles as well as some carbines.

·38–55 Ballard†

Synonym: ·38–55 Winchester. Case type: straight tapered, rimmed. Ignition: centre-fire. Case length: 2130. Diameters: head 505, body 390, bullet 380. Typical velocity: 1,320fs with a 255-grain bullet (987 ft-lb). This cartridge was introduced for the Ballard No.4 target rifle in 1884. Marlin and Winchester subsequently produced lever-action rifles chambering it, while Remington adapted the Lee bolt-action rifle and many single-shot guns appeared. ·38–55 had lost favour completely by 1940, but was put back into production for Winchester commemorative rifles in the 1970s and is now also chambered in some Shiloh Sharps. Care should be exercised with old guns, as the new ·375 Winchester (q.v.) may also chamber in them.

·38–56 Winchester
Case type: necked, rimmed. Ignition: centre-fire. Case length: 2100. Diameters: rim 605, shoulder 445, neck 405, bullet 376. Typical velocity: 1,395fs with a 255-grain bullet (1,102 ft-lb). Introduced in 1887 for the Winchester Model 86 lever-action rifle, this moderate-power sporting cartridge was discontinued prior to the Second World War and only recently resurrected. Loaded to its full potential, it is entirely adequate on medium game and can be elevated into the ·30–30 class; however, pressures climb uncomfortably and full-power loads should not be fired in old rifles! The ·38–56 currently chambers in some modern Shiloh Sharps rifles, which are sturdy enough for the heaviest loads.

·380 ACP
Synonyms: 9mm Auto Pistol, 9mm Corto, 9mm Kurz, 9mm Short. Case type: straight, rimless. Ignition: centre-fire. Case length: 675. Diameters: rim and body 375, neck 370, bullet 356. Typical velocity: 955fs with a 95-grain bullet (192 ft-lb). Designed by Browning and Fabrique Nationale and introduced in Europe in 1912, this has been the service pistol cartridge in several European armies – as well as extremely popular commercially. It is also the smallest cartridge that can be taken seriously for personal defence, but may be limited by its jacketed bullets. However, anything the 7·65mm Auto round does well, the 9mm Short does much better. Generally regarded as a handgun cartridge, it is sometimes shared with replica rifles and small carbines.

·40–50 Sharps†
Case type: necked, rimmed. Ignition: centre-fire. Case length: 1720. Diameters: rim 580, shoulder 490, neck 425, bullet 403. Typical performance: 1,465fs with a 265-grain bullet (1,263 ft-lb). Among the shortest of the Sharps cartridges, dating from c.1875, this was originally chambered in Sharps, Remington and similar single-shot rifles. Powerful enough for use on small or medium game out to 150–200yd, it is now available principally in some of the Shiloh Sharps.

·40–65 Winchester†
Case type: straight tapered, rimmed. Ignition: centre-fire. Case length: 2100. Diameters: rim 605, neck 425, bullet 406. Typical performance: 1,420fs with a 260-grain bullet (1,164 ft-lb). Developed in the late 1880s for the Winchester Model 86 rifle, this was also chambered in the Marlin Model 95 and some single-shot rifles. Developed to provide a comparatively hard-hitting round suited to lever actions, ·40–65,

discontinued in the 1930s but recently resurrected, is adequate for use on medium game at 200yd or less. It currently chambers only in Shiloh Sharps rifles.

·40–70 Sharps Necked†
Case type: necked, rimmed. Ignition: centre-fire. Case length: 2250. Diameters: rim 595, shoulder 500, neck 425, bullet 403. Typical performance: 1,420fs with a 330-grain bullet (1,478 ft-lb). Introduced in the 1870s, this was popular among buffalo hunters and target shooters alike, combining excellent accuracy and with an acceptable punch. It is currently chambered only in Shiloh Sharps rifles.

·40–70 Sharps Straight†
Case type: straight, rimmed. Ignition: centre-fire. Case length: 2500. Diameters: rim 535, neck 420, bullet 403. Typical performance: 1,260fs with a 330-grain bullet (1,164 ft-lb). Dating from c.1879–80, this round chambered in Sharps, Remington, Winchester and similar single-shot rifles before being discontinued in the 1930s. It was resurrected in 1989 for Shiloh Sharps rifles.

·40–90 Sharps Necked†
Case type: necked, rimmed. Ignition: centre-fire. Case length: 2630. Diameters: rim 600, shoulder 500, neck 435, bullet 403. Typical performance: 1,475fs with a 370-grain bullet (1,788 ft-lb). Never especially popular, this Sharps rifle cartridge appeared in c.1876. Many bullets were made to accept a ·22 Short rimfire blank in their noses, in the forlorn hope that the blank would explode on contact with a target. ·40–90 now chambers only in some modern Shiloh Sharps rifles.

·40–90 Sharps Straight†
Case type: straight, rimmed. Ignition: centre-fire. Case length: 2500. Diameters: rim 535, neck 420, bullet 403. Typical performance: 1,385fs with a 370-grain bullet (1,576 ft-lb). Whether this pre-1885 round is genuinely a Sharps design has been contested, as Ballard and Remington rifles have also been chambered for it. Despite being discontinued in the 1930s, the cartridge design has recently been exhumed for Shiloh Sharps rifles.

·404 Jeffrey
Synonym: ·404 Rimless Nitro Express. Case type: necked, rimless. Ignition: centre-fire. Case length: 2875. Diameters: head 545, neck 450, bullet 422. Typical performance: 2,315fs with a 400-grain bullet (4,761 ft-lb). This adaptation of the ·450/400 Nitro Express appeared shortly before the First World War. It is usually chambered in Mauser-action sporters or double rifles by leading British gunmakers, such as Jeffrey, Gibbs or Cogswell & Harrison. Suited only to big-game shooting, ·404 is much too powerful for lesser tasks.

10·3× 60
Case type: necked, rimless. Ignition: centre-fire. Case

Above
Developed by Smith & Wesson at the turn of the century, the ·38 Special cartridge may be chambered in carbines and some replica rifles. It is not at its best in a longarm, however, and has generally lost ground to ·357 Magnum.
By courtesy of Dynamit Nobel AG.

Above
Introduced in Britain shortly before the First World War began, powerful ·404 Jeffrey has been popular with big-game hunters.
By courtesy of Dynamit Nobel AG.

length: 2350. Diameters: rim 465, body 510, neck 440, bullet 415. Typical performance: believed to be about 2,050fs with 330-grain bullets (3,080 ft-lb). An adaptation of a rimless case derived from the standard Mauser Reichspatrone 71, this is now apparently confined to the Mauser 77S Magnum. It has a slightly undersized rim and a very distinctive shallow shoulder midway along the case-body. The large-diameter bullet and appreciable velocity suit the 10·3× 60 to all but the largest game.

·41 Magnum
Case type: straight, rimmed. Ignition: centre-fire. Case length: 1280. Diameters: rim 490, neck 430, bullet 410. Typical performance: 1,305fs with a 210-grain bullet (793 ft-lb).‡ Introduced in 1964 by Smith & Wesson, for the Model 57 revolver, this is often adjudged a failure compared with ·357 and ·44 Magnums, this is the best all-round sporting cartridge of the three. It is currently chambered in the Marlin 1894S lever-action and comparable rifles.

·416 Rigby Magnum★
Case type: necked, rimless. Ignition: centre-fire. Case length: 2885. Diameters: rim 590, neck 445, bullet 416. Typical performance: 2,370fs with a 410-grain bullet (5,115 ft-lb). Derived from ·404 Jeffrey by John Rigby, and introduced in 1911 with suitable Rigby Mausers, this powerful cartridge is currently only available with Belgian Dumoulin bolt-action sporters. The ·416 Rigby is comparable to ·458 Winchester (q.v.), but is too much for anything other than the largest African game.

10·75× 68 Mauser
Case type: necked, rimless. Ignition: centre-fire. Case length: 2675. Diameters: head 495, neck 455, bullet 424. Typical performance: 2,230fs with a 347-grain bullet (3,833 ft-lb). Developed by Mauser and introduced for the company's bolt-action sporters c.1923, this is primarily a big-game cartridge – and thus much too powerful for lesser applications unless drastically under-loaded. As smaller cartridges such as ·375 H&H Magnum offer better all-round performance, 10·75× 68 is rare outside Europe.

·44 Magnum★
Case type: straight, rimmed. Ignition: centre-fire. Case length: 1285. Diameters: rim 515, neck 455, bullet 432. Typical performance: 1,760fs with a 240-grain bullet (1,651 ft-lb). Introduced by S&W in 1955, after consultation with Elmer Keith, this is among the most powerful of revolver cartridges and will also be encountered in the Ruger semi-automatic carbine. The cartridge is capable of excellent accuracy, and the large bullets perform impeccably on small game.

·44 S&W Special★ †
Case type: straight, rimmed. Ignition: centre-fire. Case length: 1160. Diameters: rim 510, body, neck and bullet 440. Typical performance: 755fs with a 246-grain bullet (311 ft-lb). Developed by S&W from

the ·44 Russian round in 1907, this was never loaded to its full potential and was subsequently eclipsed by the ·44 Magnum derived directly from it. However, ·44 Special fires a large bullet with good knock-down capabilities, and has found renewed popularily in pseudo-replica rifles and light carbines.

·44–40 Winchester★ †
Synonym: ·44–40 WCF. Case type: necked, rimmed. Ignition: centre-fire. Case length: 1305. Diameters: rim 525, body 455, neck 445, bullet 440. Typical performance: 1,310fs with a 200-grain bullet (762 ft-lb). Introduced to accompany the Winchester Model 1873 lever-action rifle, and subsequently also chambered in the Colt Peacemaker revolver, this cartridge holds a special place in the history of the Wild West. Very weak by modern rifle standards, it is now restricted largely to handguns and Italian-made Winchester replicas. Though current US factory loadings are designed only for revolvers, ·44–40 can easily be hand-loaded to enhance performance in rifles.

·44–77 Sharps†
Synonym: ·44–77 Remington. Case type: necked, rimmed. Ignition: centre-fire. Case length: 2250. Diameters: rim 525, shoulder 500, neck 465, bullet 446. Typical performance: 1,460fs with a 365-grain bullet (1,728 ft-lb). Introduced in the mid-1870s for the Sharps rifle, this was also chambered in the Remington-Hepburn. Very popular on the target-range, where its accuracy was greatly appreciated, ·44–77 makes a passable mid-range hunting round. It currently chambers only in some of the modern Shiloh Sharps.

·44–90 Sharps†
Case type: necked, rimmed. Ignition: centre-fire. Case length: 2630. Diameters: rim 625, shoulder 505, neck 470, bullet 446. Typical performance: 1,270fs with a 520-grain bullet (1,863 ft-lb). Introduced in 1873, this was originally destined for the Sharps Creedmoor rifle. It is basically a longer version of the ·44–77 (q.v.), but had a short life: ·44-calibre Sharps rifles were discontinued in 1878, though ammunition was still being made at the turn of the century. Resurrected in 1989, ·44–90 cartridges now chamber only in Shiloh Sharps rifles.

·444 Marlin
Case type: straight, semi-rim. Ignition: centre-fire. Case length: 2160. Diameters: rim 515, body 470, mouth 455, bullet 431. Typical muzzle velocity: 2,310fs with a 240-grain bullet (2,844 ft-lb). Developed in the early 1960s and released in 1974, this originally chambered in the Marlin 336 lever-action rifle. Despite its blunt-nose bullet – necessitated by the Marlin rifle's tube magazine – ·444 is an excellent game cartridge.

·45 ACP
Case type: straight, rimless. Ignition: centre-fire.

Above

Developed to compete with ·375 H&H Magnum and ·404 Jeffrey, 10·75×68 appeared in Germany in the early 1920s. It was originally a proprietary Mauser cartridge, but is now also associated with double rifles.

By courtesy of Dynamit Nobel AG.

Case length: 900. Diameters: rim 475, neck 470, bullet 450. Typical performance: 1,100fs with a 230-grain bullet (618 ft-lb). One of the best known cartridges of all time, this was conceived by John Browning in 1905 and adopted by the US Army in 1911. It is extremely powerful and a very good man-stopper although the conventional jacketed bullets are a hindrance. Consequently, it is not chambered as widely in carbines as ·44 Magnum (q.v.).

·45 Colt Revolver★ †
Case type: straight, rimmed. Ignition: centre-fire. Case length: 1285. Diameters: rim 510, body and neck 480, bullet 455. typical velocity: 800fs with a 255-grain bullet (363 ft-lb).‡ Introduced in 1872–3, this was the cartridge that tamed the Wild West along with ·44–40 Winchester. It is very accurate, a good man-stopper, and one of the most powerful revolver cartridges obtainable prior to the advent of the ·44 Magnum. The ·45 Colt may chamber in certain single-shot carbines.

·45–70 US Government★ †
Case type: straight, rimmed. Ignition: centre-fire. Case length: 2105. Diameters: rim 610, body 505, mouth 480, bullet 458. Typical muzzle velocity: 1,300fs with a 405-grain bullet (1,520 ft-lb). Adopted by the US Army in 1873 for the 'Trapdoor Springfield' rifle, this chambers in Ruger No.3 carbines, some Shiloh Sharps and a collection of pseudo-replicas.

·45–90 Winchester†
Case type: straight, rimmed. Ignition: centre-fire. Case length: 2400. Diameters: rim 595, neck 475, bullet 457. Typical performance: 1,510fs with a 350-grain bullet (1,772 ft-lb). A longer version of the ·45–70 Government cartridge (see above), this was introduced for the Winchester Model 86 lever-action rifle – but also chambered in Winchester and possibly some Sharps single-shot rifles. Currently chambered only in Shiloh Sharps rifles, ·45–90 is entirely adequate on medium game out to 200 yards but – like most cartridges of its type – has a looping trajectory that makes range gauging difficult. Most rifles chambering ·45–90 can also fire the shorter-case ·45–70 if the need arises.

·45–100 Sharps†
Case type: straight, rimmed. Ignition: centre-fire. Case length: 2600. Diameters: rim 595, neck 490, bullet 451. Typical performance: 1,360fs with a 550-grain bullet (2,259 ft-lb). Dating from c.1878, one of a series of similar straight-case cartridges, ·45–100 was chambered in Sharps and other single-shot rifles. Theoretically long obsolete, it has recently been reintroduced for Shiloh Sharps rifles.

·45–120 Sharps†
Case type: straight, rimmed. Ignition: centre-fire. Case length: 3250. Diameters: rim 595, neck 490, bullet 451. Typical performance: 1,520fs with a 500-grain bullet (2,566 ft-lb). One of the longest of all the cartridges in its class, this was introduced for the

Sharps-Borchardt rifle in 1878–9; however, as the Sharps Rifle Company failed in 1881, few guns and only a handful of cartridges were ever made. The ·45–120 had been consigned to history until resurrected for Shiloh Sharps rifles in recent times. Owing to the great weight of its bullet, the cartridge is entirely satisfactory for all but the largest soft-skinned game. However, low velocity gives a notably looping trajectory.

·450 Nitro Express 3¼"
Case type: straight, rimmed. Ignition: centre-fire. Case length: 3250. Diameters: head 625, neck 480, bullet 458. Typical performance: 2,150fs with a 480-grain bullet (4,928 ft-lb). One of the earliest big-game cartridges to be loaded with smokeless propellant, this was designed by John Rigby and announced commercially in 1898. Generally chambered in double rifles, the cartridge is still loaded for use in Africa. The obsolete ·450 No.2 Nitro Express had a necked 3½-inch case.

·458 Winchester
Case type: straight, rimless. Ignition: centre-fire. Case length: 2500. Diameters: head 530, body 480, bullet 458. Typical performance: 2,130fs with a 500-grain bullet (5,038 ft-lb). Another of the super-power big-game cartridges, ·458 Winchester made its début with the Model 70 African bolt-action rifle in 1956 and has established itself as the bench-mark for its class. Though factory loads are monumentally over-strength for medium game, some American hand-loaders have produced cartridges that duplicate ·45-70 ballistics for lesser tasks. This certainly extends the utility of the rifles, as a 405-grain bullet fired at 1,670fs will down medium game far more effectually than any ·30–30 load.

·460 Weatherby Magnum
Case type: necked, rimless. Ignition: centre-fire. Case length: 2908. Diameters: head 580, body 560, neck 480, bullet 460. Typical performance: 2,700fs with a 500-grain bullet (8,095 ft-lb). The most powerful of all mass-produced sporting-rifle cartridges, and arguably the most useless, this was introduced in 1958 solely to wrest the "World's Most Powerful" title from the ·600 Nitro Express. Nearly four foot-tons of muzzle energy requires an extremely heavy rifle and a shooter of Herculean proportions. Cartridges of this power will simply atomize medium game; consequently, they are useful only against the largest and most powerful animals Africa has to offer.

·470 Nitro Express★
Case type: necked, rimmed. Ignition: centre-fire. Case length: 3250. Diameters: rim 645, shoulder 570, neck 500, bullet 471. Typical performance: 2,150fs with a 500-grain bullet (5,133 ft-lb). Said to have been developed by Joseph Lang in about 1907, this owes its existence to bans placed on ·450 in Britain's African and Indian colonies as unsatisfactory against elephant. Essentially similar to ·458 Winchester

Above
The legendary ·45 ACP, powerful by handgun standards and regarded as a good man-stopper, is occasionally encountered in light rifles and carbines.
By courtesy of Dynamit Nobel AG.

Magnum, ·470 Nitro Express is much too powerful for all but the largest game. It is generally chambered in double rifles.

·475 No.2 Nitro Express

Case type: necked, rimmed. Ignition: centre-fire. Case length: 3500. Diameters: rim 675, neck 505, bullet 483. Typical performance: 2,100fs with a 520-grain bullet (5,093 ft-lb). A specialized big-game cartridge, so powerful that it is suited to no other application, this originated in the early twentieth century and was normally chambered in double rifles made by Jeffrey, Gibbs and other British gunmakers. Though obsolescent, ·475 Nitro Express No.2 has recently been put back into production to satify demands from Africa. It must not be confused with the ·475 Nitro Express, which had a straight rimmed case.

·50 Browning

Synonyms: ·50 BMG, 12·7× 99. Case type: necked, rimless. Ignition: centre-fire. Case length: 3910. Diameters: rim 800, neck 555, bullet 510. Typical performance: 2,800fs with a 708-grain bullet (12,328 ft-lb). Designed for the ·50-calibre Browning heavy machine-gun shortly after the end of the First World War, this is an awesome chambering for shoulder rifles and outranks even the legendary ·460 Weatherby Magnum. It is currently used only in the AMAC and Barrett 'Light Fifty' long-range sniper/anti-vehicle/anti-helicopter rifles.

·50–70 US Government†

Case type: rimmed (see remarks). Ignition: centre-fire. Case length: 1750. Diameters: rim 560, body 565, neck 535, bullet 515. Typical muzzle velocity: 1,260fs with a 450-grain bullet (1,587 ft-lb). This was the official US Army service cartridge in 1866–73, later developing into the ·45–70 (q.v.). The original cases had a slight-but-perceptible neck, but the current '·50–70' pattern offered with some of the single-shot rifles such as the Shiloh Sharps is virtually straight-sided.

·50–100 Winchester†

Case type: straight, rimmed. Ignition: centre-fire. Case length: 2400. Diameters: rim 605, neck 535, bullet 512. Typical performance: 1,605fs with a 300-grain bullet (1,716 ft-lb). Introduced as the ·50–110 Winchester at about the turn of the century, to be chambered in the Model 86 lever-action rifle, this cartridge was discontinued in the mid 1930s. It has recently reappeared for Shiloh Sharps rifles. (Note: a high-power smokeless load generated up to 3,300 ft-lb, but was not suited to the Model 86.)

·505 Gibbs Magnum★

Case type: necked, rimless. Ignition: centre-fire. Case length: 3150. Diameters: rim 640, neck 535, bullet 505. Typical performance: 2,300fs with a 525-grain bullet (6,168 ft-lb). One of the most powerful of all sporting rifle cartridges, suited to nothing other than big-game hunting, this cartridge was introduced

shortly before the First World War. Most ·505 rifles embody Mauser actions, one of the few bolt systems sturdy enough the handle the pressures involved. A variant of the Kimber Magnum bolt-action rifle chambering ·505 Gibbs was announced in 1989.

·577 Nitro Express 3″

Case type: straight, rimmed. Ignition: centre-fire. Case length: 3000. Diameters: rim 750, neck 605, bullet 584. Typical performance: 2,050fs with 750-grain bullet (7,000 ft-lb). The largest and most powerful of all the classic British sporting-rifle cartridges, excepting ·600 Nitro Express, this has recently gone back into small-scale production to satisfy demands from Africa. Rifles chambering these blockbusters rarely weigh less than 15lb, and require a strong and well-practised marksman to use them. The shorter but otherwise similar ·577 Nitro Express 2¼″ developed considerably less power.

Sights

The modern rifle will be encountered with a variety of sights, from an open notch to the most sophisticated illuminated-reticle optical sight.

Open back sights include standing notched leaves; folding leaves, particularly favoured on European double rifles (and often known as 'Express Sights'); the distinctively North American semi-buckhorn sight in which a notched elevator generally controls a sprung leaf; tangent-leaf sights; and aperture or 'peep' sights ranging from the simplest battle pattern to micro-adjustable competition diopter with integral filters and adjustable irises. Front sights generally consist of a simple blade or barleycorn (inverted V) on a ramp, which may often be provided with a sheet-steel cover. Luminous and coloured inserts or white beads are often in vogue, though fashions change rapidly. Anything that can provide contrast against a dark background may be an asset, but it must not be so gaudy that it distracts aim or reflects light in less than ideal circumstances.

Among the best of the open sights are the Williams ramp, favoured by very many manufacturers, and the competition sights made by the principal European target-rifle makers – Anschütz, Feinwerkbau, Grünig & Elmiger ('Elite' brand), Tanner and Walther. For field work, however, optical sights have been finding such favour since the 1960s that they are now universal in some applications – e.g., long-range varmint shooting.

Above

A typical modern military 'rocking L' aperture back sight, in this case on an FNC.
By courtesy of Fabrique Nationale Herstal SA.

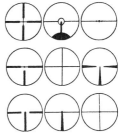

Above

A selection of cross-hair designs offered by Hertel & Reuss of Karlsruhe, on Hertels & Reuss and Nickels-branded sights.

Left

This range of 'Hubertus'-brand optical sights, made in Japan for Albrecht Kind ('Akah'), is typical of those offered by many of the larger gunmakers and wholesalers. They generally range from simple 4×28 to sophisticated 3–12× zoom patterns.
By courtesy of Karl Schäfer.

151

The modern optical sight consists of a drawn seamless aluminium tube containing a series of lenses and a reticle, generally with a means of adjusting focus.

Most modern lenses are a composite of several elements, that farthest from the shooter's eye being called the **objective**. This lens forms the 'primary image', which, were it not for a separate erector lens, would appear upside-down; the erector inverts the primary image, presenting it to the eyepiece correctly. The image then enters the pupil of the firer's eye. Optical sights normally magnify the image; variable-magnification patterns are called **zoom sights**, and are almost always heavier than fixed-power patterns. They are also more delicate.

Owing to their basic construction, and the great accuracy with which the composite lenses must be made, optical sights have several inherent weaknesses. Most of these, understandably, arise from flaws in the lens – though ineffectual seals are also potentially troublesome.

It is virtually impossible to grind a single-element lens to avoid distortion; consequently, well-known phenomena will often be seen even though their effects may be minimized by multiple lens elements. **Chromatic aberration** is caused by the inability of a lens to focus differing light rays at a single point. Ordinary 'white' light is composed of a rainbow in which the wavelength (and hence focal length) of each component differs; if the lens is badly corrected, a blurred image with a coloured corona or 'halo' may be visible. Sandwiches of thin glass are used to unify focus, each diffracting a portion of the light at a different angle.

Spherical aberration arises when light rays from the outer margins of the lens focus ahead of those from the middle, blurring the image. Though this can be minimized by super-accurate grinding, the work must not disturb essential colour corrections. **Image distortion** occurs when the lens or lens-system has been ground so out-of-true that parts of the image may seem twisted or bent. **Field-curvature** arises when the erector lens-system (particularly) produces an image with blurred edges and a pin-sharp centre –

or, conversely, when the centre is blurred while margins are crystal clear. **Astigmatism**, common enough in human eyes, is an inability to focus lines that cross each other at widely diverging angles. The most common cause is poor lens grinding. **Coma** occurs when a lens, unable to focus light passing through it obliquely, 'smears' an image outward towards the edges.

Though these problems are all potentially serious, most reputable optical-equipment manufacturers have so much experience that bad mistakes are rare: even the cheapest modern budget-price optical sights offer acceptable performance, particularly at comparatively short range. Of course, the time and care lavished on the most expensive sights by Zeiss or Schmidt & Bender is reflected in their price. Many marksmen would claim that performance justifies the cost; others regard such views as 'brandname snobbery'.

The easiest problems to detect on second-hand sights are fractured reticles and visible spotting or fogging of the lens-element coatings or interface adhesive. If the image is properly focused and no obvious coloured halo or corona effects are visible, particularly around small objects, the lens system has been corrected satisfactorily for chromatic aberration. It will usually be labelled 'achromatic'. Assuming that differing parts of the image do not focus separately when adjustments are made, then the lenses ('aplanatic') have been corrected for spherical aberration. Focusing on a brick wall or similar grid-like pattern in the middle distance will show whether horizontal and vertical lines are straight, and whether they focus sharply across the entire field of view simultaneously. If the sight passes this examination, the chances are that its 'orthoscopic' lenses have been corrected for image distortion, field-curvature and coma.

Repeating the test on chicken-wire or similar diagonal-link fences should show whether the strands running from left to right are as clear as those running right to left. If they are, then there is little or no astigmatism in the lens system.

B

Left

Pot pourri: a Soviet PSO-1 (A), with an integral passive infra-red detection system, mounted on an SVD (Dragunov) sniper rifle; a Zeiss Dialyt-ZA 6×42 optical sight on a Sauer 200 bolt-action rifle (B); and a sturdy Parker-Hale PH5E/83 aperture sight on one of the company's M84 Mk II target rifles.

By courtesy of Ian Hogg, J.P. Sauer & Sohn GmbH and Parker-Hale Ltd.

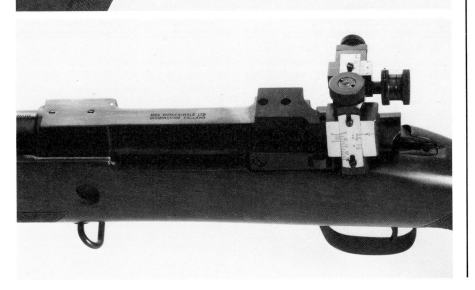

C

Many modern marksmen wear spectacles, a bane of modern life that creates additional difficulty when shooting with optical sights. Contact-lens wearers will usually look through the same part of the lens each time they sight the gun, but spectacle-wearers may look through a different part of their lenses when canting their heads. The spectacle lens then interferes with the performance of the lens-system in the sight. This is especially true of astigmatism corrections, which may unwittingly disturb out the anastigmatic correction already applied to the sight lenses!

Some shooters cannot focus on the target and the reticle at the same time, which becomes increasingly obvious with age. Problems can often be minimized by concentrating hard on the target before looking through the sight.

It is far better to adjust the sight to compensate for deficiencies in eyesight – assuming the sight is capable of doing so – than discard the spectacles, in case the predator should creep up on a myopic marksman. Target shooters can have prescription lenses inserted in aperture sights, but the less fortunate field shooter has no such way of improving his performance.

Telescope sights come in great profusion, offering wide-ranging magnification, 'enhanced resolution', 'maximum objective lens diameter', 'superior image brightness', 'TV-style field of view' or 'parallax correction'. These are not always of much value.

Magnification is simply the size of the object seen through the sight compared with that seen with the naked eye. The true magnification can be assessed, somewhat roughly, by keeping the second eye open and comparing the two images. Alternatively, a piece of thin paper can be placed over the eyepiece of a sight pointed at a bright light. As the paper is drawn backwards, the circle of light diminishes until it reaches a minimum and then begins to grow. This establishes the **eye-point** – the optimum distance at which the eye should be placed – and the diameter of the circle of light at its smallest point is the **sight aperture**. Magnification is often expressed by dividing the sight aperture into the diameter of the objective lens, though prone to give a false figure.

The **resolution** of a lens in a small-diameter telescope is limited by the performance of the human eye. The average eye is capable of resolving detail as fine as a minute of arc (i.e., one sixtieth of one degree), though sharp-sighted people can read notices at considerably greater distances than others with equally 'perfect' vision. To find the potential acuity of the eye when presented with a magnified image, it is simply necessary to divide the minute of arc by the true magnification: a 4✕ sight would improve the resolution to a quarter of a minute of arc (15 seconds of arc). Provided the objective lens diameter is sufficient to satisfy this eye-performance – say 12mm – all sights will perform adequately. As larger objectives have no effect on resolving power, there is no reason why a 4✕ 20 sight should not perform as well as a 4✕ 40.

Enlarging the objective lens diameter improves the relative brightness of the lens system, while allowing the firer's eye the luxury of additional vertical and lateral movement. It has no effect on magnification. To determine the relative brightness of a particular sight, the result of dividing the effective objective lens diameter by the sight aperture is simply squared. If a telescope sight has an objective lens diameter of 40mm (6✕ 40) and a sight aperture of 5mm, then its relative brightness is $64 - (40 \div 5)^2$ – while a 4✕ 20 sight with a comparable sight aperture would register 16.

Transmission of light is limited by the iris in the human eye, which adjusts automatically to ambient light. Iris diameter rarely exceeds 3mm in daylight and, therefore, any relative brightness greater than nine is wasted: at dusk, the iris can expand to a little over 5mm for an optimal relative brightness of 25–30. As some of the larger sights may provide relative brightnesses as great as 100, their value lies in allowing the eye to resolve detail in conditions where ambient light is insufficient to satisfy even the fully-opened iris.

A superior image brightness is obtained in telescope sights with coated lenses, identifiable by their purple-blue or strawed colour. As much as a third of the incidental light is lost travelling through the lenses of an ordinary sight, partly in the glass itself but mostly by reflection at the air/glass interfaces. Matt-black internal finish minimizes the losses, yet reflected light still bounces around the sight-tube; if the problems are bad enough, the final image may lack colour or display an inferior ghosted image.

The development of non-reflective lens coatings has done much to improve image quality, simply by enhancing transmission of light. Instead of losing up to a third of light during the passage, therefore, the primary image of a modern coated-lens telescope may lose less than a sixth.

Field of view depends not on the size of the objective lens, but on a combination of the effective diameter of the eye-piece lens, magnification and eye relief. An enormous objective lens contributes little to performance unless the eye-piece lens is also enlarged: field of view results solely from dividing the angle of view by magnification. Too restricted a view makes target acquisition difficult, though this has little importance in shooting against immobile targets. However, the same cannot be said of hunting. Here, too narrow a view prevents the marksman seeing much more than the quarry itself. Should the quarry move, it is difficult for the marksman to adjust quickly enough and a loss of target often ensues. The British Army has always accepted that 4✕ sights offer the best compromise of magnification and field-of-view. This opinion is shared by fieldsmen, even though varmint shooters prefer 8✕ for use against their tiny animate targets. Alternatively, the Austrian Bundesheer has recently promoted 1·5✕, claimed to maximize field of view and reduce body-tremor effects ('shake') while still allowing the firer to keep both eyes open.*

Fields of view can be enlarged by increasing the diameter of the eye-piece lens or shortening the eye relief. Moving the eye nearer the eye-piece is hazardous, particularly where powerful cartridges are used. This has always been a problem with military rifles such as the P14 and US M1917 Enfield, where aperture sights are mounted on the bridge at the rear of the receiver; when used for target shooting, the sights are easily driven back into the marksman's face.

* Provided the magnification is not excessive, the dominant eye will see the target clearly provided it is the eye behind the sight. Marksmen with a strongly dominant eye may be able to use virtually any optical sight with both eyes open.

Below

Large optical sights often offer additional features. Thus the Habicht 3–12×50P (A) incorporates zoom facility as well as parallax adjustment, while the anonymous 8×56 example (B) offers BDC as well as parallax-correction facilities.

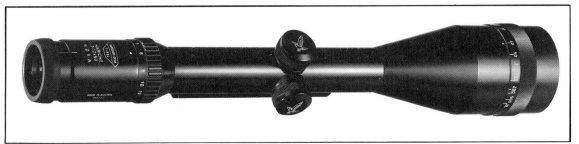

A

B

Right

A selection of Weatherby's own sights, made in Japan to the highest specifications. From top to bottom: 1·75–5×20 Supreme, 4×34 Hunting Supreme, 2–7×34 Supreme, 4×44 Hunting Supreme and 3–9×44 Supreme.

By courtesy of Weatherby, Inc.

† At all other times, the primary image focusses behind the reticle (at short range) or in front of it (at longer distances).

A 'TV' or wide-screen image is obtained from rectangular rather than circular objective lenses; however, unless associated with a suitably enlarged eye-piece or reduced eye-relief, the claim is a sham. A 'wide screen' sight generally performs no differently to a sight with a circular objective lens.

If the reticle cross-hairs wander over the target when the head is moved vertically or laterally, then **parallax** is present. Most ordinary telescope sights are corrected for particular distances – usually 100 yards – so that when aim is taken at this precise range, the crosshairs stay motionless on the target independently of head movement. This occurs because the objective lens of the sight is designed to superimpose the primary image on the plane of the reticle and relative movement is impossible. However, this only happens at one specific distance.†

Adjustable-parallax sights work efficiently provided the firer can gauge range accurately – though their value is reduced by setting the corrector for 130 yards when the target is actually at 180. 'Parallax hysteria' is greatly over-stated, as the phenomenon *cannot* occur (regardless of range) when the eye, the centre of the reticle and the target-image all lie on the longitudinal axis of the sight.

Many reticle designs are available, among the most popular being conventional crosshairs, crosshairs-and-dot, duplex (a combination of thick and thin hairs), cross-on-circle or vertical post. Attempts have been made to include 'range-finding' features, particularly in military sights. As all soldiers are

much the same size – the average is usually taken to be 5ft 7in tall – range-finding sights are quite useful. Their application to sporting sights is much less obvious; a stereoscopic range-finder of the type used by golfers provides a much better method of gauging distances at the shoot.

The provision of BDC ('Bullet Drop Computer') systems on the elevation adjusting-drum is supposed to synchronize the points of aim and impact automatically as range changes. A locking screw permits the cap to be rotated to a zero-point without moving the drum itself; the screw is then tightened and the new 'zero' locked in place. Considerable skill is required to use these sights, particularly when cartridge loads are changed, and their utility is questionable.

Illuminated reticle sights are another recent innovation, powered by small batteries. These sights are often most useful when shooting into dark ground, against which conventional cross-hairs are invisible. The most useful of all illuminated-reticle sights are those where the colour of the cross-hairs can be altered to suit the prevailing conditions.

Novice riflemen invariably begin by purchasing cheap 4× 20 or 4× 28 sights for their ·22LR rimfires. The best of these sights will perform acceptably, provided they are study enough to withstand the battering of recoil: even 4× 15 sights generally offer elevation and azimuth adjustments. The adjustors are protected by screw-on caps or (in at least one case) pivoting plastic sliders. However, the integral mounts are rarely suitable for powerful sporting rifles unless a supplementary arrestor block is fitted.

4× 32 and 4× 40 are amongst the most popular of the bigger 4× sights, the latter being favoured owing to its superior performance in poor light. Fixed-power sights of this group are usually sturdy, effectual and offer good optical performance.

Sights are usually supplied with detachable lens caps, the translucent patterns doubling as filters for use on particularly bright days. Others will be encountered with range-finding graticles and some even offer rubberized 'armour', which is useful for field use.

6× 40, 6× 42 and 6× 45 fixed-power sights are notably popular among the larger magnifications, though 8× 56, 8× 58, 9× 56 and others up to 18× or more may be obtained. Most of the large sights, with bodies as long as the gun-barrel, are used for long-range target, bench-rest or varmint shooting. They are rarely durable enough for arduous field use, and magnify body tremors so greatly that the image is difficult to stabilize.

Many shooters opt for variable-power or 'zoom' systems, though there has been a move towards compact scopes – such as the excellent Beeman 2·5× 16 SSl and 3× 21 SS2 Blue Ribbon patterns, or the Bushnell Scopechief series. These small sights perform as well as some of the 'magnum' versions with a considerable economy of weight.

Among the most popular zoom sights is 3−9× , which offers a good range, though 1·5−6× , 1·75−5× , 3−6× , 3−7× and 3−12× will also be encountered. Large magnification may prove a boon in awkward conditions, but is far from ideal for normal shooting. In addition, variable-power sights are heavier and less durable than fixed-power rivals. Care should be taken to ensure that focus stays constant throughout the zoom range; there is nothing more annoying than an optical sight (or binocular) that needs constant adjustment as the power changes.

Many leading gunmakers offer 'own brand' telescope sights through the courtesies of the principal Japanese contractors, and the differences among the various 4× 32 sights – for example – amount largely to markings

and external finish. Apart from 'Made in Japan', the sights rarely give a direct clue to their manufacturer. Brandnames include Kassnar and Tasco, Bushmaster, Bisley, Tikka, Optima, Bentley and Nikko Stirling. In Europe, however, several companies still make their own sights – including Zeiss and Schmidt & Bender in Germany, or Kahles and Swarovski-Optik in Austria. Most offer impeccable quality at a high price, and are rarely seen outside competition shooting. Bushnell, Bausch & Lomb and Weaver still make their own lenses in the USA; but, regrettably, no British manufacturers survive.

No optical sight is much use without mounts. Many of 4× 15 and 4× 20 telescope slghts are supplied with integral mounts, but these are of little use on anything other than a rimfire rifle. Unfortunately, gunmakers still use a variety of dovetail-groove widths and a selection of proprietary mounting rails that demand compatible mounts. This should be investigated before buying a sight.

The most popular form of mount is a double ring, which can be spaced as far apart as necessary along the dovetail groove to suit the length of the sight and the positioning of the reticle adjusting block. These mounts are simple, cheap and can be obtained with base-widths suiting particular makes of gun. The upper part of the split-ring is generally retained by two or four slotted-head bolts, though cap-head bolts are sometimes substituted. Among the best mounts are the German Ernst Apel brand,   but they are phenomenally expensive: more expensive, indeed, than some complete rifles. The tendency is, therefore, towards the cheaper anodized aluminium patterns emanating from Japan. Though these are strong enough for their purposes, the finish is not especially durable and care should be taken that the edges of the clamp-rings (which are sometimes surprisingly sharp) do not bite into the telescope-sight body. A ring of tape generally suffices as protection.

The recoil of most sporting guns, particularly the large magnums, necessitates special mounts. The most common is a pin, generally integral with the base, which locates in a hole drilled in the receiver to prevent

The largest sights – this is a 16× Redfield – are confined to long-range shooting

A Weaver 1·5× 15 sight in a special proprietary mount

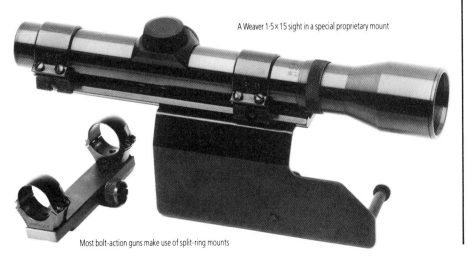

Most bolt-action guns make use of split-ring mounts

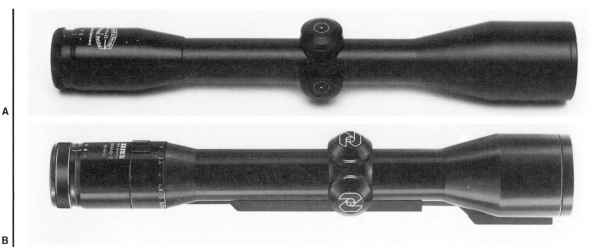

the mount sliding backward; other systems use hooks, or short bolts. But it is essential to ensure that the sight and mounts are adequate for the relevant guns and applications.

The easiest way to zero a rifle is by bore-sighting. The bolt is removed and the gun clamped in such a way that the desired target can be seen simply by looking through the bore from the breech. The sight is then added, and aligned on the same target – as a result of which, more or less accurately, the projectile will strike the right spot. Firing a few shots will suffice to make final adjustments, avoiding the alternative trial-and-error method. In this, the initial fall of shot may be so far from the intended target that it cannot even be seen. For guns where bore-sighting is inappropriate, such as lever-action Winchesters or auto-loaders, a bore collimator – made by Redfield and others – may be used. This comprises a large lens system and a base from which a short exchangeable rod projects. The idea is simple: a rod of bore diameter is selected, fitted to the collimator and pushed into the gun-muzzle. This allows a specific target to be selected in the same fashion as true bore sighting. Once the collimator has been removed, the sight is then fixed on the gun and aligned on target.

Once the approximate sight/bore alignment has been found, a five-shot group should be fired to allow a centre-point to be determined: corrections should never be made on a shot to shot basis! An arrow on the azimuth adjusting screw, marked 'L' or 'R'. shows the direction in which the screw must be turned; if the gun is shooting to the left, the desired movement is towards the right and the screw should be turned towards 'R' or away from 'L'.

Repeating the process to determine vertical displacement (the control drum for which will be marked 'Up' or 'Down' with an arrow) should complete the process.

Very little trouble is encountered with modern optical sights, though tampering with the lenses and breaking seals understandably invalidates manufacturers' guarantees. Mistreating the reticle by attempting to

force the adjustor screws past their stop point is also quite common, and the flimsiest sights do not take kindly to clamp-rings tightened beyond normal limits. Neat rings of tape around the sight-body in the clamps prevent damage to the comparatively delicate anodized finish, while a small sliver of tape in the dovetail groove may minimize 'creep' on rimfire guns where the mounts are not drilled and tapped for a stop-bolt or pin.

It is essential that an optical sight fits the gun for which it is intended. Sights with objective-lens diameters exceeding 40mm may require special high mounts, and the bell of super-power sights may foul the back sight . Some large-bell sights have rails to the underside of the bell, which slide directly into channels on the receiver; this removes the need for a second mount. Many lever-action rifles, especially Winchesters made prior to the 94XTR Angle and Side Eject series, throw spent cases upward from the top of the receiver; this necessitates an offset sight-mount, or high mounts and a suitable case deflector. Bolt-action rifles usually present few problems, excepting the few, such as the older Mannlichers, with split-bridge receivers; for these, however, one-piece mounting rails can generally be attached to the side of the receiver.

Above

A Redfield bore collimator, used during sighting-in to prevent unnecessary wastage of ammunition. Short exchangeable rods adapt the device to differing bore diameters.

Information

abbreviations

DJV: Deutsche Jägerschafts-Verband, the German national shooting organisation.

ft-lb: one foot-pound – a measure of energy obtained by squaring the velocity (in feet per second, or fs^{-1}), multiplying it by the projectile weight in grains and dividing the answer by 450,240 (a constant arising from the fact that there are 7,000 grains in a pound and that the value of g, the gravitational constant, has been assumed to be 32·16fs^{-2}). 1 ft-lb equates to 1·3558 joules.

fs (correctly written as fs^{-1}): feet per second.

ft: one foot – 12in or 305mm.

gm: one gram – 0·03525oz or 15·432gn.

gn: one grain: 0·002286oz or 0·0648gm.

in: one inch, 25·4mm.

ISU: International Shooting Union (see also UIT).

Joule (or 'J'): a measure of energy, one Joule equates to 0·7376 ft-lb.

kg: one kilogram – 2·2046lb or 15,432·2gn.

lb: one pound – 16oz or 453·59gm.

m: one metre – 39·37in, 3·2808ft or 1·0936yd.

mm: one millimetre – 0·03937in.

oz: one ounce – 28·2495gm or 437·5gn.

UIT Union Internationale de Tir, the French name for the International Shooting Union (ISU).

yd: one yard – 36in, 3ft or 914·4mm.

conversions

Grains to grams: multiply by 0·0648

Grains to ounces: multiply by 0·002286

Grams to grains: multiply by 15·432

Grams to ounces: multiply by 0·03525

Kilograms to pounds: multiply by 2·2046

Ounces to grains: multiply by 437·5

Ounces to grams: multiply by 28·2495

Pounds to kilograms: multiply by 0·45359

Feet to metres: multiply by 0·305

Inches to millimetres: multiply by 25·4

Metres to feet: multiply by 3·2808

Metres to yards: multiply by 1·0936

Millimetres to inches: multiply by 0·03937

Yards to metres: multiply by 0·9144

Bibliography

ALBRECHT, Walter; KNOTHE, Manfred; REINHART, Christian; and SALLAZ, Kurt: *Waffen Digest*. 1988 edition; Verlag Stocker-Schmid AG, Dietikon-Zürich, Switzerland. Published annually.

BARNES, Frank C. (Ken Warner, editor): *Cartridges of the World*. Fifth edition; DBI Books, Inc., Northbrook, Illinois, USA. 1985.

BEARSE, Ray: *Sporting Arms of the World*. Outdoor Life/Harper & Row, New York, Evanston, San Francisco and London. 1976.

DE HAAS, Frank (John T. Amber, editor): *Bolt-Action Rifles*. DBI Books, Inc., Northfield, Illinois. 1971.
– *Single Shot Rifles and Actions*. DBI Books, Inc., Northfield, Illinois, USA. 1969.

EZELL, Edward C.: *Small Arms Today*. Second edition; Stackpole Books, Harrisburg, Pennsylvania, USA. 1988.

HOGG, Ian V. (compiler): *Jane's Infantry Weapons*. Jane's Publishing Co. Ltd, London. 1988– 89 edition. Published annually.
– and WEEKS, John S.: *Military Smallarms of the 20th century* ("A comprehensive illustrated encyclopedia of the world's small-calibre firearms"). Fifth edition; Arms & Armour Press, London. 1985.

MURTZ, Harold A. (editor): *The Gun Digest Book of Exploded Firearms Drawings*. Second edition; DBI Books, Inc., Northfield, Illinois, USA. 1977.

MUSGRAVE, Daniel D., and NELSON, Thomas B.: *The World's Assault Rifles & Automatic Carbines*. TBN Enterprises, Alexandria, Virginia, USA. Undated (*c*.1969).

OTTESON, Stuart: *The Bolt Action, A Design Analysis*. Winchester Press, New York, USA. 1976.

SMITH, Walter H.B. (Joseph E. Smith and Edward C. Ezell, revisers): *Small Arms of the World*. Eleventh edition; Stackpole Books, Harrisburg, Pennsylvania, USA. 1977.

STEVENS, R. Blake: *The FAL Rifle* (incorporating "North American FALs", "UK and Commonwealth FALs" and "The Metric FAL"). Collector Grade Publications, Inc., Toronto, Canada. 1987.
– and EZELL, Edward C.: *The Black Rifle: M16 Retrospective*. Collector Grade Publications, Inc., Toronto, Canada. 1987.

WAHL, Paul (John E. Traister, reviser): *Gun Trader's Guide*. Fourteenth edition; Stoeger Publishing Corporation, South Hackensack, New Jersey, USA. 1990.
– *Paul Wahl's Big Gun Catalog*. Two volumes, A– L and M– Z; Paul Wahl Corporation, Bogota, New Jersey, USA. 1988.

WALTER, John D.: *The German Rifle* ("A comprehensive illustrated history of the standard bolt-action designs, 1871– 1945"). Arms & Armour Press, London. 1979.
– *The Pistol Book*. Second edition; Arms & Armour Press, London. 1988.

WARNER, Ken (editor): *Guns Digest* ("The World's Greatest Gun Book"). 43rd edition; DBI Books, Inc., Northbrook, Illinois, USA. 1989. Published annually.

WEISE, Robert E. (editor): *Shooter's Bible* ("The World's Standard Firearms Reference Book"). 80th edition; Stoeger Publishing Company, South Hackensack, New Jersey, USA. 1989. Published annually.